TAKING UP THE CROSS

LESSONS LEARNED IN THE WILDERNESS
(BOOK 5)

KENNETH A. WINTER

JOIN MY READERS' GROUP FOR UPDATES AND FUTURE RELEASES

Please join my Readers' Group so i can send you a free book, as well as updates and information about future releases in the series.

See the back of the book for details on how to sign up.

* * *

Taking Up The Cross

Book #5 in the ***Lessons Learned In The Wilderness*** series

Published by:

Kenneth A. Winter

WildernessLessons, LLC

Richmond, Virginia

United States of America

kenwinter.org

wildernesslessons.com

Cover Design: Melanie Fisher-Wellman

ISBN 978-1-7328670-3-1 (soft cover)

ISBN 978-1-7328670-2-4 (e-book)

Library of Congress Control Number: 2019937344

DEDICATION

But these are written so that you may continue to believe that Jesus is the Messiah, the Son of God, and that by believing in Him you will have life by the power of His name.
John 20:31

* * *

With gratitude
To my wife, LaVonne, for your life partnership in this continuing faith journey,
To our daughter, Lorél, for your patient and meticulous editing and corrections,
To our son, Justin, for your creative and technical insights,
To Joanne, Amanda, Aaron and Kordan, for your love and support along the way,
To Melanie, for your creative and artistic touch,
To our community group, for your encouragement and support in so many ways,
To a great group of advance readers, for your feedback and encouragement

And, most importantly,
To my Lord and Savior Jesus Christ, for Your love, Your grace and Your mercy, and without Whom there would be no one to follow and nothing to tell!

CONTENTS

SCRIPTURE REFERENCE AND DAY OF THE WEEK LISTING BY CHAPTER

* * *

Palm Sunday

1 Everyone Loves Him! (Matthew 21:1-11)

Monday

2 Created To Bear Fruit (Mark 11:12-14)
3 Cleansing The Temple (Matthew 21:12-16)

Tuesday

4 The Withered Fig Tree (Mark 11:20-26)
5 Who Gave You The Right? (Mark 11:27-33)
6 Which Son Truly Obeyed (Matthew 21:28-32)
7 The Wicked Farmers (Mark 12:1-12)
8 The Marriage Feast (Matthew 22:1-14)
9 Give To God What Belongs To Him (Luke 20:20-26)
10 One Bride For Seven Brothers (Matthew 22:23-33)
11 The Most Important Commandment (Mark 12:28-34)
12 Whose Son Is He? (Matthew 22:41-46)
13 It's Not The Seat That Makes The Man (Matthew 23:1-12)
14 The Eight Woes (Matthew 23:13-36)
15 The Widow's Treasure (Mark 12:41-44)
16 What About The Temple? (Mark 13:1-4)
17 The Parousia (Matthew 24:3-8)
18 In The Coming Days (Mark 13:9-13)
19 Perilous Times (Matthew 24:15-28)

* * *

A WORD OF EXPLANATION

For those of you who are new to my writing.

* * *

You will notice that whenever i use the pronoun "I" referring to myself, i have chosen to use a lowercase "i". It is not a typographical error. i know that is contrary to proper English grammar and accepted editorial style guides. i drive editors (and "spell check") crazy by doing this. But years ago, the LORD convicted me – personally – that in all things i must decrease and He must increase. And as a way of continuing personal reminder, from that day forward, i have chosen to use a lower case "i" whenever referring to myself. Because of the same conviction, i use a capital letter for any pronoun referring to God. The style guide for the New Living Translation (NLT) does not share that conviction. However, you will see that i have intentionally made that slight revision and capitalized any pronoun referring to God in my quotations of Scripture from the NLT. If i have violated any style guides as a result, please accept my apology, but i must honor this conviction.

Lastly, regarding this matter – this is a personal conviction – and i share it only so that you will understand why i have chosen to deviate from normal editorial practice. i am in no way suggesting or endeavoring to have anyone else subscribe to my conviction. Thanks for your understanding.

* * *

PREFACE

Then He said to the crowd, "If any of you wants to be My follower, you must give up your own way, take up your cross daily, and follow Me."
Luke 9:23

* * *

As we reviewed in chapter 36 of *Walking With The Master*, the disciples thought that they were getting ready to step into positions of power. For those in the crowd who were beginning to see Jesus as the Messiah, they thought they would soon be out from underneath the rule of Rome and would be their own masters. But to their surprise, Jesus said (paraphrased), "if you want to follow Me, you must give up your right to be your own master, and you must take up an instrument of death." That was not the message they were expecting! And Jesus went on to say (paraphrased), "if you try to keep your life, you'll lose it. *But if you give up your life for My sake, you will save it.*" The people were thinking about what the Messiah was going to do for them, and instead, Jesus told them that they must die to themselves.

Jesus lived in a day when religious leaders taught one thing, but lived another. (Regrettably, that is too often true today.) But Jesus not only lived out what He taught, He made the way for <u>us</u> to be able to live it out. Otherwise, we would have been doomed to fail. Only One could live up to what He taught – and that was Jesus Himself. So, it is only through the power of His Holy Spirit living within us that we can possibly live it out.

Remember, Jesus was not telling them how they could be "saved" from the penalty of sin. Salvation is not a work that we do. There is absolutely nothing we can do to earn salvation. It is the free gift of God extended by His grace and received by us purely through faith in Him. Jesus is talking about the result of our salvation, not the cause of it. We must first be saved in order to have His Spirit living within us. And we must have His Spirit living within us in order to truly be His follower.

Now, if we don't desire to follow Him, then we need to question whether we truly have surrendered our lives to Him as our Savior. Salvation and followship are two sides of the same coin. We can't separate them. Though the way we often live out our lives would indicate that we think we can.

In the sixty-one chapters of this fifth book of the ***Lessons Learned In The Wilderness*** series, we're going to look at what it means to take up the cross – the cross He has chosen for us – and follow Him. And the backdrop for our time will be the last forty-seven days of His earthly ministry, picking up at the triumphal entry into Jerusalem and continuing to the day He ascended into heaven. Jesus knew from before the beginning of time that the day would come when He would literally carry His cross to that hill on Golgotha. He knew that His work of salvation could not be completed without the cross. It would require death – a death that once and for all would conquer sin, death and the grave. And the cross would not only be the instrument through which that would be accomplished, but it would also forever be a reminder of that completed work. That's why it was fitting for Him to tell us that if we are going to follow Him, we must take up our cross – that instrument that is also the reminder of His work – our salvation.

i don't believe there was ever a moment that Jesus was not mindful of the cross that was before Him. He often talked about the fact that His time had not yet come. He knew that the work of the cross was before Him. It was the defining moment of God's eternal plan. It was the primary reason that the Father sent the Son. It was the way that the Father ultimately brought glory to His Name through the redemption of a lost world unto Himself.

And in many respects, the same is true for us. Our salvation is not God's end game for our lives. It's not just about ourselves – though too often we act like it is. In many respects, our salvation is a starting point. He has reconciled us unto Himself and then given us an opportunity to be a part of His eternal plan. As followers of Jesus, He has called us to be ambassadors of Christ, ministers of the gospel, and missionaries of His redemptive work, all for His purpose and His glory. And He has equipped us and empowered us to be a part of His plan by placing His Holy Spirit within us.

So, He reminds us that first, we must give up our own way. Our lives cannot be about our comfort and our personal preferences. Life cannot be about "what's in it for me". i must surrender my soulish ambition. i must relinquish control of my life and surrender it to Him. i must be about His agenda and His purpose – whatever it is – and wherever it is. My only choice will be whether i follow Him or not. If i choose to follow Him, i don't get to choose where, what, when or how. If He leads me to go halfway around the world, or halfway across the room, i don't get to say "no". He is in control.

Secondly, He tells us that we are to take up the cross that He has set before us. That cross will look different for each of us. In John 21:21, after Jesus had told Peter what was in store for him, Peter asked, *"What about him, Lord?"* (Peter was referring to John.) Jesus responded by saying, *"What is that to you? As for you, follow Me"* (John 21:22). The Father has a unique role for each of us. He has equipped and placed us uniquely. He has shaped the cross we are to take up. We don't get to shape it. We are simply to take it up – splinters and all.

Thirdly, He reminds us that taking up the cross is a daily – and a continuous – act. It is not a "one and done". It is an act of surrender and obedience that continues every moment and every day until we are in heaven with Him. We are never too young or too old, or too busy. We are never retired or otherwise engaged. We are never "between jobs". It is "job one"! We are followers of Jesus – each day, every day.

Lastly, He makes sure we understand that we are to follow Him. We are not to go out and do our own thing, or make our own path. He is the One who goes before us, not the other way around. The great news about that is that we don't need to figure it all out – we just follow Him. i have often said that i look forward to meeting Enoch one day in heaven. We read in Genesis 5 and Hebrews 11 that Enoch walked with God. Enoch never had to figure out which way to turn. All he had to do was keep his eyes on God. And as he did, one day the Lord took him home. i want to have that kind of intimate walk with the Lord. One moment walking with Him here, and the next walking with Him in heaven. And since i don't know when that moment will be, i don't want to be off doing my own thing when that moment arrives. i want to be following Him.

Over the next sixty-one chapters, we will see through the Gospels what "taking up the cross" looked like in the life of Jesus and what He has determined it will look like in our lives. He doesn't promise that there won't be a cost – there will be. And He doesn't promise that it will be easy – it won't be. But it is the journey He has set before us – a journey that will further His purpose in and through our lives – and a journey that will lead to His glory.

My prayer is that this book encourages you along the way!

* * *

1

EVERYONE LOVES HIM!

As Jesus and the disciples approached Jerusalem, they came to the town of Bethphage on the Mount of Olives. Jesus sent two of them on ahead. "Go into the village over there," He said. "As soon as you enter it, you will see a donkey tied there, with its colt beside it. Untie them and bring them to Me. If anyone asks what you are doing, just say, 'The Lord needs them,' and he will immediately let you take them." This took place to fulfill the prophecy that said, "Tell the people of Jerusalem, 'Look, your King is coming to you. He is humble…, riding on a donkey's colt.'" The two disciples did as Jesus commanded. They brought the donkey and the colt to Him and threw their garments over the colt, and He sat on it. Most of the crowd spread their garments on the road ahead of Him, and others cut branches from the trees and spread them on the road. Jesus was in the center of the procession, and the people all around Him were shouting, "Praise God for the Son of David! Blessings on the One who comes in the name of the Lord! Praise God in highest heaven!" The entire city of Jerusalem was in an uproar as He entered. "Who is this?" they asked. And the crowds replied, "It's Jesus, the prophet from Nazareth in Galilee."

Matthew 21:1-11

* * *

It's the first day of the week, and everyone loves Jesus! Well, maybe not everyone. But, at this moment, you would think everyone does, by the way that the crowd is acting. There were probably two million people in and around Jerusalem for the celebration of Passover that year. The celebration always brought pilgrims to Jerusalem. But the crowd was unusually large that day. The people had seen that Jesus always came to

Jerusalem for the religious festivals. They knew that Passover would be no exception. Thus, large numbers had come that year for the express purpose of seeing Jesus. Many had traveled down from Galilee, having witnessed the miracles He performed there. His fame and notoriety had spread throughout Judea as well, particularly after He raised Lazarus from the dead (John 12:17-18). The people wanted to see Jesus perform more miracles.

But most of them were blinded to the truth of who Jesus really was. They were blinded by the teachings of their religious leaders. Instead of pointing the people to the truth of the Word, they had pointed the people to their man-made traditions (Luke 11:52). The leaders had never been interested in the truth. They merely sought to protect their own self-interests of position, power and prestige. And the people themselves were also blinded by their own selfish desires – desiring only what Jesus could do for them.

Those very desires are what prompted them to cry out, "Hosanna!" This Hebrew word means "Save Now!" They were quoting from Psalm 118:25-26: *"Please, Lord, please save us. Please, Lord, please give us success. Bless the one who comes in the name of the Lord. We bless you from the house of the Lord."* But their emphasis was on save us! Give us success! Do for us! And they lavished Him with praise, welcoming the Miracle Worker into their midst, expecting to be rewarded by His miracles.

Jesus had planned for this day – from before the beginning of time. This was the only time in the ministry of Jesus that He planned and promoted a public demonstration. Up until then, He had deliberately avoided public scenes. But now, the defining moment of time and space had arrived. Up until now, each time that Jesus had entered Jerusalem, He had done so unobtrusively through the "sheep gate". But on this day, He entered conspicuously as King through the "Golden Gate" (aka the "Eastern Gate"). (It is worthy to note that when He returns, He will again enter Jerusalem from the east. Though men have now sealed up the current eastern gate and made it humanly impassable, one day all of those man-made "barricades" will fall away, and the gates will open to our returning King!)

Jesus had not only planned this day from eternity past, He had also planned for it the previous time He was in Jerusalem. He had made arrangements for a donkey and its colt to be available. The keeper of the animals was to expect two of His disciples, and have everything ready for them. Everything was to be as the prophet Zechariah had recorded: *Rejoice, O people of Zion! Shout in triumph, O people of Jerusalem!* ***Look, your King is coming to you.*** *He is righteous and victorious,* ***yet He is humble…, riding on a donkey's colt.*** (Zechariah 9:9).

And yet, Zechariah was writing simultaneously about two different occurrences when Jesus would enter into Jerusalem. The portion of the verse that i have emboldened relates to this entry into Jerusalem as we see quoted above in Matthew 21. On that day, the crowd was not witnessing the arrival of their victorious, judging King. The triumph had not yet occurred. It was still a few days away. They were welcoming the arrival of their saving King. A donkey's colt was the royal animal of Jewish monarchs. It symbolized Jesus' station as King. But it was also a symbol of peace – the peace and the salvation that He was bringing to all people. It was a picture of Jesus, the humble Savior and Servant. He was presenting Himself as King, approaching His cross – not as a victim – but as the coming Victor.

(Bear in mind, Zechariah is also giving us a glimpse of Jesus' triumphal entry on the day still yet to come when He returns. The underlined portion of that verse speaks to the day He will return in triumph and victory – a day that is rapidly drawing near!)

On what we now call "Palm Sunday", His time had arrived. The "spontaneous" demonstration of praise and accolades from the people frightened the leaders and left them to conclude if they did not destroy Jesus now, they would be destroyed. Jesus was forcing the religious leaders to act now, in the time and way He had chosen. Don't lose sight of the fact that He was in complete control of what was about to unfold. No, everyone did not love Jesus, but by this act of obedience to the Father, the Father and the Son both demonstrated their love for everyone.

Jesus knew what was in the minds and hearts of everyone in the crowd, and each one of the religious leaders. He knew that the shouts of praise today would turn into shouts to crucify Him in just a matter of days. He was no more disillusioned or distracted by the shouts of praise than He would be by the shouts that He be crucified. That's the lesson for us to grasp. If we are following Jesus, there will be days that we are experiencing the adulation and praise and "love" from the crowd. Those are the days that are easier to experience – but don't be deceived by them. Because, if we truly are following Jesus in obedience, we will encounter days when many of that same crowd turn against us. If they did it to Jesus, why should we expect anything different?

But don't lose sight that regardless of how the crowd acted, Jesus loved them. He loved them from the back of a donkey's colt, and He loved them from the vantage point of His cross. As you take up the cross and follow Him, ask Him to give you that same love for the crowd around you, no matter what your vantage point is today. That kind of love doesn't exist within us apart from Him. But ask Him to position your heart so that He can love them through you.

* * *

2

CREATED TO BEAR FRUIT

The next morning as they were leaving Bethany, Jesus was hungry. He noticed a fig tree in full leaf a little way off, so He went over to see if He could find any figs. But there were only leaves because it was too early in the season for fruit. Then Jesus said to the tree, "May no one ever eat your fruit again!" And the disciples heard Him say it.
Mark 11:12-14

* * *

It's the second day of the week. Jesus and His disciples are returning to Bethany each evening. More than likely, they are lodging with Lazarus, Martha and Mary, then each morning they are returning to Jerusalem. En route, Jesus was hungry. Apparently, Martha hadn't fed them breakfast that morning. He saw a fig tree beside the road, and it was in *"full leaf"*. Both Matthew and Mark tell us that Jesus *"went over to see if He could find any figs"*.

Let's stop and consider that a moment. Jesus knew whether or not that tree had figs on it long before He went over to see it. Our God is all-knowing. Jesus Himself had taught, *"What is the price of five sparrows — two copper coins? Yet God does not forget a single one of them"* (Luke 12:6). There isn't a detail that escapes His view or His knowledge. Just as Jesus knew everything about each of the men that accompanied Him – the one who would betray Him, the one who would deny Him, the one who would doubt Him – He knew there was no fruit on that fig tree. Some of the

Pharisees had already discovered that Jesus knew the sins that they had committed in the shadows, even though they had thought no one else knew (see *Walking With The Master,* chapter 43). He knows all things past, present and future. So, if He was hungry, why was He walking over to a fig tree that He already knew was barren? And secondly, Jesus had turned a little boy's lunch into a feast for thousands. If He was hungry, why didn't He just turn some of the leaves into fruit? Something tells me that there is a whole lot more to this than what meets the eye!

One other fact about fig trees before we move on: in that part of the world, fig trees produce leaves in March/ April, then bear mature fruit twice each year – the first at the beginning of June, and the second from August through October. Since this event would have taken place during the March/ April timeframe, Mark rightly records that *"it was too early in the season for fruit."* But, during this time of year as fig trees were becoming fully-leafed, they would produce a crop of small knobs, called "taqsh" (pronounced "tuhk-wAAsh"). In essence, they are a forerunner to the mature figs and drop off the tree before the "real" fruit is formed. Most often, the taqsh were left to fall off the tree, but on occasion they would be eaten by hungry peasants. If, however, there are no "taqsh", it is an indication that there will be no figs. So, it was evident to Jesus that the absence of taqsh meant that there would be no figs when the time came.

Thus, the example of the fig tree proved to be a lesson to be learned. The tree gave the outward appearance that it was healthy and growing. It was pleasing to the eye, and all indications were that in its time, it would produce a bountiful harvest. But Jesus knew, and on closer inspection showed the disciples, that the tree was not healthy. God created the tree with one purpose – His purpose – to bear fruit. He didn't create it to be a fruitless tree. And though harvest time had not yet arrived, it was obvious by the condition of the tree that it would be fruitless.

In a parallel passage, Luke writes that as Jesus *"came closer to Jerusalem and saw the city ahead, He began to weep."* He knew that *"It is too late, and peace {was} hidden from {their} eyes. Before long your enemies… will crush you into the ground… because you did not recognize it when God visited you"* (Luke 19:41-44). The Father had created and called His people, Israel, to bear fruit to His glory – to bear witness to His Majesty and to worship Him through their very lives. And yet, they had rejected Him. They had turned their focus upon themselves to the point that they no longer even recognized Him – when He stood in their presence. Though the destruction of

Jerusalem had not yet taken place, all of the signs were already present. It was obvious that the nation – God's people – would be fruitless. But the lesson did not stop with them.

In just a few days from then as we see recorded in John 15, Jesus would teach the disciples that each one of them was to be a branch – attached to Him, grafted into the Vine. Their purpose as a branch would be to bear fruit – fruit that brings glory to the Father, fruit that remains, and fruit that multiplies. He would remind them that a branch cannot bear fruit on its own. It can only bear fruit when it is attached in a healthy way to the vine. We will look at the John 15 passage further in chapter 36, but for now suffice it to say that the life and sustenance for the fruit to be borne can only come from the vine. The branch's role is but to remain grafted into the vine in order for it to be used to bear fruit. If the branch pulls away from the vine it will become fruitless.

That picture of the branch and the vine is a picture of how we are to walk with Jesus. He said, *"Yes, I am the Vine; you are the branches. Those who remain in Me, and I in them, will produce much fruit. For apart from Me you can do nothing"* (John 15:5). We were created – and we have been redeemed – in order to be used by our Master to bear fruit. We don't produce the fruit; He does! But in His sovereignty, He has chosen to use us as the branches through whom He produces His fruit. We are to be prepared in season and out of season (2 Timothy 4:2) to bear fruit – whether it is March/ April, June, August thru October – or any moment of any day. That is true for us as individual followers of our Master, and that is true for us as local bodies of believers.

Regrettably, too many of us as followers, and too many of us as local churches, look like that fig tree. On the outside we present with a full crop of leaves, seemingly healthy and growing. But our Master knows all too well that our lives are fruitless and not producing a harvest.

Jesus has called us to turn from ourselves, take up the cross and follow Him – that includes being branches that remain in Him – healthy branches that are usable by Him to bear His fruit. So, what does the Master see in your life? Are you a healthy growing branch with leaves and taqsh or mature fruit? Or are you a branch that appears to be healthy but is really barren? Allow Him to make you into that usable branch today – *"ready for the Master to use you for every good work"* (2 Timothy 2:21).

* * *

3

CLEANSING THE TEMPLE

Jesus entered the Temple and began to drive out all the people buying and selling animals for sacrifice. He knocked over the tables of the money changers and the chairs of those selling doves. He said to them, "The Scriptures declare, 'My Temple will be called a house of prayer,' but you have turned it into a den of thieves!" The blind and the lame came to Him in the Temple, and He healed them. The leading priests and the teachers of religious law saw these wonderful miracles and heard even the children in the Temple shouting, "Praise God for the Son of David." But the leaders were indignant. They asked Jesus, "Do you hear what these children are saying?"

"Yes," Jesus replied. "Haven't you ever read the Scriptures? For they say, 'You have taught children and infants to give You praise.'"

Matthew 21:12-16

* * *

It's still the second day of the week. Yesterday, Jesus entered the city as King. Today, He enters as High Priest to cleanse His temple.

This was the second time that Jesus cleansed the temple in Jerusalem. The first time was at the beginning of His earthly ministry, as we see recorded in John 2:13-22. That time, Jesus made a whip from some ropes and chased them all out of the temple. Unfortunately, He didn't chase them far enough and they had slithered back inside.

. . .

Now three years later, nothing had changed. The outer court of the Gentiles had again become a marketplace where visiting Jews could exchange their money for temple currency and purchase animals to be sacrificed. The practice had originally been borne out of convenience for the travelers from out of town, but it had denigrated into a VERY profitable business. The outer court had originally been intended to be a place where "non-believers" could enter and learn about the one true God of Israel. But its use as a market had transformed the space from one being used for a missionary purpose to one now being used for a mercenary purpose.

Every Israelite, rich or poor, who had reached the age of twenty was required to pay a temple tax of one-half shekel into the temple treasury. This tax was to be paid using a Hebrew half shekel. At Passover, all adult males who wished to worship at the temple would bring his "offering". Since foreign money with any foreign image was considered to be "corrupt and unclean", the money changers would sell "temple coinage" at a very high rate of exchange and add an additional charge for their services. The judges, who inspected the offerings that were brought by the pilgrims, were quick to detect any blemish in the non-temple coinage, which further increased the exchange trade.

The dealers charged exorbitant prices, but no one could oppose them. They profited from the wealthy by providing four-legged animals for sacrifice, and they profited from the poor by selling them doves. It had become the ultimate "convenience store". The former high priest, Annas, was the manager of the enterprise, assisted by his sons, and they operated under the protection of the current high priest, his son-in law, Caiaphas. Their motivation was greed and extortion. It had truly become a "den of thieves". They were using their religion to cover up their sin. As we mentioned earlier, two million people were in Jerusalem that week to celebrate Passover. Do not lose sight that this had become BIG business!

Jesus was not the first to be sent by the Father to rebuke the religious leaders and the people of Israel for this practice of turning the temple into a marketplace. Over six hundred years earlier, God had sent the prophet Jeremiah to deliver the same rebuke. *"Don't you yourselves admit that this Temple, which bears My name, has become a den of thieves? Surely, I see all the evil going on there. I, the Lord, have spoken!"* (Jeremiah 7:11) The leaders had rejected that word from God just as they had rejected the first rebuke from Jesus.

. . .

Jesus repeats the words of the prophet Isaiah, *"My Temple will be called a house of prayer for all nations"* (Isaiah 56:7). It is to be a place where prayer bears evidence of dependence upon God and reliance on His Word. As He demonstrated in the healing of the blind and the lame, His Temple was to be a place where people were welcomed and received the help that they needed. It was to be a place where God's power was evident in the transformation of lives. And as evidenced by the children, as they gave praise, it was to be a place where God was praised and belief in God was displayed. Jesus reminded them of the Scripture – *"You have taught children and infants to tell of Your strength ("to give You praise"* – Greek version*), silencing Your enemies and all who oppose You"* (Psalm 8:2). Not only had the temple become as fruitless as the fig tree; it had become a stumbling block to true seekers desiring to worship the one true God.

And we read that the leaders were indignant and plotted even more fervently how to kill Jesus. They could think of nothing else, *"because all the people hung on every word He said"* (Luke 19:48). He threatened their financial enterprise. He threatened their power over the people. He threatened their position of leadership. There was nothing godly within them. Their hearts were as cold as stone. They could think of nothing else, but how they would rid themselves of Jesus. That which had been building for three years in their hearts had now escalated to the point of action. They would not be dissuaded. They were afraid of Him. They needed to act now! Little did they know that they did not control the timing, the Father did.

If we would take up the cross, there are many lessons for us in the cleansing of the temple – in our own lives, and in the local church bodies of which we are a part. First – the abomination that the marketplace practices became began with a simple and subtle compromise. It was a means to make it easier for foreigners to participate in worship. Those who had begun the practice probably did so to enhance worship, never intending to hamper it. It is a reminder to us to guard every facet of our worship and not compromise or redirect our focus from the One we worship, no matter how seemingly inconsequential our redirect might be. Second – our lives and our local body are to bear evidence of our dependence upon God and our reliance on His Word. We are to be welcomers and helpers of all who God brings across our path. His presence and His power are to be conspicuously evident in our lives, in our praise, our beliefs and our actions. Third – we must never lose sight that we have been called to be ambassadors of the gospel to all nations – through our prayer and through our actions.

The apostle Paul wrote, *"Don't you realize that all of you together are the temple of God and that the Spirit of God lives in you?"* (1 Corinthians 3:16). The lesson of the cleansing of the temple is much like the lesson of the barren fig tree. We have been called to be fruit bearers. Let's be certain that we have allowed the Master to cleanse our temple, so that we are fit for His purpose and His glory.

* * *

4

THE WITHERED FIG TREE

The next morning as they passed by the fig tree He had cursed, the disciples noticed it had withered from the roots up. Peter remembered what Jesus had said to the tree on the previous day and exclaimed, "Look, Rabbi! The fig tree you cursed has withered and died!" Then Jesus said to the disciples, "Have faith in God. I tell you the truth, you can say to this mountain, 'May you be lifted up and thrown into the sea', and it will happen. But you must really believe it will happen and have no doubt in your heart. I tell you, you can pray for anything, and if you believe that you've received it, it will be yours. But when you are praying, first forgive anyone you are holding a grudge against, so that your Father in heaven will forgive your sins, too."

Mark 11:20-26

* * *

It's now the third day of the week. For the third day in a row, Jesus and the disciples are headed back to Jerusalem after overnighting in Bethany. As they walk, they pass a dead fig tree. The disciples notice that the tree has withered from the roots up. It has withered due to a complete lack of water and nutrients. And Peter is the one who remembers that the Master had cursed this tree the day before. In one day, a tree that was full of leaves and had given the outward appearance of health and growth had now shriveled and died. A process that should have taken weeks, or maybe months, had occurred overnight. Not only was it seemingly cut-off from its source of water at its roots, but also all of the moisture that had existed within the tree had immediately dried up.

. . .

In chapter 2, we looked at the fact that a tree that had been created to be fruitful had been found by Jesus to be fruitless. Now, immediately after Peter points out the dead tree, Jesus begins to teach the disciples about faith. Though it seems like an abrupt change of subject, it's not!

Remember, Jesus was using this tree as a practical illustration of the spiritual health of the people of Israel. But He was also using it to teach His disciples – then and now – what it means to truly follow Him and abide in Him. If we follow and abide in Him, we will be His disciples indeed (John 15:5), and He will bear fruit through our lives. His Living Water will flow through us (John 7:38-39) and we will reflect His Light (John 8:12). Our fruitfulness is not based upon our effort, it is based upon our abiding. Without His Living Water flowing and His Light reflecting through us, we are a dead branch – withered – just like that fig tree. Fruitfulness is not intended for our glory, it is for His. In a few days from now, Jesus will tell them, *"if you remain in Me and My words remain in you, you may ask for anything you want, and it will be granted! When you produce much fruit, you are My true disciples. This brings great glory to My Father"* (John 15:7-8).

Jesus now turns the conversation from fruit to faith, because fruit will not occur apart from faith. We must live in an attitude of total dependence on Him – acting and asking in alignment with His Word. When Jesus speaks His Word, and His Word "remains" in us, it requires a response on our part – and that response is either faith or faithlessness. We can't remain in a neutral place. That would be like the servant in the parable of the talents who buried his talent. He took no action – which was faithlessness.

And Jesus is telling the disciples here, that if a mountain – otherwise known as some significant, immovable impediment – is standing between us and what God has told us to do, we must step out in faith, trusting and asking God to move the mountain. The prophet Zechariah wrote of Zerubbabel when he was chosen to lead the Jews back to Jerusalem, *"Nothing, not even a mighty mountain, will stand in Zerubbabel's way; it will become a level plain before him!* (Zechariah 4:7a). Why couldn't a mighty mountain stand in his way? Because he was walking in obedience to God on His mission. Nothing could stand in His way! No mountain can stand in our way, if we are walking in obedience to God's Word and His will. So, we must be certain that we are praying in response to a word from God and in alignment with the will of God (1 John 5:14-15). If that is so, we will see God take those mountains and "throw them into the sea"! Let's be clear – Jesus is not saying that, if we pray hard enough and long enough, and really believe, God is obligated to answer our prayer no matter what we ask. That is not faith in God; that's faith in our feelings. True faith must be rooted in God's Word – it is our <u>response</u> to His truth.

Then Jesus went on to talk about forgiveness. We are to walk – not only in the word of God, according to the will of God, but also – abiding in the love of God (John 15:7-14). If the branch is to abide in the Vine, there can't be anything standing between ourselves and God, or ourselves and another person. If we hold a grudge, or fail to forgive, we are sinning and inhibiting our abiding relationship with the Vine. So, Jesus says, before you pray, make sure you are not holding unforgiveness in your heart. Forgive that individual, and where possible make amends. But let me hasten to add that our forgiveness does not obligate God to act, it simply unblocks the pathway.

Earlier, i mentioned the parable of the talents. We will look at it in detail in chapter 22. But if you recall, the master in the parable takes the talents he had left with that faithless servant and gives them to one of the faithful servants (Matthew 25:28). Once judgement is declared by the master, the faithless servant is left with nothing. It wasn't gradual; it was immediate.

Through a simple fig tree, Jesus taught His disciples about fruitfulness, faithfulness and forgiveness. If we would take up the cross and follow Jesus, we too must heed the lesson of the withered fig tree.

How long does it take for a fruitless fig tree to wither after the Master has judged it and found it to be barren? It's immediate. And the same is true of us!

* * *

5

WHO GAVE YOU THE RIGHT?

Again they entered Jerusalem. As Jesus was walking through the Temple area, the leading priests, the teachers of religious law, and the elders came up to Him. They demanded, "By what authority are You doing all these things? Who gave You the right to do them?" "I'll tell you by what authority I do these things if you answer one question," Jesus replied. "Did John's authority to baptize come from heaven, or was it merely human? Answer Me!" They talked it over among themselves. "If we say it was from heaven, He will ask why we didn't believe John. But do we dare say it was merely human?" For they were afraid of what the people would do, because everyone believed that John was a prophet. So they finally replied, "We don't know." And Jesus responded, "Then I won't tell you by what authority I do these things."

Mark 11:27-33

* * *

This is the day after Jesus has cleared out the temple. The leading priests, teachers and elders are all still stinging from His rebukes the day before. They are indignant and combative. They are out for Jesus' blood. Up until yesterday, they had been fearful of what Jesus was doing. Up until then, they had viewed Him as one who was challenging their authority. But yesterday, He had completely undermined their authority. He had shut down their financial enterprise. He had taken action that demonstrated a flagrant disregard for their position. And their fear turned into unadulterated hatred of Him. Now they were singularly focused on His destruction. They were now on His trail, like bloodhounds of hate.

• • •

A sticking point for them had always been that Jesus didn't respect their official authority as the leaders of their religion. He had never once come to them seeking their approval to do anything that He did. They had never delegated Him any authority. And He had been running roughshod over them for far too long. Of all of the things that Jesus had said and done, that was His major offense to them. So, it's no wonder that, as He returned to the temple that morning, their first question – or should i say their first accusation – is a challenge to His authority. *"**Who gave You the right to do what You are doing?**"*

Jesus did not demean Himself by directly answering their question. He knew their motive. He knew that they did not desire to follow Him. They now sought to crucify Him. They were not seeking truth. They were looking for evidence to use to destroy Him. Jesus never rebutted sincere questions from sincere seekers. He always gave genuine answers to sincere inquiries. But there was nothing sincere about what these men were asking. It was just a part of their plot. Instead, Jesus very deftly countered their question with another question, and in so doing, exposed their hypocrisy and their hard-heartedness.

Why did Jesus ask them about John the Baptist? Because He was the forerunner that the Father had sent to speak His truth to His people. Remember, there had been silence for over 400 years. God had not spoken to His people during that time – until He sent John to prepare the way for His Son. And the truth that John spoke, the religious leaders rejected. There is a principle here that we need to grab onto. **God will not teach us new truth if we have rejected the truth that He has already given us**. The leaders would never accept the truth of Jesus because they had rejected God's truth through John. Bear in mind, if they had received God's message through John, they would have submitted to the authority of Jesus and the accounts of the Gospels would have looked VERY different. But God knew how they would respond – long before He sent John!

Now the Pharisees had another dilemma. How should they respond to Jesus' question? They weren't considering "what is true?" or "what is right?" but rather, "what is safe?". The Pharisees knew, whichever way they answered Jesus, the crowd would turn on them, and their authority, position and prestige would be totally lost. So, they refused to answer by pleading ignorance.

. . .

In an environment of ever-increasing political correctness, that has become an operative strategy in our day and time as well. Too often, we are compromising "what is true" and "what is right" in favor of "what is safe". How often are we following the way of the Pharisee instead of following the way of our Master?

God has given us His Word, His gospel and His truth. We have a choice. Do we accept it, or do we reject it? And if we accept it, we cannot compromise it for what is "safe". His truth is what sets sinners free (John 8:31-32). Compromised truth is no longer truth. It has become a lie. That was true with the Pharisees, and it's just as true today.

Jesus said, *"I have been given all authority in heaven and on earth. Therefore, go and make disciples of all the nations.... Teach these new disciples to obey all the commands I have given you"* (Matthew 28:18-20). Jesus, of course, never required any authority from the religious leaders. He had been given all authority from the Father. The Father gave Jesus the right! It was His "birthright" as the eternal Son of God. And as His followers, we have "the right" as children of God. We have the right – and the mandate – to go and make disciples of all peoples. We cannot step back. We must press forward under His authority – under His right. And we must proclaim His truth boldly and rightly – which, my friends, will probably not be "safely". After all, He called us to take up the cross and follow Him – and there wasn't anything safe about His journey.

* * *

6

WHICH SON TRULY OBEYED?

"But what do you think about this? A man with two sons told the older boy, 'Son, go out and work in the vineyard today.' The son answered, 'No, I won't go,' but later he changed his mind and went anyway. Then the father told the other son, 'You go,' and he said, 'Yes, sir, I will.' But he didn't go. "Which of the two obeyed his father? They replied, "The first." Then Jesus explained His meaning: "I tell you the truth, corrupt tax collectors and prostitutes will get into the Kingdom of God before you do. For John the Baptist came and showed you the right way to live, but you didn't believe him, while tax collectors and prostitutes did. And even when you saw this happening, you refused to believe him and repent of your sins."

Matthew 21:28-32

* * *

It's still the third day of the week. Jesus had arrived in the temple to teach, and immediately the priests and elders came to confront Him. As we saw in chapter 5, Jesus has just responded to their demand to tell them by whose authority He does what He does, by asking them from whom John the Baptist's authority came. Because of their rejection of John and the message of God's truth that he delivered, combined with their realization that if they now denounced John then the people would rise up against them, they had refused to answer Jesus' question. Before the religious leaders can scatter to avoid any further light being shone on their sin, Jesus immediately confronts them with a trilogy of parables. Here is the first of the three:

A man with two sons told the older boy, 'Son, go out and work in the vineyard today.' The son answered, 'No, I won't go,' but later he changed his mind and went anyway. Then the father told the other son, 'You go,' and he said, 'Yes, sir, I will.' But he didn't go. "Which of the two obeyed his father?

As Jesus later explains, the first son represents the tax collectors and prostitutes – those who the religious leaders would deem unworthy. That first son initially rejects his father and refuses to go out into the vineyard. But later in the day, he changes his mind. He repents and, in so doing, makes a 180 degree turn and does what the father told him to do. The second son tells the father that he will work in the vineyard, but, in fact, does not do so. He represents the religious leaders, who on the outside want everyone to believe that they are obedient sons of God, whereas in reality they have rebelled against Him and rejected His word. Jesus left no doubt with the priests and elders as to who was who in the parable. Although the religious leaders answered rightly as to which son truly obeyed the father, they took even greater offense from Jesus' remarks instead of being convicted of their sin.

This parable is as relevant today as it was the day Jesus taught it. There are still many who want to give an outward appearance of godliness. Like the religious leaders that Jesus is confronting, they know the jargon. They know the rituals. They know how to act. They are active in church. They may possibly be leaders in the church. But in all reality, there has been no transformation in their lives. The apostle Paul cautioned Timothy that in the last days, the numbers of these people within the church would be on the increase. He said, "*They will act religious, but they will reject the power that could make them godly. Stay away from people like that*" (2 Timothy 3:5).

Paul described that transformation clearly to the church in Corinth when he wrote, "*So we have stopped evaluating others from a human point of view. At one time we thought of Christ merely from a human point of view. How differently we know Him now! This means that anyone who belongs to Christ has become a new person. The old life is gone; a new life has begun!*" (2 Corinthians 5:16-17).

A number of years ago, we moved from Southeast Florida to Central Virginia. We tell folks that we moved "south" to Virginia. Even though geographically we didn't, culturally we did. For the first time in our lives, we lived in the "proper south". We quickly observed that unlike South Florida, there is more of a pretense of religion in the "proper south". We observed churches on most every corner. But we quickly began to recognize that there were many who "acted religious" but had truly never experienced "new life".

As i write this, i am reminded of two dear friends who, when i first met them, didn't know one another. Their names are Mike and Bill. i met them both within a matter of days after they had surrendered their respective lives to Christ. They were both middle-aged and had lived their younger lives apart from a relationship with Jesus. Both of them had the scars to prove it. They hadn't learned the religious jargon yet. They were both as new in their faith as you can possibly be. But though they didn't know all of the right words, there was an aura about them that reflected a changed life – a life that reflected Christ. There wasn't anything contrived. There was a genuine, authentic and transparent transformation. And i am grateful to be able to tell you, over twenty years later, that genuine and authentic walk with Christ has not dimmed. These guys had been transformed by Christ into "new persons", scars and all!

i pray that has been your experience. i pray that, like the "first son" in Jesus' parable, you have repented of your sin, surrendered your life to Christ and been transformed by the power of the gospel – scars and all! The first son may have come "late", but gratefully he came.

The last days that Paul references in 2 Timothy 3 have never been closer than they are right now. These cannot be days for religious pretense and jargon. *"For God says, 'At just the right time, I heard you. On the day of salvation, I helped you." Indeed, the "right time" is now. Today is the day of salvation'"* (2 Corinthians 6:2).

The religious leaders walked away from Jesus offended, bitter and hardhearted. They had a religion of exterior decorations, with nothing real inside. Don't make that same mistake! Jesus didn't come to redecorate your life; He came to make it new! If you would take up the cross and follow Him, first make sure that your life has been made new. Then head on out into the vineyard. The Father is waiting for you.

* * *

7

THE WICKED FARMERS

Then Jesus began teaching them with stories: "A man planted a vineyard. He built a wall around it, dug a pit for pressing out the grape juice, and built a lookout tower. Then he leased the vineyard to tenant farmers and moved to another country. At the time of the grape harvest, he sent one of his servants to collect his share of the crop. But the farmers grabbed the servant, beat him up, and sent him back empty-handed. The owner then sent another servant, but they insulted him and beat him over the head. The next servant he sent was killed. Others he sent were either beaten or killed, until there was only one left — his son whom he loved dearly. The owner finally sent him, thinking, 'Surely they will respect my son.' But the tenant farmers said to one another, 'Here comes the heir to this estate. Let's kill him and get the estate for ourselves!' So they grabbed him and murdered him and threw his body out of the vineyard. What do you suppose the owner of the vineyard will do?" Jesus asked. "I'll tell you — he will come and kill those farmers and lease the vineyard to others. Didn't you ever read this in the Scriptures?

'The stone that the builders rejected has now become the cornerstone.
This is the Lord's doing, and it is wonderful to see.'"

The religious leaders wanted to arrest Jesus because they realized He was telling the story against them — they were the wicked farmers. But they were afraid of the crowd, so they left Him and went away.
Mark 12:1-12

* * *

Once more, Jesus confronted the religious leaders, before they could scatter away, using the second parable of the trilogy with imagery that was very clear to them. The prophet Isaiah had described the vineyard as the nation of Israel (Isaiah 5:1-7). God had planted His people. He had led them out of bondage. He had made them a mighty nation, holy unto Himself. He had provided for them. He had protected them. He had "cultivated" them. Their whole purpose for existence was to worship Him, and to be a people through whom He made His Name known and brought glory to Himself. The religious leaders were blind to a lot of things, but they were not blind to that! So as Jesus told this story, there was no mistaking who and what He was talking about. Jesus was speaking to the religious leaders in the most pointed and direct parable of His ministry.

The owner and planter of the vineyard is the Father. The vineyard is supposed to bear the fruit of worship and obedience. The servants He sends are the prophets. The wicked tenant farmers are the religious leaders. Obviously, the son whom the Father "loved dearly" is Jesus. Their plan to kill Jesus so that they can "maintain control" is clearly exposed. Jesus has again shined His light on their darkness and their sinful plans. Jesus then asks the leaders, *"What do you suppose the owner of the vineyard will do?"* Matthew in his account records, *"The religious leaders replied, 'He will put the wicked men to a horrible death and lease the vineyard to others who will give him his share of the crop after each harvest'"* (Matthew 21:41). In so replying, they condemned themselves.

With every fiber of their being raging inside them, they wanted to extinguish the light and arrest Him right then. But they feared how the crowd might react, so they looked for a way to hastily slither away. But before they could get away, Jesus continued by telling them the judgement they would experience. That judgement was in fact fulfilled in 70 A.D. when Titus, then a Roman military commander, besieged and captured Jerusalem, destroying the city and burning and destroying the Temple. The people were killed, or enslaved and taken to Rome.

As Jesus concluded the parable, He quoted the Messianic Psalm 118:22-23 – *"The stone that the builders rejected has now become the cornerstone. This is the Lord's doing, and it is wonderful to see."* In so doing, He again brought judgement on the Pharisees, because they were the "builders" who had rejected Jesus, their promised Messiah. To them, He had become a stumbling block, threatening their plans and their selfish ambitions. And their rejection was manifested in His coming crucifixion. But Jesus very clearly told them that there was nothing they could do to Him that had not been permitted by the Father. The Pharisees may have plotted to kill Jesus, but it was all a part of the Father's plan of redemption. As the prophet Isaiah wrote, *"Therefore, this is what the Sovereign Lord says: 'Look! I am placing a foundation stone in Jerusalem, a firm and tested stone. It is a precious cornerstone that is safe to build on. Whoever believes need never be shaken'"* (Isaiah 28:16). Jesus is the Cornerstone – the One through whom the Father has reconciled His creation back to Himself, through His crucifixion and His resurrection. He is the One – and only One – on whom the true temple can be built. Jesus, in essence, was saying to the religious leaders the same thing Joseph had said to his brothers: *"you meant evil against me, but God meant it for good in order to bring about this present result, to preserve many people alive"* (Genesis 50:20 NASB).

Several weeks later, after Pentecost, the apostles Peter and John were standing before these very leaders. And they recalled what Jesus had said on this day in the temple, as they too bore witness:

"Then Peter, filled with the Holy Spirit, said to them, 'Rulers and elders of our people, are we being questioned today because we've done a good deed for a crippled man? Do you want to know how he was healed? Let me clearly state to all of you and to all the people of Israel that he was healed by the powerful name of Jesus Christ the Nazarene, the man you crucified but whom God raised from the dead. For Jesus is the one referred to in the Scriptures, where it says,
'The stone that you builders rejected
has now become the cornerstone.'
There is salvation in no one else! God has given no other name under heaven by which we must be saved"
(Acts 4:8-12).

This parable was a condemnation of the religious leaders, and it stands as a condemnation of anyone who would deny Jesus as the Messiah, the Son of the Living God. But if we are to take up the cross and follow Him, we can take it up with the confidence and assurance that He is our Cornerstone, our One Foundation, by Whom we are saved and by Whom all must be saved. The religious leaders were the wicked farmers that slithered away, but we must be His faithful followers that boldly proclaim that Good News from the rooftops!

* * *

8

THE MARRIAGE FEAST

Jesus also told them other parables. He said, "The Kingdom of Heaven can be illustrated by the story of a king who prepared a great wedding feast for his son. When the banquet was ready, he sent his servants to notify those who were invited. But they all refused to come! "So he sent other servants to tell them, 'The feast has been prepared. The bulls and fattened cattle have been killed, and everything is ready. Come to the banquet!' But the guests he had invited ignored them and went their own way, one to his farm, another to his business. Others seized his messengers and insulted them and killed them. "The king was furious, and he sent out his army to destroy the murderers and burn their town. And he said to his servants, 'The wedding feast is ready, and the guests I invited aren't worthy of the honor. Now go out to the street corners and invite everyone you see.' So the servants brought in everyone they could find, good and bad alike, and the banquet hall was filled with guests. "But when the king came in to meet the guests, he noticed a man who wasn't wearing the proper clothes for a wedding. 'Friend,' he asked, 'how is it that you are here without wedding clothes?' But the man had no reply. Then the king said to his aides, 'Bind his hands and feet and throw him into the outer darkness, where there will be weeping and gnashing of teeth.' For many are called, but few are chosen."

Matthew 22:1-14

* * *

Just before the religious leaders scattered, Jesus had one more indictment for them through this third parable of the trilogy. In the first parable (chapter 6), He indicted them for failing to be obedient sons. In the second (chapter 7), He called them out for their attempts to commandeer the Kingdom for their own selfish ends, persecuting and killing God's messengers, the prophets, and even His Son. In this third of the three, Jesus rebuked them for throwing away the honor and privilege of their covenant relationship with God, thereby dishonoring the Almighty and the Son.

The main character of this parable is the king, representing God the Father. His son represents Jesus the Messiah. Although He is not an active character in the parable itself, He is central to its meaning, serving as the reason for the wedding banquet. The feast represented the future union of the bridegroom (Jesus) with His bride (the church). Participation in this celebration presupposes that he/she has placed his/her faith in Jesus and become a part of His people (His church). The invitation to the feast was an invitation to salvation and it was an invitation to enjoy the king's blessing – the "food" of the feast, as well as the honor of being invited.

As in the second parable, the king sent two groups of servants as messengers. The first group went out to those who had been invited to the banquet to tell them to come. The invitees, representing Israel, God's chosen people (and its leaders in particular), knew they were supposed to attend the celebration – they had already been invited. The messengers (the prophets) informed them that it was time to attend. However, the invitees refused to accept the invitation. But this invitation was truly a command. To disregard this invitation was not an option; rejection went beyond discourtesy to the point of rebellious disobedience. Israel had not been invited but *commanded* to pay the price and reap the blessing of Kingdom citizenship. And yet they rejected his invitation and, in so doing, rejected the king.

But the king was patient, even in the face of such discourtesy, to send a second group of messengers to the people. This group conveyed the Lord's patient pleading with His rebellious people over the centuries through His prophets, as well as John the Baptist, and would continue through the apostles. The message they carried to the people was, "I have gone to a lot of trouble and great expense to prepare this banquet. Dinner is on the table. It is a magnificent feast! Only the best has been prepared. Come celebrate with us!" Participation in the feast, in honor of the king's son, was both a responsibility and a privilege. The king was appealing, "Come honor my son and enjoy the honor of my blessing."

. . .

This second group of messengers received two responses – apathy and aggression. Some people invited to the wedding feast thought they had more important things to do. They chose to ignore the messengers and tend to their fields and businesses – the everyday pursuits that had taken possession of their hearts. But others responded like the tenants in the second parable, mistreating and killing the messengers. The one significant difference between the action of these invited wedding guests and that of the tenants in the second parable was that the wedding guests had no motive for mistreating and killing the king's servants. The murder of the messengers and the message of rejection to the king and his son were irrational, since the king intended only good by his invitation.

God's offer of a covenant relationship with Israel carried a price for those who accepted it, but the blessing and honor that the Kingdom citizen received would far outweigh the cost of discipleship. God offered redemption, forgiveness, salvation, and reward. Those who rejected God's grace were displaying blindness to the point of insanity. They returned a curse for God's blessing.

Because of their perverted attitude, the king sent a third messenger, his army. They would serve as messengers of judgment for the irrational rebellion of these unwilling wedding guests. The armies destroyed the murderers and burned their cities. This signified God's judgment of those who reject His covenant relationship.

Meanwhile, the celebration was waiting; the son was yet to be honored. So the king sent out his messengers again – but to a different set of invitees this time. The original invitees did not deserve to come. Their self-absorption and irrationality had displaced their loyalty to the king and his son. The new guests were those who would be honored by such an invitation. These were the riff-raff, the outcasts of society, that the messengers would find along the byways, including every possible prostitute and tax collector.

The messengers went out into the streets and invited all the people they could find, both good and bad. Whereas those who should have been "good" (Israel, God's chosen people) had shown themselves to be evil, the king treated all who were evil as though they were good. The impartiality of the king represented the impartial grace of God, inviting all people of all nations into the Kingdom. By extension, we can identify the king's servants or messengers now to include the apostles, the New Testament believers, and us, if we are faithful to be ambassadors of His Good News.

It was as shocking then, as it is now, that God accepts the worst of sinners unconditionally. As long as a sinner shows a willingness to accept God's grace by faith, God will transform him or her into a Kingdom citizen. With such a group of people, the king filled his wedding hall. It was a blend of good and evil, Jew and Gentile, slave and free, wealthy and poor. Truly, the Lord will fill His Kingdom with all peoples from all nations. He will reject those who refuse His invitation into honor and privilege, replacing them with true worshipers – those restored from sin by His grace.

At this point, Jesus clarified exactly who could take part in His celebration of faith. After the guests had gathered in the wedding hall, the king inspected them and discovered a man not dressed properly. In that day, wedding clothes (sometimes supplied by the host) were not a particular style of garment. But they were to be the cleanest and best clothes each person had to wear. This man was displaying disrespect by wearing less than the best available to him. The king addressed the man as "friend", implying that he was open to an explanation. But when questioned, the man had no answer. He was guilty of failure to honor the king's son in a proper manner. The proper garment represents the righteousness of Christ provided through His death. To refuse it is to refuse Christ's sacrifice. To refuse Christ is to refuse life. The invitation has gone out to everyone, but only those wearing the righteousness of Christ can enter into the marriage feast. There is an open invitation to the wedding feast, but there is a dress code.

There will be many shocked church attenders when the Lord returns, who think that they have responded to the Lord's invitation to come to the banquet of heaven, but in fact have never really, with their hearts, surrendered their lives to enter into His presence. They walked in the door of the church, but they never opened the door of their heart to Him. With their lips they honor Him, but their hearts are far away. It's as though they were never even there. When the Master says, "Change your clothes," they adjust their collars or shine their shoes, or tidy up their shirts or pants, but they won't take off those cherished habits. They won't strip away their selfish ambition, or the love of money, or the addiction to pornography, or whatever else has control of their lives. They want the hope of heaven, but they won't dress for heaven. They won't change their clothes. And Jesus says in the end on the graduation day, "Bind him hand and foot and cast him into outer darkness. He never really enrolled with his heart. It was all a show."

This disrespectful man was recognized as ill-prepared as every imposter will be. At the king's command, he was bound and thrown into the darkness. This represents exclusion and separation from the celebration in the Kingdom of light and truth. The weeping and gnashing of teeth indicates eternal extreme pain and sorrow.

Jesus' closing statement had a proverbial tone. Note that He did not say that *all* men and women are called. But *many* are invited. God has issued to a wide audience His invitation (command) to join with Him in covenant relationship. But few are chosen. Not everyone who is invited will be among the chosen. The adjective *chosen* suggests that the "decision" is not totally in our hands, but it is a response to God's sovereign election. In particular, the unbelieving religious leaders were among those called but not chosen.

The parable's basic lessons are clear. The king issued a gracious invitation to people he wished to view as friends. They rejected the invitation. Their rejection sparked a severe judgment from the king. Their rejection caused the king to extend the invitation even further to anyone who would come. Their refusal served to open the gates wide. But though the gates were thrown wide open, those actually chosen were limited by specific criteria – the righteousness of Christ.

We are invited guests. There is a seat at the celebration with our name on it if we have surrendered our life to Christ. But we have also been called to be the messengers extending the king's invitation to those who have not yet heard it. The gates are open wide – whomsoever will may come. But many have yet to hear that they have been invited. There is no substitute for the true gospel – the Good News. There is only one way by which we can be saved. But as we have previously said – it's only Good News if it gets there in time!

* * *

9

GIVE TO GOD WHAT BELONGS TO HIM

Watching for their opportunity, the leaders sent spies pretending to be honest men. They tried to get Jesus to say something that could be reported to the Roman governor, so he would arrest Jesus. "Teacher," they said, "we know that You speak and teach what is right and are not influenced by what others think. You teach the way of God truthfully. Now tell us — is it right for us to pay taxes to Caesar or not?" He saw through their trickery and said, "Show Me a Roman coin. Whose picture and title are stamped on it?" "Caesar's," they replied. "Well then," He said, "give to Caesar what belongs to Caesar, and give to God what belongs to God." So they failed to trap Him by what He said in front of the people. Instead, they were amazed by His answer, and they became silent.

Luke 20:20-26

* * *

The religious leaders withdrew from the courtyard in the temple to escape the light that Jesus was shining on them and their sinful motives. They sequestered themselves behind closed doors – and away from piercing eyes – so that they could discuss their dark plans to kill Jesus safely away from the light. They needed to catch Jesus saying something that would be so egregious that the Roman authorities would permit His crucifixion. So the logical first attempt was to trap Him in making a statement against Roman authority. And who better to pose the question than supporters of King Herod (Herodians)?

Though the Pharisees and the Herodians were enemies of one another,

Jesus was their common enemy. The Herodians saw Jesus as a threat to Roman rule. Without Roman support, King Herod would be unable to retain the power and position that Roman soldiers guaranteed him. Without Herod, the Herodians would lose whatever benefits and advantages they enjoyed as loyal supporters of King Herod. Though the Pharisees resented Rome, they had learned how to survive (and profit) within the rule of their Roman oppressors. And though they viewed Herod and his Edomite supporters as interlopers, Jesus was now a much bigger threat to their continued profit and power over the people. Believing the principle that "the enemy of my enemy is my friend", the Pharisees and the Herodians formed an alliance to entrap Jesus.

The Herodians began their questioning by flattering Jesus in an attempt to disarm Him. *"Teacher, we know that You speak and teach what is right and are not influenced by what others think. You teach the way of God truthfully."* Jesus knew their hearts. He knew the evil motivation behind their question. He wasn't drawn in by their feeble attempt to manipulate Him through flattery. We, however, would be wise to remember that one of the most common ploys of Satan is to begin his attempts of manipulation through flattery or half-truths. Though we rarely will have the clear understanding that Jesus had of the true motivation behind questions that are being asked of us, be wary of questions that are preceded by veiled flattery.

Next came their big question. *"Is it right for us to pay taxes to Caesar or not?"* i think it was difficult for them to mask the smug smiles that were in their hearts after they asked their question. They were confident that they had just trapped Jesus. There was no good way for Him to answer that question. All they needed to do now was to wait for Him to answer the question in one way or the other, and He would no longer be a problem. The people of Israel were an occupied nation required to pay taxes to their Roman oppressors. Every tax payment was another expression of the Roman boot pressing down on the necks of the people. If Jesus spoke in favor of paying the tax, the Jews would rise up against Him. If Jesus opposed the tax, He would be in trouble with Rome. Regardless, the Herodians had Jesus right where they wanted Him.

At that moment, Jesus had a choice. He could call out the Herodians and the Pharisees for their evil intent and their hypocrisy and refuse to answer them. Or He could use this moment as an opportunity to silence His enemies and teach the people an important truth.

. . .

Either Jesus didn't have a coin in His pocket, or He wanted to reinforce that the Kingdom of God was about so much more than money. So, Jesus asked His questioners to produce a coin. In so doing, they illustrated that they possessed the coins, and, in their use of them, showed that they deemed them to have value. As they did, He asked, *"Whose picture and title are stamped on it?"* By the simple fact that the coins bore the image of Caesar, they were acknowledging and accepting His authority. At that point, Jesus differentiated between that which belongs to Caesar and that which belongs to God, and in so doing, taught them – and us – several important truths.

If we would honor God, we must honor and obey the rulers whom God has placed, or allowed to be placed, in authority over us. Paul would later write. *"Everyone must submit to governing authorities. For all authority comes from God, and those in positions of authority have been placed there by God.... So you must submit to them, not only to avoid punishment, but also to keep a clear conscience.... Give to everyone what you owe them: Pay your taxes and government fees to those who collect them, and give respect and honor to those who are in authority"* (Romans 13:1-7). (By the way, bear in mind that Nero, the persecutor of Christians, was the Roman emperor when Paul wrote these words.) As followers of Christ, we have dual citizenship. Though heaven is our home, we must respect our earthly authority, by obeying the laws – unless they are in direct violation of God's law (Acts 5:29). We must pay our rightful taxes, being above reproach in how we do so. In this answer, Jesus was clearly teaching that taxes were merely the citizen's responsibility to pay back for services performed. And we must pray for all of those who are in authority – whether we agree with them or not – and whether they are acting in a godly way or not. In honoring earthy authority, we are honoring God.

An important, quick side road: Respecting and honoring those in authority does not mean that we blindly and silently accept injustice and sinful actions. We have been called to be salt and light. We are to be voices for what is right, what is God-honoring, and that which aligns with the truth of His Word. We are not to sit silently by as injustice is being perpetrated by governmental authority. BUT, we must challenge and work to change it in a way that is God-honoring and is respectful of positions of authority. We are living in a day and time when godless actions are being confronted in ungodly ways by people who profess to be God's people. We would be wise to pay heed to the words of Jesus and the apostle Paul!

. . .

Second, we must honor and obey God. He is our creator. He has stamped each one of us with His image. All that we have – and all that we are – is from Him. Our honor to Him is not through simple coinage; our honor to Him is through the submission of the totality of our lives in worship of Him. This is the primary truth Jesus was teaching that day. The religious leaders wanted to elevate the issue of money and taxes to entrap Jesus because they failed to live out this important truth. Honoring and obeying include surrender and submission to the Father, His Son and His Spirit. We are most like the Pharisees and the Herodians when we elevate issues of money over being wholly submitted and surrendered to our Lord.

If we would take up the cross and follow Jesus, yes, we must give to "Caesar what belongs to him", but more importantly, we must give to God all that belongs to Him – our very lives!

* * *

10

ONE BRIDE FOR SEVEN BROTHERS

That same day, Jesus was approached by some Sadducees — religious leaders who say there is no resurrection from the dead. They posed this question: "Teacher, Moses said, 'If a man dies without children, his brother should marry the widow and have a child who will carry on the brother's name.' Well, suppose there were seven brothers. The oldest one married and then died without children, so his brother married the widow. But the second brother also died, and the third brother married her. This continued with all seven of them. Last of all, the woman also died. So tell us, whose wife will she be in the resurrection? For all seven were married to her." Jesus replied, "Your mistake is that you don't know the Scriptures, and you don't know the power of God. For when the dead rise, they will neither marry nor be given in marriage. In this respect they will be like the angels in heaven. "But now, as to whether there will be a resurrection of the dead —haven't you ever read about this in the Scriptures? Long after Abraham, Isaac, and Jacob had died, God said, 'I am the God of Abraham, the God of Isaac, and the God of Jacob.' So He is the God of the living, not the dead." When the crowds heard Him, they were astounded at His teaching.

Matthew 22:23-33

* * *

The Herodians had their time at bat, and Jesus struck them out! So now it's the Sadducees time at bat. Hopefully you are seeing that none of these questions are being asked of Jesus "by chance" or at random. These questions are all being orchestrated from behind the scenes with one clear purpose in mind.

. . .

Though the Pharisees and Sadducees both made up the ruling body called the Sanhedrin, the groups were deeply divided over doctrinal beliefs. The Pharisees accepted the authority of the five Books of Moses (known as the Torah), as well as the oral teachings of laws, commands and traditions handed down over the years (known as the Talmud). The Sadducees, however, did not accept the authority of the Talmud, or any of the wisdom or prophetic books. The Pharisees believed in the resurrection of the dead, but the Sadducees did not believe in angels, the spirit world or the resurrection of the dead (Acts 23:8). As you can imagine, the two groups often debated their differences to no satisfactory conclusion. i am of the belief that this question being posed to Jesus is one that the two groups had debated ad nauseam. But today the two groups had come to at least one point of agreement – to pose the question to Jesus. Finally, unbeknownst to them, they brought the question to the only One who could answer them with complete authority!

i have entitled this chapter "One Bride For Seven Brothers". i'm playing off the title of a 1954 American musical film entitled "Seven Brides For Seven Brothers". Set in the mid-1800's, it is the story of *"Adam, a backwoodsman, who is the eldest of seven brothers, and goes to town to get a wife. He convinces Milly to marry him that same day. When they return to his backwoods home, she discovers he has six brothers - all living in his cabin"* (Source: IMDb). She is only married to one, but she finds she is having to care for seven – all at the same time. And the story goes from there. In this question being posed to Jesus, there is only one bride, and her husband has died. According to the Jewish law of "levirate" marriage (levirate meaning "a husband's brother"), *"if two brothers are living together on the same property and one of them dies without a son, his widow may not be married to anyone from outside the family. Instead, her husband's brother should marry her…"* (Deuteronomy 25:5). The purpose of the custom was to preserve a man's name if he should die without a male heir. (Incidentally, levirate marriage is still practiced today in parts of the world.) Apparently in the scenario being posed to Jesus, each of the remaining six brothers, after having fulfilled his responsibility to the Law by taking her to be his wife, dies. Thus, she has been married to each of the seven. This premise was, in fact, one of the reasons that Sadducees refused to believe in the resurrection.

Though the Pharisees believed in the resurrection of the dead, their understanding was errant. They believed that the afterlife was merely an extension of the present. They believed that whatever relationships, whatever physical defects or deformities, whatever scars, even to the point that whatever clothes you had on when you died, is exactly what you'd be like in the next life. Their false thinking assisted in the false thinking of the Sadducees. Thus, the idea that a woman could have multiple husbands was inconceivable. Therefore, as their logic played out, the resurrection of the dead was inconceivable.

And how does Jesus respond? He doesn't pull any punches! He says, *"Your mistake is that you don't know the Scriptures, and you don't know the power of God."* These were probably two areas on which the Sadducees prided themselves as being the authority – knowing the Scriptures and knowing the power of God. And Jesus challenged them right at the heart of their pride. To quote John MacArthur, Jesus in essence is saying, *"Had you known the Scriptures you would have known God promises resurrection. Had you known the power of God you would have known that God can raise people in a state where that's not going to be an issue. If you knew the power of God, you would know that He wouldn't recreate people with the same problems as here. He's not limited to that, as if God has spent all His creative power on the way we are and can't improve on it? If you knew the power of God and if you knew the Scriptures, you wouldn't be so spaced-out in your thinking."* Jesus tells them with authority that there will be no marriage in heaven. There will be no death. There will be no childbirth. It will no longer be necessary to bear children to replace those that die. Sex, marriage, reproduction, childbirth, all that is for this life only, not the next life. God's creation of life will be complete. God is raising up worshipers in this life that will worship Him for eternity in the next life. We, too, can become disoriented – just like the Pharisees and the Sadducees – when we view the next life as a mere extension of this one.

We can also become disoriented when we think of life on this side of glory as our primary life. The reality is that life on this side is preparation for eternity; the other side is eternity. As Jesus said, *"Long after Abraham, Isaac, and Jacob had died, God said to Moses, 'I am the God of Abraham, the God of Isaac, and the God of Jacob.' So He is the God of the living, not the dead. You have made a serious error"* (Mark 12:26b-27).

And when Jesus concluded, you could have heard a pin drop. The crowd was astounded by His teaching and the authority with which He spoke. And the Sadducees were silenced. As Luke writes, *"No one dared to ask Him any more questions"* (Luke 20:40).

There are still questions even in our minds. Though Scripture and Jesus are clear about the fact of the resurrection and the work that Christ has completed to "prepare a place for us" (John 14:2), there are still questions we have that won't be answered until we are there. There is a great cloud of witnesses who have gone before us who now understand. And, if we are followers of our Lord Jesus Christ, we, too, will one day join them either at the time of our death – or upon His return – whichever occurs first.

As we take up the cross and follow our Master, let us be careful to not make a serious error. There is but one bride – the Church – and one day soon, we are going to meet our Groom – our Lord and Savior, Jesus Christ!

* * *

11

THE MOST IMPORTANT COMMANDMENT

One of the teachers of religious law was standing there listening to the debate. He realized that Jesus had answered well, so he asked, "Of all the commandments, which is the most important?" Jesus replied, "The most important commandment is this: 'Listen, O Israel! The Lord our God is the one and only Lord. And you must love the Lord your God with all your heart, all your soul, all your mind, and all your strength.' The second is equally important: 'Love your neighbor as yourself.' No other commandment is greater than these." The teacher of religious law replied, "Well said, Teacher. You have spoken the truth by saying that there is only one God and no other. And I know it is important to love Him with all my heart and all my understanding and all my strength, and to love my neighbor as myself. This is more important than to offer all of the burnt offerings and sacrifices required in the law." Realizing how much the man understood, Jesus said to him, "You are not far from the Kingdom of God." And after that, no one dared to ask Him any more questions.

Mark 12:28-34

* * *

Some of the greatest teaching from Jesus was in response to questions that were intended to trap Him. As we look at this encounter, it's still the second day of the week. The Sanhedrin has put forth the Herodians and the Sadducees, both of whom have failed miserably in trapping Jesus. So they sent out a lawyer – an expert in religious law.

As we saw in chapter 50 of ***Walking With The Master***, the scribes (the lawyers) had determined that the Jews were obligated to obey 613 mitzvah (precepts and commandments) recorded in the Torah. 365 of them were negative commands to abstain from certain acts. Interestingly, that was one for each day of the year (excluding leap years). 248 were positive commandments which outlined acts to be performed. It was said that the number 248 coincided with the number of bones and main organs in the human body. And that was just in the Torah! That didn't include the exhaustive code of conduct to be practiced as it related to rituals, worship practices, God-man and interpersonal relationships that made up the Talmud. That was a lot of which to keep track! No wonder they needed a team of lawyers to keep a close eye! One of the favorite pastimes of the scribes was discussing which of these divine commandments was the greatest. These men, who were considered to be the greatest religious minds in the land, had spent countless hours in debate over the answer to that question, and had never come to a resolution. So, at the behest of the Sanhedrin in their "game" of "let's trap Jesus", one of them poses the question to Jesus, *"Of all the commandments, which is the most important?"*

Bear in mind, the scribes had debated this ad nauseam. But Jesus never blinked an eye or hesitated for even a moment. He immediately – and authoritatively – replied, quoting the confession of faith that pious Jews recited each morning and evening, called "The Shema", from Deuteronomy 6:4-5:

> *"Listen, O Israel! The Lord is our God, the Lord alone. And you must love the Lord your God with all your heart, all your soul, and all your strength."*

And He followed it up by quoting Leviticus 19:18:

> *"… love your neighbor as yourself…."*

The teachings of the religious leaders of the day had little to do with love. Their teaching stressed duty, obligation and rules. Even though they would regularly quote "The Shema", it was by rote and in word only. Very little was said or taught about love, let alone lived out. But Jesus made love the most important thing. He was teaching that love for God and love for our neighbor was the purpose of the Law and the fulfillment of the Law. He was revealing to them the truth that Paul would later write:

"Owe nothing to anyone—except for your obligation to love one another. If you love your neighbor, you will fulfill the requirements of God's law. For the commandments say, 'You must not commit adultery. You must not murder. You must not steal. You must not covet.' These—and other such commandments—are summed up in this one commandment: 'Love your neighbor as yourself.' Love does no wrong to others, so love fulfills the requirements of God's law" (Romans 13:8-10).

Warren Wiersbe says it well when he writes that Jesus was telling them that *"if we love God, we will experience His love within and will express that love to others. We do not live by rules, but by relationships – a loving relationship {with} God that enables us to have a loving relationship with others."* Again, i believe you could have heard a pin drop. The crowd – and the scribe – had never heard that truth expressed. Time and again, they had debated the Law and missed the very point of it! As Jesus' answer began to sink in, we see a moment of transparency and authenticity. The scribe, who had intended to trap Jesus, now sincerely commended Him. Imagine the Pharisees' anger as they heard their representative commending Jesus and confessing the very truth that Jesus had just spoken. The Word of God had just spoken to the man's heart and he was beginning to understand. Further Scripture came to his mind:

"You do not desire a sacrifice, or I would offer one. You do not want a burnt offering. The sacrifice You desire is a broken spirit. You will not reject a broken and repentant heart, O God" (Psalm 51:16-17).

"What can we bring to the Lord? Should we bring Him burnt offerings? Should we bow before God Most High with offerings of yearling calves? Should we offer Him thousands of rams and ten thousand rivers of olive oil? Should we sacrifice our firstborn children to pay for our sins? No, O people, the Lord has told you what is good, and this is what He requires of you: to do what is right, to love mercy, and to walk humbly with your God" (Micah 6:6-8).

So what did Jesus mean when He said to the scribe, *"You are not far from the Kingdom of God"*? i believe He was affirming the scribe as he was now facing truth honestly. The scribe was now testing his beliefs against the Word of God and not against the teachings of men. There hadn't yet been a complete change of heart, but the man had made a quantum leap in his journey toward the Kingdom of God. i pray that he made it the rest of the way. And if so, i look forward to meeting him one day in heaven. Because if i do, i believe his testimony will be very similar to that of the man who once was physically blind – *"I once was blind, but now I see"* (John 9:25).

Three up! Three down! Jesus had pitched a no-hitter. The Sanhedrin didn't have anyone else to put before Jesus that day. But as we know, they weren't done trying.

As we've seen, in every instance, Jesus responded with truth. As you take up the cross to follow Him, remember that, no matter who you face in your journey today, lies and deceit cannot survive in the light of truth. And the core of that truth is *"love the Lord your God with all your heart, all your soul, all your mind, and all your strength."* And *"love your neighbor as yourself!"* Live out that truth – and add words where appropriate!

* * *

12

WHOSE SON IS HE?

Then, surrounded by the Pharisees, Jesus asked them a question: "What do you think about the Messiah? Whose son is He?" They replied, "He is the son of David." Jesus responded, "Then why does David, speaking under the inspiration of the Spirit, call the Messiah 'my Lord'? For David said, 'The Lord said to my Lord, Sit in the place of honor at my right hand until I humble Your enemies beneath Your feet.' Since David called the Messiah 'my Lord,' how can the Messiah be his son?" No one could answer Him. And after that, no one dared to ask Him any more questions.
Matthew 22:41-46

* * *

In the preceding chapters, we have looked at how the Sanhedrin sent their ambassadors to ask questions of Jesus that they thought would trap Him. These were questions that they frequently debated among themselves, never able to come to agreement. In each instance, Jesus had responded with the absolute truth. The crowd had been amazed by His teaching. The religious leaders, having been shut down in each of their attempts, dared not ask any more questions of Jesus.

Now, Jesus has a question for them. Unlike the questions they asked of Jesus, His question to them was one in which all of them could agree upon the answer – at least initially. *"Whose son is the Messiah?"* All of them – the Pharisees, the Sadducees, the Herodians and the scribes – could confidently answer, *"He is the son of David."* They presumed that Jesus was asking them a theological question – just as they had asked Him. And this one was in their "wheel house". They knew the answer to this. They knew the promises of God through the prophets, including Jeremiah, who wrote:

"The day will come, says the Lord, when I will do for Israel and Judah all the good things I have promised them. In those days and at that time I will raise up a righteous descendant from King David's line. He will do what is just and right throughout the land. In that day Judah will be saved, and Jerusalem will live in safety. And this will be its name: 'The Lord Is Our Righteousness.' For this is what the Lord says: David will have a descendant sitting on the throne of Israel forever. And there will always be Levitical priests to offer burnt offerings and grain offerings and sacrifices to Me"
(Jeremiah 33:14-17).

But for Jesus, this was not a theological question, this was a personal question, on par with when He asked His disciples, *"Who do you say that I am?"* (Matthew 16:15). So Jesus followed up with a second question, *"Why does David, speaking under the inspiration of the Spirit, call the Messiah 'my Lord'?"* He was quoting David, from Psalm 110:1:

"The LORD said to my Lord, "Sit in the place of honor at My right hand until I humble Your enemies, making them a footstool under Your feet."

Every one of these religious leaders knew that this passage referred to the Messiah, and they knew that only the Messiah could sit at the right hand of the Lord God Jehovah. Not a one of them could question the authority or the accuracy of the text. Which led Jesus to ask His third question: *"Since David called the Messiah 'my Lord,' how can the Messiah be his son?"* How can the Messiah be both David's Son and David's Lord? Not one of the religious leaders dared to consider the possibility of the Messiah being both. Like the other theological issues we have looked at, the leaders had debated this truth but never come to agreement. One picture of the Messiah in the Old Testament had been as the Son of Man (Jeremiah 33), another as the Son of God (Psalm 110). Another picture had shown Him to be a Suffering Servant (Isaiah 53). Still others showed Him to be a Reigning Monarch (Zechariah 9). Were there to be two Messiahs? How could God's Servant suffer and die? Peter would later write, *"This salvation was something even the prophets wanted to know more about when they prophesied about this gracious salvation prepared for you. They wondered what time or situation the Spirit of Christ within them was talking about when He told them in advance about Christ's suffering and His great glory afterward"* (1 Peter 1:10-11).

The fact of the matter is that the Answer was standing right before them, but their eyes – and hearts – were blind to the truth. Because the only answer is that as God, the Messiah is David's Lord and, as man, He is David's Son. The Messiah is both the Son of God AND the Son of Man. He could not be one or the other, He must be both. The crowds had already declared Jesus to be the Messiah. They had shouted it throughout the city as Jesus entered two days before. In so doing, they were unknowingly declaring His deity, as well as His humanity. But the leaders refused to consider that possibility. It was a question whose answer could only be given with praise. But their response was silence. Two days earlier, as He entered Jerusalem, some of the Pharisees had told Him to rebuke the crowd for declaring Him to be the Messiah. Jesus had responded, *"I tell you, if these were silent, the very stones would cry out"* (Luke 19:40). i believe as the Pharisees stood there now in silence, the stones were crying out – but regrettably their ears were deafened to hear them. The Pharisees didn't have the courage to question Him further, nor did they have the courage to face the truth and act on it. And in so doing, they condemned themselves to eternal damnation.

In the 4th century, Augustine wrote the confession, *"Christ is both David's Son and David's Lord: David's Lord always, David's Son in time. David's Lord, born of the substance of his Father; David's Son, born of the Virgin Mary, conceived by the Holy Spirit. Let us hold fast both."*

Every one of us have stood, or are standing, at the crossroad of that life or death decision. It is not a theological question; it's a personal question. Before we can ever take up the cross to follow Jesus, we must answer the question of Whose Son He is. The religious leaders were so blinded by tradition, selfish ambition, and pride that they would not see the truth and act on it. Will we stand silent with them, or stand boldly and join Augustine in confessing who Jesus is – and be saved?

* * *

13

IT'S NOT THE SEAT THAT MAKES THE MAN

Then Jesus said to the crowds and to His disciples, "The teachers of religious law and the Pharisees are the official interpreters of the law of Moses. So practice and obey whatever they tell you, but don't follow their example. For they don't practice what they teach. They crush people with unbearable religious demands and never lift a finger to ease the burden. "Everything they do is for show. On their arms they wear extra wide prayer boxes with Scripture verses inside, and they wear robes with extra-long tassels. And they love to sit at the head table at banquets and in the seats of honor in the synagogues. They love to receive respectful greetings as they walk in the marketplaces, and to be called 'Rabbi'. "Don't let anyone call you 'Rabbi,' for you have only one teacher, and all of you are equal as brothers and sisters. And don't address anyone here on earth as 'Father,' for only God in heaven is your Father. And don't let anyone call you 'Teacher,' for you have only one teacher, the Messiah. The greatest among you must be a servant. But those who exalt themselves will be humbled, and those who humble themselves will be exalted."

Matthew 23:1-12

* * *

Before we delve into this passage, just a few reminders about the Pharisees, so that we have some context. The role of the Pharisees did not exist prior to the middle of the 2nd Century BC. The Hellenistic rule of Judea and the surrounding area was overthrown through the Maccabean Revolt of 165 BC. Soon after, a new monarchy was formed which established priests as the political, as well as religious, authority. The Pharisee (or "separatist") party emerged as a sect of scribes and sages from within the larger group. The Pharisees were considered the most expert and accurate expositors of Jewish law. In contrast to the Sadducees, who came from the more wealthy and elite strata of Jewish society, the Pharisees were more eclectic and popular with the common people. In addition to the written Scriptures, the Pharisees were the preservers and promoters of the oral law and traditions. Pharisaic Judaism is considered by many to be the progenitor of Rabbinic Judaism which influences all mainstream forms of Judaism today. Though the Pharisees were initially more welcoming to Roman rule because they believed it would enable the more Hellenistic influence of the Sadducees on Judaism to be diminished, the tide turned at the end of the 1st Century BC. Thus, in the time period of the Gospels, the Sadducees were more politically aligned with Rome, and controlled the Temple and the financial enterprise of Judaism, whereby the Pharisees controlled the synagogues and enjoyed more of the favor of the common Jews. In Jesus' day, there would have been approximately 6,000 Pharisees. They were seen as, and set themselves up to be, the authorities of the Law and the religious rulers over the people. They enjoyed a followship by the people. That is until John the Baptist, and then Jesus, arrived on the scene and began to call them out.

Now, it is important to remember that not all Pharisees were identical in their beliefs. Though the majority had come to the place of seeing Jesus as a threat to their position and power, there were some in their midst who were drawn to the teachings of Jesus – Nicodemus, Joseph of Arimathea, the unnamed Pharisee in Mark 12:33-34 that we looked at in chapter 11, and possibly Gamaliel (Acts 5:34), to name a few.

In this passage, we see our Lord's last public message, and it is a scathing denunciation of the false religion created by the Pharisees that paraded under the guise of truth. Bear in mind that given the popularity of the Pharisees, many of the people in the crowd would have been aghast at Jesus' remarks as He called them out for sitting in seats for which they were not worthy.

<u>First, they had placed themselves in the seat of Moses</u> (vs. 2), as interpreters and arbitrators of the Law. They were not given that authority by God through Scripture. Therefore they had no God-given right to interpret or establish Law. Anything that they taught that was outside of Scripture was without foundation. The authority was Scripture and not their position. Jesus told the people that they were to obey the Word of God that the Pharisees taught, but not their traditions and man-made rules.

. . .

What's more, Jesus said, they were not practicing and obeying Scripture themselves. They were teaching one way, and living another. Jesus denounced their hypocrisy (vs. 3), both for their outward actions and their inner hearts (vs. 4). They were practicing a religion of rules and not a life of loving, honoring and following the Father. It was a religion that placed crushing demands and burdens on the people, but never reflected the love of God. Jesus taught that His yoke is easy to bear, and His burden is light (Matthew 11:30). The Pharisees had been teaching the absolute opposite and placing unreasonable burdens on the people.

Second, they had placed themselves in the seat of honor (vs. 6). They sought to draw attention to themselves. They loved the recognition, the respect, the prestige and the honor of their position. This meant using religious ornaments to call attention to their piety. They sought the accolades of man and to be served by all around them. No wonder the disciples had been confused when they saw Jesus get up from His seat to wash their feet. Jesus had come to seek and to serve. The religious leaders, whose teachings they had grown up under, had come to be served and be honored. They lived for the pomp and the circumstance, and the adulation of the crowd. Whereas Jesus had taught, "Do not sit in the seat of honor" (Luke 14:8). There is a quote from Albert Einstein that in many ways communicates what Jesus was saying: *"Try not to become a man of success, but rather try to become a man of value."*

Third, they had placed themselves in the seat of God (vs. 9). The Pharisees prided themselves on their titles. They loved to receive the greeting of Rabbi (or teacher), or even to be addressed as Father. And Jesus told them clearly that there is but one Father, and one Teacher. And the Teacher was standing before them.

Jesus closed this portion of His message by saying, *"The greatest among you must be a servant. But those who exalt themselves will be humbled, and those who humble themselves will be exalted."* In essence He was saying, your worth does not lie in the place you sit. Servants don't sit – they serve. Servants don't exalt themselves – they serve in humility. Servants will not be exalted in heaven because of where they sat – they will be exalted in heaven for Who they served.

. . .

As you and i take up the cross, there is much in this word from Jesus that applies to us, just as it did to the Pharisees. When we serve, are we seeking the applause of men or the applause of heaven? Are we seeking earthly rewards or heavenly rewards? Are we seeking rewards at all? Or are we simply following our Savior, serving as He does, as we serve Him? Don't look for the seat in the front row, look for the towel and the basin in the corner. Because it's definitely not about the seat!

* * *

14

THE EIGHT WOES

... Woe to you, scribes and Pharisees, hypocrites, because you shut off the kingdom of heaven from people; for you do not enter in yourselves, nor do you allow those who are entering to go in.
Woe to you... because you devour widows' houses, and for a pretense you make long prayers; therefore you will receive greater condemnation.
Woe to you... because you travel around on sea and land to make one proselyte; and when he becomes one, you make him twice as much a son of hell as yourselves.
Woe to you... who say, 'Whoever swears by the temple, that is nothing; but whoever swears by the gold of the temple is obligated.'
...Woe to you... for you tithe mint and dill and cummin, and have neglected the weightier provisions of the law: justice and mercy and faithfulness; but these are the things you should have done without neglecting the others. You blind guides, who strain out a gnat and swallow a camel!
Woe to you... for you clean the outside of the cup and of the dish, but inside they are full of robbery and self-indulgence.
Woe to you... for you are like whitewashed tombs which on the outside appear beautiful, but inside they are full of dead men's bones and all uncleanness.
Woe to you... for you build the tombs of the prophets and adorn the monuments of the righteous, and say, 'If we had been living in the days of our fathers, we would not have been partners with them in shedding the blood of the prophets....'
Matthew 23:13-36 (NASB)

* * *

When we think of Jesus, we most often think of Him as our Loving Savior. He and the Father loved us so much that Jesus came to this earth to pay the penalty for our sin. *"There is no greater love than to lay down one's life for one's friends"* (John 15:13). Jesus was not only pronouncing His love for us; He was calling us His friends. We also often think of Jesus as the Gentle Servant, who lived humbly and served selflessly. But we water down the gospel when we fail to recognize Him as the Righteous Judge. Though we see Him most often in the Gospels as the Loving Savior, we see Him upon His return in the Book of Revelation as the Righteous Judge. And just as He, as our Savior, has extended His salvation to each and every one of us – each and every one of us will stand before Him as our Judge.

On that day in the temple, three days before He would be crucified, He stood as Judge over the scribes and Pharisees rendering His verdict and His pronouncement over them. Do not think for a moment that Jesus had allowed His emotion to get the better of Him. This was not like you or i might do – allowing our anger to seize control of our tongue and spew venom upon those who have hurt us. He was speaking out of an anger that was godly and a judgement that was righteous. Let us be mindful, on that day when we stand before Him as Judge, there are three things that we never want to hear Jesus say to us!

The first is, **we never want Jesus to call us hypocrites**. Throughout this pronouncement, Jesus repeatedly referred to the scribes and Pharisees as hypocrites, who taught and said one thing, but lived another.

- Through their false leadership and false teaching, they prevented others from making their way to heaven. Instead of teaching truth, they taught lies that the people accepted as truth. And though each of us are responsible for our own decisions, these men carried an even greater weight because of their part in keeping the people blinded to the Truth.
- Though they made great pretense through lengthy and showy prayers that they were servants of God, they failed to demonstrate any compassion for those around them, and actually took advantage of them, including the widows, for their own selfish greed.
- Though they made great show of teaching others the Law, they were converting others to their man-made beliefs and not leading them to become followers of the Almighty God. They

were promulgating a religion and not introducing anyone into a personal relationship with God.

- The Pharisees had contrived a system whereby people would make oaths in the temple by swearing on gold or objects of value. Thereby those elements became "dedicated to God" and could not be used for anything else. It enabled the Pharisees to build rich treasure chests for personal gain but still appear to be pious in their practice.
- The Pharisees majored on the minors. They had rules for every minute area of life. But they would totally ignore the most important things – loving God and loving their neighbor. As an example, Jesus was not denouncing the practice of tithing, He was correcting them that they were not to tithe out of obligation to a set of rules, they were to tithe as an expression of love, thanksgiving and worship to a loving Heavenly Father Who entrusts us with everything we possess.
- The Pharisees were more concerned about their outward appearance than the spiritual condition of their hearts. They sought the praise of men, and were therefore most concerned about what could be seen on the outside. But God, who could see on the inside, saw their greedy and self-indulgent hearts.
- Jesus used the example of the tombs related to ceremonial cleansing to illustrate the same truth. The Pharisees placed all of their attention on the outside appearance and totally ignored the death and decay of their hearts.
- Finally, throughout much of their history, the religious leaders had rejected the prophets of God, and, in many instances, they had been complicit in their murder or persecution. Three contemporary examples to this group would be their treatment of John the Baptist and, in the days ahead, of Jesus Himself, followed by His apostles and other believers. They were guilty of building monuments to the very prophets they had murdered. And though these Pharisees in most instances had not had a personal hand in their murder, their hearts reflected the same attitudes.

The second is, **you never want Jesus to address you by saying, *"woe to you!"*** "Woe" is a word of judgement. It signifies that impending condemnation, doom, and wrath await you. Whatever reward the Pharisees enjoyed in this life was but momentary. What awaited them was an eternity of damnation separated from God. Their "outward" appearances and feeble attempts to earn God's forgiveness through their works was all for naught. Jesus knew their hearts and He knew the judgement that awaited them.

i can't finish this chapter without including a third statement that you never want to hear Jesus say to you. Though He did not speak these words on this day to the scribes and Pharisees, they were included in His Sermon on the Mount. And again, though He did not speak them here, the scribes and Pharisees would have said to you that they were spokespersons for God to the people. So it is fitting to include this statement here as well. **You never want to hear Jesus say to you, *"I never knew you; depart from Me"*** (Matthew 7:23 – NKJ).

As you take up your cross and follow Jesus, remember that the only outcome of playing at religion is "woe". The Pharisees rejected the Savior and rejected the salvation that can only come through Him. Jesus is the only way. Our salvation is from Him and through Him. Our walk with Him is empowered by Him. He is not fixated on our outer appearance. He sees our heart. And if our heart is truly where it needs to be – cleansed of our sin, seeking Him, loving Him and obeying Him – then the outside is going to look just the way it should – like Jesus!

* * *

15

THE WIDOW'S TREASURE

Jesus sat down near the collection box in the Temple and watched as the crowds dropped in their money. Many rich people put in large amounts. Then a poor widow came and dropped in two small coins. Jesus called His disciples to Him and said, "I tell you the truth, this poor widow has given more than all the others who are making contributions. For they gave a tiny part of their surplus, but she, poor as she is, has given everything she had to live on."
Mark 12:41-44

* * *

It is fitting that after Jesus spent the day shining His light on the hypocrisy of the Pharisees, He concluded His day by illuminating the genuineness of a widow's faith. Jesus did something that would be very inappropriate for you or me to do. He sat down near the collection box and watched as the people placed their offerings in the box. He watched how and what the people gave. But He really wasn't watching how much each person gave. He was watching how much each one kept for themselves. And, by the way, He still does!

Compared to the overall budget for the upkeep and operation of the temple, two small coins would seem to be inconsequential. But in God's economy, she gave more than all the others combined. Her gift did not represent the least; it represented the most – her very all. She kept nothing for herself but gave it all to Him. And that, too, is an important distinction, she was not giving to the temple, or a cause, or a budget, she was giving to God. Many others had given generously, but she gave out of her full devotion to God. Many others had given what the law required, but she gave as a debtor of grace, knowing that all that she had belonged to God. She knew that she wasn't an owner, she was simply a steward of what had been entrusted to her. So, as she gave, she was merely returning to the Owner that which He already owned.

Jesus commended the woman for giving in the way that Paul commended the churches in Macedonia to the church in Corinth:

> *"… They gave not only what they could afford, but far more. And they did it of their own free will. …Their first action was to give themselves to the Lord and to us, just as God wanted them to do. …You know the generous grace of our Lord Jesus Christ. Though He was rich, yet for your sakes He became poor, so that by His poverty He could make you rich. …Whatever you give is acceptable if you give it eagerly. And give according to what you have, not what you don't have"* (2 Corinthians 8:3-12).

There is so much for us as 21st century followers of Jesus to learn from this "poor widow" about the way we are to give of our finances – but also, of our lives.

1. Do we give in order to receive the approval of others, or do we give to honor God? Jesus observed that many who gave did so in a way to bring attention to themselves, in order for them to garner the esteem of the crowd. Earlier in His ministry, Jesus had taught, *"When you give…, don't do as the hypocrites do – blowing trumpets in the synagogues and streets to call attention to their acts of charity! I tell you the truth, they have received all the reward they will ever get"* (Matthew 6:2). Paul would later write to the church in Galatia, *"Obviously, I'm not trying to win the approval of people, but of God. If pleasing people were my goal, I would not be Christ's servant"* (Galatians 1:10).
2. Do we give in order to receive the appreciation and thanks of others, or do we give as an expression of our thanksgiving and appreciation to God? Too often we give expecting to be thanked in return. The fact of the matter is that our giving is to be an expression of our thanksgiving to God. When Zacchaeus gave half of his possessions to the poor (Luke 19:8), it was out of a grateful heart to Jesus for his salvation. He did not give to receive thanks; he gave to express his thanks to God.

3. Do we give in order to receive back, or do we give in order to "pay it forward" and extend the grace that has been extended to us? Granted we can't outgive God as we give sacrificially. He promises that if we give with our whole heart, with an open palm and not a tightened fist, that we will receive back *"in full – pressed down, shaken together to make room for more, running over, and poured into [our] lap"* (Luke 6:38). We have already received more than we could ever repay – we have received His free gift of eternal life.
4. Do we give out of joy, or do we give out of duty? *"Take delight in the Lord, and He will give you your heart's desires"* (Psalm 37:4) Yes, He has commanded us to delight in Him, but that is because He delights in every detail of our lives (Psalm 37:23). And He does not want us to give reluctantly or merely out of duty, but joyously. *"…don't give reluctantly or in response to pressure. 'For God loves a person who gives cheerfully'"* (2 Corinthians 9:7).
5. Do we give out of our contentment in Christ, or do we give out of obligation? Paul wrote, *"… I have learned how to be content with whatever I have. I know how to live on almost nothing or with everything. I have learned the secret of living in every situation, whether it is with a full stomach or empty, with plenty or little"* (Philippians 4:11-12). We must learn how to not only live out of contentment, but also, to give out of contentment.
6. Do we give out of faith, or do we determine what we give out of our plenty? The writer of Hebrews wrote, *"…it is impossible to please God without faith"* (Hebrews 11:6). And that also is true in both the way we live, as well as the way we give. The widow gave all that she had by faith, knowing that her provision came from God.

Whose approval are you seeking? Winston Churchill once said, *"We make a living by what we get, but we make a life by what we give."* As you take up the cross, Jesus is leading – but He is also watching. He is watching to see if we have learned from this "poor widow". She, too, stands as a part of that great cloud of witnesses. They all are watching to see if we will give everything. After all, He loves us so much that He gave everything for us, and He has given everything to us. How can we give any less?

* * *

16

WHAT ABOUT THE TEMPLE?

As Jesus was leaving the Temple that day, one of His disciples said, "Teacher, look at these magnificent buildings! Look at the impressive stones in the walls." Jesus replied, "Yes, look at these great buildings. But they will be completely demolished. Not one stone will be left on top of another!" Later, Jesus sat on the Mount of Olives across the valley from the Temple. Peter, James, John, and Andrew came to Him privately and asked Him, "Tell us, when will all this happen? What sign will show us that these things are about to be fulfilled?"
Mark 13:1-4

* * *

It's the end of the third day of the week. It has been a long day for Jesus that started with the withered fig tree, continued through the various ploys of the religious leaders to trap Him which culminated in His rebuke of the leaders, then was followed by the beautiful contrast of the faithful widow. Jesus and the disciples were now leaving the Temple and heading to the Mount of Olives to spend the night.

Let's add some context for the moment. It's halfway between His triumphal entry and His crucifixion. Jesus is as aware of what will occur over the next few days as He is of what has occurred during the last few. He sees, not only what is behind, but also, what lies ahead – over the course of the next week – and over the millennia that will follow. Imagine if you will that it is September 10, 2001, and you are standing at the top of one of the towers of the World Trade Center. You are looking out at the panoramic view of New York City and admiring the impressiveness of this architectural marvel. In your wildest imagination, you cannot possibly conceive that the place you are standing right then will no longer exist within less than twenty-four hours. Now, imagine Jesus is standing there right beside you. He too can see the physical marvel before your eyes, but He is able to see the destruction that will take place the next morning.

The first Temple (originally built by King Solomon) was destroyed by the Babylonians in 586 B.C. The second Temple was built as a modest structure in 516 B.C. by Jewish exiles who had returned to Jerusalem from Babylon under the leadership of the appointed governor Zerubbabel. During the reign of King Herod the Great in the 1st Century B.C., the Temple was refurbished and transformed into a compound of magnificent structures. Work would have been completed on or about the time of Jesus' birth and the birth of many of His disciples. Thus, for them, because of its complete refurbishing, it was a "modern" structure.

Each of them had been to the Temple many times before in their lifetimes, so the sight was not a new one. But, in an effort to decompress from the many tensions of the day, they turned their conversation to reflect on the "impressive" and "magnificent" buildings that made up the Temple compound. And as they did, Jesus replied, *"Yes, look at these great buildings. But they will be completely demolished. Not one stone will be left on top of another!"* This was not merely conjecture on the part of Jesus, nor was it solely a prophetic word. The patriarchs and prophets of the Old Testament had prophesied about events that would take place in the future. They had prophesied about the Messiah by faith. They had not seen the Messiah. They only knew of the promise of the Messiah. But this wasn't like that. As Jesus spoke, He literally could see the destruction of the Temple. Jesus saw this event, as well as the other future events we will look at in the next few chapters. These were not speculations or possible outcomes. These were actual events that He could see. We now know that the second Temple was destroyed by the Romans in 70 A.D., within less than fifty years from when this conversation took place. And in a matter of days, the True Temple, where the glory of God resides, would be crucified. "It" would be rebuilt in three days' time as Jesus arose from the dead as He had also prophesied (John 2:19). Imagine the shock and dismay of Jesus' disciples when they heard that the physical Temple would be destroyed. And bear in mind, they still were not clear on all that what was about to occur within the next few days.

• • •

This begins what is often referred to as the "Olivet Discourse" (because it took place on the Mount of Olives) in which Jesus unfolds the eschatological (meaning "end things") events which will end this age. This discourse is recorded in Matthew 24, Mark 13 and Luke 21. Again, we will look at the discourse over the coming chapters. Mark (bear in mind his source would have been Peter) is the only Gospel in which we see that this was a "private" conversation that Peter, James, John and Andrew had with Jesus. Matthew infers it, and Mark's Gospel would have been Luke's source.

It is very significant that this conversation unfolded on the Mount of Olives, for three reasons. The first reason was very personal to Jesus. It was because this was the place to which Jesus often retreated when He was in Jerusalem in order to spend One-on-One time with the Father. It was the place that They would have long conversations in prayer. The second was somewhat pragmatic. It was the place where Judas would betray Him in two nights' time. The Father had ordained that Jesus would be arrested and led away from the Mount of Olives. The first three days of this time in Jerusalem, Jesus and the disciples had overnighted in Bethany. But now He switched to the Mount of Olives, so He could clearly establish a nightly pattern – a pattern that Judas would use to lead the posse that would arrest Him. Jesus was not only using this time to teach about the end of the world, He was using it to further order the steps of His last days leading to His crucifixion. And this second reason ties very clearly with the third, which is prophetic. The Mount is just to the east of Jerusalem. It is just outside the gates of the city. And when Jesus returns to establish His Kingdom, *"His feet will stand on the Mount of Olives"* (Zechariah 14:4). The place of His intimate times with the Father, the place of His betrayal and arrest, and the place of His return are all right there at the Mount of Olives.

And on that coming day, the new Temple – the everlasting Temple – will be established. The second Temple, for all of its magnificence, will pale in comparison.

On that day the sources of light will no longer shine, yet there will be continuous day! Only the Lord knows how this could happen. There will be no normal day and night, for at evening time it will still be light.
On that day life-giving waters will flow out from Jerusalem, half toward the Dead Sea and half toward the Mediterranean, flowing continuously in both summer and winter. And the Lord will be King over all the earth.
On that day there will be one Lord – His name alone will be worshiped.

(Zechariah 14:6-9)

And what a great day that will be! And as that day approaches, take up the cross and follow Him!

* * *

17

THE PAROUSIA

Later, Jesus sat on the Mount of Olives. His disciples came to Him privately and said, "Tell us, when will all this happen? What sign will signal Your return and the end of the world?" Jesus told them, "Don't let anyone mislead you, for many will come in My name, claiming, 'I am the Messiah.' They will deceive many. And you will hear of wars and threats of wars, but don't panic. Yes, these things must take place, but the end won't follow immediately. Nation will go to war against nation, and kingdom against kingdom. There will be famines and earthquakes in many parts of the world. But all this is only the first of the birth pains, with more to come.

Matthew 24:3-8

* * *

The Greek word "Parousia" (pronounced pair-oo-see-ah) is a noun that means "a coming" or "a presence."[1] Most commonly in the New Testament, the word refers to the coming return of our Lord Jesus Christ. And on the evening of this passage, Jesus sat with Peter, James, John and Andrew on the Mount of Olives and answered their questions about the Parousia.

As we saw in chapter 16, as they were walking to the Mount, Jesus had declared to the disciples that the Temple would be completely demolished. That prompted these disciples to ask three questions:

1. When will all this happen?
2. What sign will signal Your return?
3. What sign will signal the end of the world?

Jesus didn't respond to their questions to satisfy idle curiosity or merely to resolve any confusion they had about end-times prophecy. And we must be careful of our motivation as well. There are many students of the Word that relish the study of biblical prophecy as an intellectual pursuit or in an effort to predict the actual arrival of our Lord's return. Jesus, in fact, was equipping them so they would not be deceived by false teaching or drawn away from following Him in His mission. He was equipping them – as He is equipping us – to be people of Issachar – who understand the times and know what to do (1 Chronicles 12:32).

Jesus actually answered their questions in reverse order by explaining the events that will lead up to what He later described in this passage as a time of tribulation. *"For then there will be a great tribulation, such as has not occurred since the beginning of the world until now, nor ever will"* (Matthew 24:21 NASB). He describes these initial events as *"the first of the birth pains"*. The analogy of "birth pains" references back to the prophecy of Isaiah:

"Scream in terror, for the day of the Lord has arrived – the time for the Almighty to destroy. Every arm is paralyzed with fear. Every heart melts and people are terrified. Pangs of anguish grip them, like those of a woman in labor. They look helplessly at one another, their faces aflame with fear. For see, the day of the Lord is coming – the terrible day of His fury and fierce anger. The land will be made desolate, and all the sinners destroyed with it. The heavens will be black above them; the stars will give no light. The sun will be dark when it rises, and the moon will provide no light"
(Isaiah 13:6-10).

The first of these "birth pains" or "pangs of anguish" are:

1. *"Many will come in My name, claiming, 'I am the Messiah.' They will deceive many."* i searched on the web for "Messiah claimants" and was over-

whelmed by the length of the list. When Jesus said "many" will come, it was no exaggeration. Here are just a few of the names[2]:

- Simon Magus – a Samaritan born soon after Christ ascended in the early 1st century, who called himself the "Standing One".
- Ann Lee (1736-1784) – a central figure to the Shakers – who considered herself to be Christ's female counterpart.
- Victor Manuel Gomez Rodriguez, who later changed his name to Samael Aun Weor – born in Colombia in 1917 and declared himself to be Messiah in 1972
- Sun Myong Moon (1920 – 2012) – founder of the Unification Church who declared himself to be the second coming of Christ to fulfill Jesus' unfinished mission.

The list goes on ad nauseam, and, as Jesus warned, each of these deceived many to follow them. The Apostle John writes in The Revelation (6:1-8) about the four seals that will be broken in the last days, the first of which is the Antichrist, the final world dictator who will declare himself to be the Messiah and will lead the nations away.

In addition to this list of false Messiahs is an unending list of false teachers teaching false doctrine, who also have deceived many. We need to be watchful. We need to be discerning of Truth. And we need to be bold to proclaim Truth and denounce false teaching.

2. *"You will hear of wars and threats of wars.... Nation will go to war against nation, and kingdom against kingdom."* Wars by themselves do not announce the end of the age. Throughout history there have been wars. Even the enforced peace of the Roman Empire in the early 1st Century disintegrated into national conflicts. The second of the seals that John writes about (Revelation 6:3-4) is the unleashing of war and slaughter. There will be increased incidents of war.

3. *"There will be famines and earthquakes in many parts of the world."* We already are seeing increased incidents of natural disasters – earthquakes, tsunamis, tornadoes, floods – that have caused countless deaths and destruction. We see increased famine resulting from those disasters, as well as from military conflicts, and ineffective use of natural resources. It

is estimated that 815 million of the 7.6 billion people in the world today are suffering from chronic undernourishment, and 9.1 million people currently die of hunger every year.[3] The third of the seals (Revelation 6:5-6) will be increased famine.

One side road while we are on this subject. Our Master has clearly called us, as we will again see in chapter 24 (Matthew 25:35), to minister to those in need around us – and specifically the basic needs of hunger, thirst, clothing, etc. Let's not be just observers of our times, let's be active in ministering to the needs of our times. There are ways that each and every one of us can be involved in meeting those needs locally – in our own communities – and globally – into the impoverished regions of the world. One of the organizations that i have seen God use first-hand to work effectively in helping to meet these needs outside of the US is Baptist Global Response (gobgr.org). i have found that in many instances they have been the first responders to needs when they occur.

4. There will be *"more to come."* The fourth of the seals (Revelation 6:7-8) will be ever-increasing death resulting from war, disaster and famine.

And Jesus said that these are but the beginning "pangs of anguish" that will "signal the end of the world".

One further side road before we close this chapter: Jesus did not address the rapture of His church in this discourse. We will look at the rapture further in the last book of this series. But it is the belief of many students of the Word who are followers of Jesus, that believers in the present age of the church will be raptured by Christ and taken to heaven before the Tribulation begins. Then at the close of the Tribulation, they will return to earth with Him. i agree with that interpretation – but i'll reserve further discussion for a later chapter.

In the meantime, we have been called to take up the cross in these days. There has never been a generation closer to the end of the age than we are. We have been called to be alert (Matthew 24:42) and we have been called to be faithful servants carrying out the Master's business (Matthew 24:45-47) and being about His mission (Matthew 28:19-20). The Parousia is drawing near. Let's not be found asleep or distracted at the post (Matthew 24:48-51)!

[1] gotquestions.org
[2] Wikipedia.org
[3] WorldHunger.org

* * *

18

IN THE COMING DAYS

"When these things begin to happen, watch out! You will be handed over to the local councils and beaten in the synagogues. You will stand trial before governors and kings because you are My followers. But this will be your opportunity to tell them about Me. For the Good News must first be preached to all nations. But when you are arrested and stand trial, don't worry in advance about what to say. Just say what God tells you at that time, for it is not you who will be speaking, but the Holy Spirit. A brother will betray his brother to death, a father will betray his own child, and children will rebel against their parents and cause them to be killed. And everyone will hate you because you are My followers. But the one who endures to the end will be saved.

Mark 13:9-13

* * *

Jesus continues to answer the questions we looked at in the last chapter that Peter, James, John and Andrew have posed to Him there on the Mount of Olives. As a reminder, it is the end of the third day of the week, two nights before He is to be arrested and betrayed. He is still unpacking what will lead up to the end of the age and signal His return.

Before we look at these next "signs" for which He instructs them to watch, let's talk about "time". The persecution that He says will occur actually began with the apostles in just a few short weeks after this very conversation. In many respects, the coming of the end of the age began right then, early in the 1st Century. The penultimate event of history is the crucifixion, burial and resurrection of Jesus. In God's plan:

- First, He created the heavens and the earth in order to raise up and gather worshipers unto Himself, through whom He would ascribe glory to His Name. But we immediately separated ourselves from our Creator through our sin and disqualified ourselves from being able to worship a Holy God, so...
- Secondly, He unfolded His redemptive plan to reconcile His sinful creation back to Himself through the death, burial and resurrection of His Son, which leads us to the final part of the plan...
- Thirdly, through the power of His Holy Spirit, now working in and through the followers of His Son, He multiplies that multitude of worshipers from every language, people, tongue and tribe, culminating in that final day when He gathers us all together before His throne (the end of the age).

So truly, the final days began after Christ completed His redemptive work and returned to the right hand of the Father, thereby enabling the Holy Spirit to be sent to earth to be about His work. The period between the first to the second part of the plan was approximately 4,000 years, and now the Holy Spirit has been about His work for the last 2,100 years since Jesus had this conversation with His disciples. There is no question we are in those final days. Only God knows how long they will continue. "*But you must not forget this one thing, dear friends: A day is like a thousand years to the Lord, and a thousand years is like a day*" (2 Peter 3:8). So, it should not come as a surprise to us that the disciples began to experience some of the very occurrences that Jesus described as being signs of the last days. Nor should it surprise us that we are.

Jesus taught that His followers would experience persecution, and that we would experience it "officially" and "personally". Believers will stand before local councils, governors and leaders and be beaten, persecuted, imprisoned and even executed for their faith in Christ. It began with Peter and John being arrested in Acts 4, and it continued with all of the apostles and many of the 1st Century followers being martyred or persecuted. And it has continued throughout history to this day. Today, it is estimated that there are 215 million Christians that are experiencing high levels of persecution in the "fifty most difficult countries in which to be a Christian"[1].

And that persecution is not confined to "official" authorities. It continues and is often even more severely inflicted "personally" by family members and neighbors.

God has used a good friend, Nik Ripken, to open my eyes to the ever-growing reality of persecution around the globe. Nik writes[2],

"Christians who live in nations where persecution is not a normal occurrence often cringe in horror upon hearing reports that their brothers and sisters around the globe are experiencing the atrocities of suffering and death for their faith in (and their witness of) Jesus Christ…. Admittedly, we cannot fully comprehend all of God's purposes in allowing Christ's followers to be persecuted. Only those purposes which are clearly articulated in Scripture may be known to us, and they are few in number. The book of Acts records the fact that the early believers left Jerusalem and scattered to other key cities as a result of intense persecution (Acts 11:19). Here, one may conclude that God purposed to use persecution to spread and multiply the Church. Persecution serves to test and strengthen one's faith (Romans 5:3-4; James 1:3, 1 Peter 1:6-7, 4:12). There is a mysterious purpose in persecution and suffering related to bringing about the Kingdom of God (2 Thessalonians 1:4-5). Scripture tells us that Jesus was "perfected" as the author of salvation and in His obedience through suffering (Hebrews 2:10, 5:8-10). This principle has limited but valid application to God's purposes for suffering in the lives of Christian leaders. And, finally, one of God's purposes in affliction and suffering is to equip His servants with the ability to comfort and sustain others who endure similar afflictions (2 Corinthians 1:3-11)."

Jesus said, *"everyone will hate you because you are My followers."* If they hated and crucified Him, why would we expect anything different? We cannot expect the world to treat us any differently than it treated Jesus. And as the end of the age draws near, this will only increase.

Jesus went on to teach, *"For the Good News must first be preached to all nations."* In the first century, the Apostles and other followers of Christ scattered to the nations to proclaim the Good News to all that had not heard. Today, men and women are still scattering to the nations, having been sent out to continue that mission. Currently 4.3 billion people live in areas where less than 2% of their population are followers of Jesus, and 932 million of those live in areas where there are no known believers or churches to provide a witness.[3] We are to be witnesses in these last days.

We must go, we must send, and we must undergird those who have been sent.

Lastly, in this passage, Jesus told them that His followers must endure to the end. Enduring faith is not the product of our profession of faith. Our profession of faith opened the door for the Holy Spirit to enter into our lives and indwell us. Enduring faith is then the product of God's Spirit at work within us and through us. John Piper said it well – "*'We must' becomes 'we will' because 'God will'.*" And the Apostles wrote these truths to those new followers of Jesus in the early church to encourage them that "God will":

"He is able to keep you from stumbling and to present you blameless before the presence of His glory"
(Jude 1:24).
"He who began a good work in you will bring it to completion at the day of Jesus Christ"
(Philippians 1:6).
"{Christ} will sustain you to the end.... God is faithful, through whom you were called into fellowship with His Son"
(1 Corinthians 1:8-9).
"The Lord will bring me safely to His heavenly kingdom"
(2 Timothy 4:18).

And those words are as true for us today as they were for them. As we take up the cross to follow Jesus – no matter what wilderness we may be walking through – we must continue to be like those people of Issachar (who we looked at in the last chapter), understanding our times, walking in the mission of our Master and enduring to the end – no matter how many days there are yet to come.

[1] OpenDoorsUSA.org
[2] NikRipken.com
[3] Global Status of Evangelical Christianity, IMB, published 3/1/2018

* * *

19

PERILOUS TIMES

"Therefore, when you see the abomination of desolation which was spoken of through Daniel the prophet, standing in the holy place (let the reader understand), then those who are in Judea must flee to the mountains. Whoever is on the housetop must not go down to get the things out that are in his house. Whoever is in the field must not turn back to get his cloak. But woe to those who are pregnant and to those who are nursing babies in those days! But pray that your flight will not be in the winter, or on a Sabbath. For then there will be a great tribulation, such as has not occurred since the beginning of the world until now, nor ever will. Unless those days had been cut short, no life would have been saved; but for the sake of the elect those days will be cut short. Then if anyone says to you, 'Behold, here is the Christ,' or 'There He is,' do not believe him. For false Christs and false prophets will arise and will show great signs and wonders, so as to mislead, if possible, even the elect. Behold, I have told you in advance. So, if they say to you, 'Behold, He is in the wilderness,' do not go out, or, 'Behold, He is in the inner rooms,' do not believe them. For just as the lightning comes from the east and flashes even to the west, so will the coming of the Son of Man be. Wherever the corpse is, there the vultures will gather."

Matthew 24:15-28

* * *

Jesus continues to answer the three questions that His disciples have asked Him about the end of the age:

1. When will all this happen?
2. What sign will signal Your return?

3. What sign will signal the end of the world?

In revealing these truths to the apostles and, through them, to us, Jesus is providing us with knowledge that should lead to an understanding and fear regarding the coming judgement of God. There should be a terror that grips the human heart when it contemplates God's judgment on sin. The apocalyptic revelations are a warning to all mankind about the end result of sin and that we had better be prepared for the Lord's return. It is a warning to the non-Christian to repent or they will suffer God's judgment, and it is a warning to us as followers of Christ to live our lives in a worthy manner.

As He talks through the events, He now comes to the most perilous of times that are triggered by what He and the prophets call "the abomination of desolation". As Matthew notes, Daniel recorded this coming event as follows:

> *"The ruler will make a treaty with the people for a period of one set of seven, but after half this time, he will put an end to the sacrifices and offerings. And as a climax to all his terrible deeds, he will set up a sacrilegious object that causes desecration, until the fate decreed for this defiler is finally poured out on him" (Daniel 9:27).*

The event will occur halfway through the seven year period of the Great Tribulation that will immediately precede Christ's return. At the beginning of that period, a man portraying himself to be a man of peace (the anti-Christ) will rise to a position of power across the entire world. His arrival and the resulting abominations are being restrained until their proper time by the Spirit of God. But in His time, He will remove His hand of restraint. During the first half of the anti-Christ's seven-year reign, he will establish a treaty of global peace and will blindly be accepted by most. But halfway through, his true nature will be revealed. He will set himself up to be worshipped and destruction will be poured out across the earth. Paul writes:

> … on that day "*… a great rebellion against God {will arise} and the man of lawlessness [will be} revealed — the one who brings destruction. He will exalt*

himself and defy everything that people call god and every object of worship. He will even sit in the temple of God, claiming that he himself is God. …And you know what is holding him back, for he can be revealed only when his time comes. For this lawlessness is already at work secretly, and it will remain secret until the One who is holding it back steps out of the way"
(2 Thessalonians 2:3-7).

The "abomination of desolation" will herald a time of danger for those who live in Judea that will occur so quickly that as soon as one hears of it, they should flee immediately without stopping to make any preparation. The ramifications will be global as the world enters into a time period of three and a half years of unprecedented destruction and desolation, so severe that it *'has not occurred since the beginning of the world until now, nor ever will."*

Daniel wrote, *"Wise leaders will give instruction to many, but these teachers will die by fire and sword, or they will be jailed and robbed. During these persecutions, little help will arrive, and many who join them will not be sincere. And some of the wise will fall victim to persecution. In this way, they will be refined and cleansed and made pure until the time of the end, for the appointed time is still to come. The king will do as he pleases, exalting himself and claiming to be greater than every god, even blaspheming the God of gods. He will succeed, but only until the time of wrath is completed. For what has been determined will surely take place. He will have no respect for the gods of his ancestors, or for the god loved by women, or for any other god, for he will boast that he is greater than them all. Instead of these, he will worship the god of fortresses—a god his ancestors never knew—and lavish on him gold, silver, precious stones, and expensive gifts. Claiming this foreign god's help, he will attack the strongest fortresses. He will honor those who submit to him, appointing them to positions of authority and dividing the land among them as their reward"*
(Daniel 11:33-39).

And this false Christ and his *"false prophets will arise and will show great signs and wonders, so as to mislead, if possible, even the elect."* But Jesus warns for His elect not to be deceived by signs and wonders, for they are but counterfeit imitations of God's power. When Jesus returns, there will be no question that it is Him! At the appropriate time, according to the Father's timetable, He will return in all majesty and power. *"For just as the lightning comes from the east and flashes even to the west, so will the coming of the Son of Man be."*

But before He returns, *"all the rulers and their armies {will gather} to a place with the Hebrew name Armageddon"* (Revelation 16:16). And the awful carnage that results from this battle will result in a massive field of death that Jesus depicts when He says, *"Wherever the corpse is, there the vultures will gather."* In the next chapter of this book, we will look at His pronouncement of His glorious return.

At this point, let me stop and take a moment to talk about why i have included this chapter, as well as the three that preceded it, to walk through Jesus' teaching of the end times. You might be asking, "what does that have to do with my wilderness journey?" Or, "what does that have to do with my taking up the cross and following Him?" The reality is that it has everything to do with both questions. We follow a Living Savior who will be returning! We may still be here to be raptured with the church just prior to these "end of the ages" events, or we may have already stepped into eternity before those events unfold. But first, we need to live and follow Him with full anticipation and expectation of His soon return. This is not hypothetical, futuristic prophecy that doesn't apply to us. Jesus is talking about the day we live in. The wilderness we are walking in is surrounded by the world events that are rapidly unfolding toward that day of His return. Let's not become so myopic with our own wilderness journey that we miss the bigger picture.

And second, let's not miss the bigger purpose! Sin destroys. The enemy deceives. We live in a world that is in a free fall toward death and destruction. God will return to judge His creation for our sin. And the verdict is eternal damnation. BUT Jesus saves. And we as His followers have that message of salvation. The very circumstances that each one of us are walking in today is but a platform through which He will make His message known and bring glory to Himself. That's why we follow! And that's why He wants us to know. Yes, perilous times lie ahead… but the cross and the empty grave lie behind. Let's be faithful to carry the cross, proclaiming the good news of the empty grave so that others can escape those perilous times in the days ahead.

* * *

20

THEN HE WILL COME!

"But immediately after the tribulation of those days the sun will be darkened, and the moon will not give its light, and the stars will fall from the sky, and the powers of the heavens will be shaken. And then the sign of the Son of Man will appear in the sky, and then all the tribes of the earth will mourn, and they will see the Son of Man coming on the clouds of the sky with power and great glory. And He will send forth His angels with a great trumpet and they will gather together His elect from the four winds, from one end of the sky to the other."
Matthew 24:29-31

* * *

Throughout the last three chapters, we have been looking at Jesus' response to the three questions that His disciples have asked Him about the end of the age:

1. When will all this happen?
2. What sign will signal Your return?
3. What sign will signal the end of the world?

As we have seen, He started His answers by responding to the third question. We have looked at the events that He tells us will signal the end of the age (the world). Now He comes to the answers to the first two questions.

. . .

What will signal His return and when will it occur? Immediately following the Battle of Armageddon (Revelation 16:16), the earth will be plunged into utter darkness! The sun will cease to shine. The moon will have no light to reflect, and the stars will fall and be snuffed out. Jesus is quoting from Ezekiel 32:7:

I will veil the heavens and darken the stars.
I will cover the sun with a cloud, and the moon will not give you its light.
I will darken the bright stars overhead and cover your land in darkness.
I, the Sovereign Lord, have spoken!

The earth will be as a darkened void – just as it was before God commanded there to be light. The darkness will be so pervasive that one will not be able to see their hand right in front of their eyes. It will be a demonstration of God's might and power – but also, a demonstration of what this world looks like absent His presence. Apart from His light, we are surrounded by darkness, covered with darkness and lost in our darkness. Without light there can be no morning, and there can be no joy (Psalm 30:5). Without light, there can be no life. Without light, there can be no hope.

Jesus said that in the midst of that absolute darkness the sign of His return will appear in the sky. He doesn't tell us how long the darkness will last. He doesn't tell us what that sign will be. Theologians have debated and conjectured what it might be. i believe it will be Him shining forth as the Light of the World. It will be a light that radiates from Him and overpowers the darkness in every corner of the earth. We already know that there is no need for artificial light in heaven because the Shekinah "*glory of God illuminates the city, and the Lamb is its light*" (Revelation 21:23). He will shine upon all of the earth as bright as the noonday sun. No darkness will be permitted to hide from His light. "*... all the tribes of the earth will mourn*" because Christ's return will finalize their defeat. The power that Satan and the principalities of this world have been permitted to exercise will now be bound – bound by Christ's might, His power and His light! To quote Paul Maxwell from his article on the *Desiring God* blog:

"The tribes of the earth — the captains of industry, the earthly-minded, the self-livers, the others-blamers, the indulgent, the wolves, the servant-abusing — they will mourn, because the Great Shepherd has come to gather His elect, to name the

faithful, to harvest His fruit. He brings great joy to the weary who have spent their lives for others in His name.... {There will be} a global mourning among those who have recklessly cast aside the free offer of Christ's grace in this life. And the unseen faithful and generous servants will finally rest."

The nations will walk in His Light and will bring their honor and glory to Him (Revelation 21:24, 26). As we saw in Matthew 24:14 (in chapter 18) – *"This gospel of the kingdom shall be preached in the whole world as a testimony to all the nations, and then the end will come."* Peoples from every language, tribe and nation will be gathered from the four corners of the world – *"from one end of the sky to the other"* – drawn to His light, drawn to His presence and drawn to His feet – where every knee will bow and every tongue will declare that Jesus Christ is Lord, to the glory of God the Father (Philippians 2:10-11).

So, as we take up the cross to follow Him, let's not lose sight of "the end" – the return of our Lord, receiving all the worship, praise, honor and glory that is due Him. In the midst of the darkness and trials of our journey, as we follow Him, let's not lose sight of the reality that His Light will prevail. Every speck of darkness will be eradicated. Every shadow will be removed. Though the enemy may appear to have the upper hand right now, he is a defeated foe. When Jesus "appears in the sky", it's all over! The psalmist David said it best:

Fret not yourself because of evildoers; be not envious of wrongdoers!
For they will soon fade like the grass and wither like the green herb.
Trust in the LORD, and do good; dwell in the land and befriend faithfulness.
Delight yourself in the LORD, and He will give you the desires of your heart.
Commit your way to the LORD; trust in Him, and He will act.
He will bring forth your righteousness as the light, and your justice as the noonday.
(Psalm 37:1-6 ESV)

In the meantime, let's dwell in the land, cultivating faithfulness, staying true to Him and His mission. Let's remain steadfast in making disciples of all peoples – those within our current traffic patterns – and those within the traffic patterns where He is sending us to engage. For that day is drawing near!

* * *

21

ONE WILL BE TAKEN, ONE WILL BE LEFT

"Now learn the parable from the fig tree: when its branch has already become tender and puts forth its leaves, you know that summer is near; so you too, when you see all these things, recognize that He is near, right at the door. Truly I say to you, this generation will not pass away until all these things take place. Heaven and earth will pass away, but My words will not pass away. But of that day and hour no one knows, not even the angels of heaven, nor the Son, but the Father alone. For the coming of the Son of Man will be just like the days of Noah. For as in those days before the flood they were eating and drinking, marrying and giving in marriage, until the day that Noah entered the ark, and they did not understand until the flood came and took them all away; so will the coming of the Son of Man be. Then there will be two men in the field; one will be taken and one will be left. Two women will be grinding at the mill; one will be taken and one will be left."

Matthew 24:32-41

* * *

As a reminder, Jesus is only two days away from His arrest and subsequent execution. His days on this earth, including those after His resurrection, are drawing to a close. Though His disciples do not know – nor are they able to comprehend – all that is about to occur, they can sense His time with them is coming to an end. And those who have walked with Him the closest want to know when He's coming back. In many respects, they are already longing for His return. In response to their questions, Jesus is describing His second coming to earth – when He will return as Judge.

. . .

When the branch on the fig tree begins to put forth its leaves, you know that spring has dawned, and summer is near. You know that the fruit of the season will arrive in its time, not far behind. You know the time is coming. And so it is with the return of the Master. The unmistakable signs of the times will herald His return. But the days of this age (or the days of "*this generation*") will not pass, and the day of His return will not occur, until all of the events that He has described have taken place. It's interesting that Jesus says that even He as the Son of Man does not know the exact moment. That day and hour is known by "*the Father alone*". That should be a reminder to us that we are not to spend our time watching for the signs of His return and obsessing on the "when", we are to be good stewards of the time He has given us now and invest our lives in being about His mission. Because, as He goes on to say, the only thing that endures will be His word – His gospel. Even heaven and earth will pass away. John writes, "*Then I saw a new heaven and a new earth, for the old heaven and the old earth had disappeared*" (Revelation 21:1).

No, we don't know the day and the hour. And there's a reason for that! The Lord wants every generation to live in expectancy, every generation to live in preparedness. We don't know what generation it's going to come upon. But when it comes, it's going to come in catastrophic proportion, and it's going to come rapidly. We don't know what generation that will be, and even the generation that it comes upon will not know the exact moment. Thus, Christians dating back to the very 1st century church have always lived in the eagerness of the coming of Christ.

Jesus compared these coming days to the days of Noah. In that day, the people lived as though God did not exist. They had rejected the word of God and did not believe that God would judge them. On the day that the rains began to fall and the flood waters began to rise, they were going about their lives as usual, without any thought of, or regard for, God. Luke includes a reference to the people of Sodom, just prior to their destruction (Luke 17:28-29), and then goes on to say, "*Yes, it will be 'business as usual' right up to the hour when the Son of Man returns*" (Luke 17:30).

But at that given moment, enough will have been enough! John also writes, "*Then another angel came from the Temple and shouted to the One sitting on the cloud* {referring to Jesus}, *'Swing the sickle, for the time of harvest has come; the crop on earth is ripe.' So the one sitting on the cloud swung His sickle over the earth, and the whole earth was harvested*" (Revelation 14:15-16). Using the imagery in this verse, the seed is planted, the grain grows to its full ripeness, and then it is harvested. The Lord has patiently waited for the final ripening of evil. He has waited for the full ripening of sin. And God is not going to return to judge this world until the harvest is ripe, and sin has run its course. He will not return until all the ungodliness has been revealed. That includes the evil of evil that is still unrevealed – as hard as it is to imagine that there is any more evil that has not yet been revealed. But when that evil has been revealed and sin has run its full, rampant course, then the sickle will be "swung" and the harvest will be ready. So, the Father is patiently waiting to allow sin to run its reckless course, to spend itself, to ripen to the point where it will be fully, finally, and forever harvested.

i believe the other reason the Lord is patiently waiting is to allow for the gathering of His church. He is waiting to gather all the saints whose names are written in the Lamb's book of life. Paul writes in his epistle to the Romans, "*... this will last only until the full number... comes to Christ*" (Romans 11:25). God is waiting to gather all of those from every language, people, tribe and nation who will throughout eternity give Him glory, give Him praise, give Him honor, give Him adoration and serve Him. He is gathering worshipers for His eternal heaven to praise and glorify His Name.

Then at that moment, "*One will be taken, and one will be left.*" Somewhere along the line, the church began to believe that Jesus was talking here about His return to rapture His bride. The idea has been taught that one will be taken to join Jesus in the clouds and one will be left on this earth to endure the tribulation. But remember, Jesus is making this statement AFTER He has described the days of the tribulation. As we will discuss in the next book as we study the epistles, the rapture of the church will have already occurred before the tribulation takes place. He is describing now His awaited return, marking the end of the tribulation. These folks who are being taken are not being raptured, they're being "taken" into judgement, and will not be entering into the millennial kingdom (the one thousand years of Christ's reign that will follow His return). The ones who remain will be those who have come to faith during the tribulation period.

Imagine that moment as men and women, young and old, are "taken" into eternal separation from God. And the moment before, they stood with one who apparently was a follower of Jesus (because he or she remained). Imagine the loss that follower will experience as that family member, or coworker, or friend is taken. Yes, there will be great joy in the return of our

Lord, but there will also be great sorrow for those who will no longer have an opportunity to follow Jesus.

As we take up the cross to follow Jesus, let's not be distracted by the things that will pass away. Let's be about His mission so that "<u>less</u> are taken", and "<u>more</u> are left".

* * *

22

LET'S BE READY

"Therefore, be on the alert, for you do not know which day your Lord is coming. But be sure of this, that if the head of the house had known at what time of the night the thief was coming, he would have been on the alert and would not have allowed his house to be broken into. For this reason, you also must be ready; for the Son of Man is coming at an hour when you do not think He will. Who then is the faithful and sensible slave whom his master put in charge of his household to give them their food at the proper time? Blessed is that slave whom his master finds so doing when he comes. Truly I say to you that he will put him in charge of all his possessions. But if that evil slave says in his heart, 'My master is not coming for a long time,' and begins to beat his fellow slaves and eat and drink with drunkards; the master of that slave will come on a day when he does not expect him and at an hour which he does not know, and will cut him in pieces and assign him a place with the hypocrites; in that place there will be weeping and gnashing of teeth.

Then the kingdom of heaven will be comparable to ten virgins, who took their lamps and went out to meet the bridegroom. Five of them were foolish, and five were prudent. For when the foolish took their lamps, they took no oil with them, but the prudent took oil in flasks along with their lamps. Now while the bridegroom was delaying, they all got drowsy and began to sleep. But at midnight there was a shout, 'Behold, the bridegroom! Come out to meet him.' Then all those virgins rose and trimmed their lamps. The foolish said to the prudent, 'Give us some of your oil, for our lamps are going out.' But the prudent answered, 'No, there will not be enough for us and you too; go instead to the dealers and buy some for yourselves.' And while they were going away to make the purchase, the bridegroom came, and those who were ready went in with him to the wedding feast; and the door was shut. Later the other virgins also came, saying, 'Lord, lord,

open up for us.' But he answered, 'Truly I say to you, I do not know you.' Be on the alert then, for you do not know the day nor the hour."
Matthew 24:42 – 25:13

* * *

Jesus begins this particular passage with the admonition to "be on the alert" and He ends with the exact same words. There are at least four "audiences" to whom Jesus was speaking those words. First, He was responding to questions from His disciples – He was speaking to them. Second, Jesus' earthly ministry was primarily to the Jewish people – He was speaking to the Jews. Third, He was speaking to those who would follow Him before the Tribulation – those who have already gone to be with Him in heaven or those who will be raptured by Him prior to the Tribulation. By the way, as His people, we will escape the Tribulation, but He never promised that we will escape tribulation. Fourth, He was speaking to His followers who will come to faith in Him during the Tribulation (after the rapture, but prior to His return).

For those of us in that third category – those of us following Him today – we live in a place between the already and the not yet. We look back to the cross, where Jesus bore our sins, and we look forward to His second coming. We live in the last days, but not yet in the last of the last days. We live with a sense of what is already true and what is yet to come to pass. We live with the excitement, thrill, and joy of looking for the coming of our Lord Jesus Christ.

Peter said it this way, *"Blessed be the God and Father of our Lord Jesus Christ, who according to His great mercy has caused us to be born again to a living hope through the resurrection of Jesus Christ from the dead to obtain an inheritance which is imperishable and undefiled and will not fade away, reserved in heaven for you, who are protected by the power of God through faith for a salvation ready to be revealed in the last time"* (1 Peter 1:3-5 NASB). We live in that "not yet" place of living hope! We are clothed in His righteousness, but we are not yet like Him in all ways. And our hearts are filled with anticipation for the day we will see Him. Those who are not His followers should look to that day when they will see Him with great fear and trembling. Paul wrote, *"Knowing therefore the terror of the Lord, we persuade men…"* (2 Corinthians 5:11). To think of the coming of our Master is either to think in hope and anticipation of His glory, or to think in fear and dread of His eternal judgement. So, we look to His return – for those of us who know the

Savior, with a living hope, and for those who do not, with fear and dread.

For us, "being on the alert" means we are to carry the cross with the awareness that one day we will stand in His presence to give an account. We do not know the day or the hour. And as He said, He will come even *"when you do not think He will"*. We must live and walk in the ready.

Blessed is the servant (or slave) that is walking in the ready and is about his master's business. Every one of us – believer and non-believer alike – have been given gifts to carry out our Creator's purpose. Every single person in the world has been given life, breath, privilege – all granted to us by God as a stewardship, for which we will be accountable. And hell will be populated not only by Satan and his angels, but by people who with unrepentant hearts wasted that privilege and who embezzled the gifts that God intended for His purpose. The servant's task is to serve the Master and those He has placed before us. And the day of accountability is coming soon!

Lastly, Jesus relates the parable of the ten virgins to teach us the suddenness and the unexpectedness of His return. It should call us to readiness, preparedness and alertness so that we are not caught in an unexpected moment unprepared for His coming. Let's be mindful that the first time Jesus came, the world was not ready. They should have been. The prophets had marked out very clearly the signs for which the world should be watching. They said there would be a forerunner. There was. They identified him as a voice crying in the wilderness. That's exactly who John the Baptist was. They said the Messiah would be born in Bethlehem, He was; born of a virgin, He was; born of the line of David, He was. They said He would come to Galilee, He did. They said He would have great power, He had it. But the world still was not prepared and not ready. John writes, *"He came into the very world He created, but the world didn't recognize him. He came to His own people, and even they rejected Him"* (John 1:10-11).

Now, the lesson of the parable is very simple. It is not complex. The parable is meant to teach us that Jesus is coming. That He is coming to judge sinners and to reward the righteous. That He is coming in a sudden and unexpected moment and everyone should be prepared. And afterward, there will be no second chance. People may knock all they want, but the door will be shut. The day of opportunity will have come and gone forever.

The church has known for over 2,000 years that Christ is returning for His bride, and yet, many of us have become lethargic and derelict in our responsibility. Among too many of us, there is no longer an excited anticipation for the soon-return of our Lord and Savior. As a result, there is little effective witness being given that the Lord is returning.

The Master has called us to "be on the alert". We have no idea how much time remains – before we are with Him in heaven, or before He returns. Let us carry the cross that He has placed before us in a way that honors Him, that brings glory to Him and furthers His mission!

* * *

23

LET'S TALK ABOUT THE TALENTS

"Again, the Kingdom of Heaven can be illustrated by the story of a man going on a long trip. He called together his servants and entrusted his money to them while he was gone. He gave five bags of silver to one, two bags of silver to another, and one bag of silver to the last — dividing it in proportion to their abilities. He then left on his trip. The servant who received the five bags of silver began to invest the money and earned five more. The servant with two bags of silver also went to work and earned two more. But the servant who received the one bag of silver dug a hole in the ground and hid the master's money. After a long time, their master returned from his trip and called them to give an account of how they had used his money. The servant to whom he had entrusted the five bags of silver came forward with five more and said, 'Master, you gave me five bags of silver to invest, and I have earned five more.' The master was full of praise. 'Well done, my good and faithful servant. You have been faithful in handling this small amount, so now I will give you many more responsibilities. Let's celebrate together!' The servant who had received the two bags of silver came forward and said, 'Master, you gave me two bags of silver to invest, and I have earned two more.' The master said, 'Well done, my good and faithful servant. You have been faithful in handling this small amount, so now I will give you many more responsibilities. Let's celebrate together!' Then the servant with the one bag of silver came and said, 'Master, I knew you were a harsh man, harvesting crops you didn't plant and gathering crops you didn't cultivate. I was afraid I would lose your money, so I hid it in the earth. Look, here is your money back.' But the master replied, 'You wicked and lazy servant! If you knew I harvested crops I didn't plant and gathered crops I didn't cultivate, why didn't you deposit my money in the bank? At least I could have gotten some interest on it.' Then he ordered, 'Take the money from this servant, and give it to the one with the ten bags of silver. To those who use well

what they are given, even more will be given, and they will have an abundance. But from those who do nothing, even what little they have will be taken away. Now throw this useless servant into outer darkness, where there will be weeping and gnashing of teeth.'"
Matthew 25:14-30

* * *

The master did not apportion his talents equally to his servants. He gave more to some and less to others. But he entrusted them all. He was the determiner of what and how much would be given to each. He was a wise master. He knew their abilities. In many ways, he knew them better than they knew themselves. He knew that too much could overwhelm, and too little would undertax their ability. Thus, he entrusted each proportionate with their ability. And then he left – for a long time.

There were several risks that the master took in what he did. First, he entrusted others with a portion of his wealth. Jesus did not say whether it was all of his wealth or only a portion, but regardless, the master was putting at least a portion of his kingdom "at risk" by investing in his servants. He determined that his work and his kingdom would be best furthered through his servants. He didn't have to make that choice. He could have grown his kingdom in any way he chose – and as a successful master, he probably could have done so in an even more effective way. But he chose to grow his kingdom through his servants.

Second, since he entrusted each servant with differing amounts, he risked creating envy and/or pride between the servants, Those who received more could become prideful over the ones who received less, and those who received less could become envious of those who received more. The servants would not have fully comprehended the master's thinking or his plan as he divided the talents in the way that he did. Thus, his allocation could have created enmity among the servants, and the kingdom work could be hampered by any strife that ensued.

Third, the master was gone a long time. Without his physical presence, the servants were free to make their own choices. Would they be diligent today in the task the master had given them, or would they find more pleasurable or satisfying ways to expend their time? The servants knew there would be a reckoning, but as time passed, the temptation would become greater to focus on the pleasures of today and allow tomorrow to take care of itself. Perhaps doubt could even begin to creep in that the master wasn't really coming back.

Fourth, for one of the servants, fear of the master created a paralysis that led to faithlessness. This servant "bought the lie" that said, "what difference can my meager talent make?" He convinced himself that the other servants could do so much better and so much more, so he followed his fear and his faithless "self-talk" and buried his talent. [Forgive a quick side road: This kind of fear and self-talk is prevalent in Kingdom work today. You've heard the adage that 20% of the people do 80% of the work. Though this principle may not be the sole factor, it is definitely a contributing factor. God's people have belittled the talent with which the Master has entrusted them, have buried it and are not using it for the Kingdom. Thus, the work and mission of the Kingdom goes undermanned and under-funded in the midst of the plentiful resources the Master has provided.]

One day, probably when they least expected it, the master returned, and the day of accountability had arrived.

The faithful servants honored their master and wanted to please him by wisely investing the talents with which he had entrusted them. Though each returned a different amount, they were rewarded equally. It is a reminder that God is a rewarder of faithfulness. His reward is not proportionate to the quantity of our talents, it is proportionate to the faithfulness of our use of the talents. They began as servants, and they were promoted to rulers. They were faithful in the few, and the master entrusted them with much more, increasing their capacity for greater service and responsibility. They had labored and toiled, and now they entered into their reward.

The unfaithful servant disobeyed and dishonored his master by doing nothing. He robbed his master of that which was due him. His one talent could have brought an increase of another talent, bringing honor to his Master. But instead, he allowed his fear of failing to keep him from trying to succeed. His fear paralyzed him from acting, and he buried his talent. As a result, even that which he had was lost. He lost his opportunity to serve – not for trying and failing, but for failing to try. He gained no praise or reward from his master. He experienced a loss of intimacy with the one who had trusted him. That's outer darkness! It could be that he looked at his talent as too meager to be of any use, as compared to the amounts received by the other two. It is a reminder to us to never disparage the amount that the Master has given us. We have been appointed as a steward of the Master, and He will take whatever He has entrusted us with and multiply it for His glory, if we will be faithful stewards.

What will the Master say to <u>us</u> upon His return? Will we have labored faithfully and stewarded wisely? Paul wrote, "*...it is required of stewards that they be found faithful*" (1 Corinthians 4:2 ESV). The measure of our faithfulness will not be in the eyes of men, but rather, in the eyes of our Master. He knows what He has entrusted us with. He knows what constitutes the cross He has called us to carry. May He find us faithful with what He has entrusted us – faithful to the end. And on that day, may we hear Him say, "Well done My good and faithful servant. Enter into the joy of your Master!"

* * *

24

SHEEP AND GOATS

"But when the Son of Man comes in His glory, and all the angels with Him, then He will sit upon His glorious throne. All the nations will be gathered in His presence, and He will separate the people as a shepherd separates the sheep from the goats. He will place the sheep at His right hand and the goats at His left. Then the King will say to those on His right, 'Come, you who are blessed by My Father, inherit the Kingdom prepared for you from the creation of the world. For I was hungry, and you fed Me. I was thirsty, and you gave Me a drink. I was a stranger, and you invited Me into your home. I was naked, and you gave Me clothing. I was sick, and you cared for Me. I was in prison, and you visited Me.' Then these righteous ones will reply, 'Lord, when did we ever see You hungry and feed You? Or thirsty and give You something to drink? Or a stranger and show You hospitality? Or naked and give You clothing? When did we ever see You sick or in prison and visit You?' And the King will say, 'I tell you the truth, when you did it to one of the least of these My brothers and sisters, you were doing it to Me!' Then the King will turn to those on the left and say, 'Away with you, you cursed ones, into the eternal fire prepared for the devil and his demons. For I was hungry, and you didn't feed Me. I was thirsty, and you didn't give Me a drink. I was a stranger, and you didn't invite Me into your home. I was naked, and you didn't give Me clothing. I was sick and in prison, and you didn't visit Me.' Then they will reply, 'Lord, when did we ever see You hungry or thirsty or a stranger or naked or sick or in prison, and not help You?' And He will answer, 'I tell you the truth, when you refused to help the least of these My brothers and sisters, you were refusing to help Me.' And they will go away into eternal punishment, but the righteous will go into eternal life."

Matthew 25:31-46

* * *

When the Son of Man first came, He came in all humility to a modest stable. He was announced by a choir of angels, and laid in a feeding trough. But when He returns – He will return in all of His glory – accompanied no longer by a choir of angels, but by the entire angelic host. He will return – not as a baby – but as the Conquering King of Kings reigning on His glorious throne. When He first came, He was ignored by most, including those who knew the prophesies and should have been watching for Him. But this time when He returns, no one will miss His return – and it will be marked by awe and dread.

When the Son of Man returns, He will gather the "ethnos" – those who are alive from every language, tribe, people and nation. Every one will stand before His presence – those who followed, those who rejected, those who rejoice in His return, and those who now stand in fear – those who *"will go away into eternal punishment"* and those who *"will go into eternal life"*.

As the Good Shepherd, *"He will separate the people as a shepherd separates the sheep from the goats"*. In the first century, it would have been very common for a shepherd to be leading a flock which included both sheep and goats. The shepherds would divide them for feeding and for resting. They would move them together and then separate them. That was necessary because sheep and goats do not feed or rest well together. Sheep are for the most part docile, gentle, easily led and easily scared. Goats, on the other hand, are unruly, rambunctious, almost fearless and they create all kinds of problems for the sheep. Thus, the shepherd needed to separate them.

"He will place the sheep at His right hand and the goats at His left." Be mindful that the right hand is the hand of blessing, the hand of honor, and the hand of inheritance. When Jacob was asked by his son Joseph to bless his grandsons, Ephraim and Manasseh, he was very careful to make sure that his right hand was placed on the grandson that was to be blessed as the child of inheritance. If you remember, he crossed his hands in order to be sure that he placed his right hand on Ephraim (Genesis 49:8-20). And that's what you have here. The sheep represent the followers of Christ, those who are entering into the inheritance, and they are placed on the right hand.

. . .

As the King of kings, He says *"to those on His right, 'Come, you who are blessed by My Father, inherit the Kingdom prepared for you from the creation of the world."* We need to understand the importance of what Jesus is saying here. If we miss this, we could walk away thinking that the "sheep" enter into eternal life because of their good works. But nothing could be further from the truth! Jesus is saying that the sheep – the saints – are entering into the Kingdom because the Father has determined to bless them because they are a part of His family through their relationship with Christ, by grace through faith. Just as Jacob's grandsons were blessed by virtue of their relationship to their father, Jacob's son, we who are followers of Jesus are blessed by virtue of our relationship to the Father's Son. Further when He says, *"inherit the Kingdom prepared for you"*, He is emphasizing that salvation by faith is what brings us into the inheritance. The Kingdom was prepared for those who are followers of Christ. Our inheritance is not because of our works. Our works are evidence of our faith. What we do evidences what we are and Whose we are.

Jesus specifically mentioned six types of mercy ministry: those who hunger, those who are thirsty, those who are in need of hospitality, those who need clothing, those who are sick, and those who are imprisoned. We are to show mercy to Christians because we see Christ in them, and we are to show mercy to unbelievers because we want to see Christ in them. We help suffering believers because they bear the name of Christ. And we help suffering unbelievers in the hope that they will come to bear the name of Christ. The Kingdom is for people who minister to others in the name of Christ in that way – who meet a need...whatever that need might be. And in the first century culture that's what the needs were. People were hungry and had no food, they could be thirsty and need a drink. They could be strangers without a place to stay, ill clothed and needing proper clothing, sick and needing someone to come and attend to their sickness, or in prison and needing someone to come and visit them to find out why they were there and work to get them out. That's what they needed in that day. And those needs still exist in our day. But so do other needs, other hurts, other problems, and other anxieties. And Jesus is saying to us that we are to demonstrate to Him that we are people of the Kingdom chosen by the Father with the mandate to meet those needs. In fact, He says if you've done that, you've done it to Me. The Kingdom is for people who do that for Christ, reflecting genuine salvation.

As the Judge, Jesus turns to the "goats", those who are not His followers, and says, *"Away with you, you cursed ones, into the eternal fire prepared for the devil and his demons."* He says, "you never demonstrated the love of God which is the mark of the manifestation of My presence. You never revealed a changed life. You never showed love for your neighbor." He's not talking about the milk of human kindness and compassion, He's talking about the love of Christ. And if the love of Christ is not within me, i have none to give. Paul was writing to the believers in the church in Galatia, *"So then, as we have opportunity, let us do good to everyone..."* (Galatians 6:10).

And note that Jesus says that those cast away are sent *"into the eternal fire prepared for the devil and his demons."* Hell was created for Satan and his demons; it was not created for people. It was never God's desire that people should enter into hell. That outcome is solely the result of rejection of the free gift of salvation which has been extended by God's grace. And the lack of compassion and mercy that He is rebuking in this passage is a reflection of the lack of Christ's presence in their lives.

But many will cry out, "Now wait a minute. We prophesied in Your name. We cast out demons in Your name. We've done many wonderful works in Your name. Are You telling us, You don't know us?" (Matthew 7:22). And there are going to be lots of folks in that line saying, "Look at all the greatness, look at all the grandeur, look at all the splendor, look at all the wonders we did in Your name." But Jesus will say, "I don't know you."

Remember, it's not just about what we have done. He is talking about sins of omission, as well as sins of commission. Not doing good is the moral equivalent of doing evil. That was the case with the third servant who got one talent. It wasn't what he did, it was what he didn't do. The servant wasn't immoral, he just did nothing. He buried the talent and paid no attention to it. That is what caused him to be into outer darkness. Also, the five virgins weren't vile, they were just negligent. People will be cast into hell for what they didn't do. And what they didn't do was believe in the Lord Jesus Christ. It is the absence of righteousness. It is the absence of the love of God that comes through faith in Christ. It is the absence of those kinds of deeds that demonstrate righteousness and demonstrate God's love. It is the presence of the sin of unbelief, and the absence of faith. And the result is an eternity cast away and separated from God.

As we take up the cross and follow Jesus, let's be a people who are watchful for the opportunities the Master gives us to meet a need – to share a cup of cold water in His Name – to be a reflection of His love and His gospel, not only in word, but also in deed. That's why He has left us here with an assignment – an assignment to be His sheep – not goats!

* * *

25

THE MASTER TEACHES WHILE THE TEACHERS CONSPIRE

Every day Jesus went to the Temple to teach, and each evening He returned to spend the night on the Mount of Olives. The crowds gathered at the Temple early each morning to hear Him.
The Festival of Unleavened Bread, which is also called Passover, was approaching. The leading priests and teachers of religious law were plotting how to kill Jesus, but they were afraid of the people's reaction.
Luke 21:37 – 22:2

* * *

Jesus was back in the Temple teaching. The crowds were surrounding Him, hoping to catch a glimpse of another miracle, or hear Him speak truth with authority to the religious leaders, or to teach the Scriptures in a way they had never heard before. And the religious leaders watched Him from the shadows.

The Feasts of Passover (also known as the Festival of Unleavened Bread, which occurs in the March/April timeframe), Pentecost (also known as the Festival of Harvest, which occurs in the May/June timeframe) and Tabernacles (also known as the Festival of Shelters, which occurs in the September/October timeframe) were the three most important feasts for the Jews (Leviticus 23). According to the Law handed down through Moses, all Jewish males were expected to go to Jerusalem to appear before the Lord for these three "pilgrimage" feasts (Deuteronomy 16:16).

• • •

As we saw in a previous chapter, it is estimated that 2 million people made their pilgrimage to Jerusalem for Passover that particular year. Many had in fact come to see and hear Jesus, more than to observe the Passover. The crowd was excited to see Him. Large crowds gathered in Jerusalem always caused the Roman leaders to be anxious of possible uprisings, and this record "excited" crowd made them more so. Passover commemorates God's deliverance of the people of Israel from the bondage of Egypt. So there were strong political overtones to this particular festival that potentially made it an ideal time for a "would-be messiah" to attempt to overthrow Rome. That's why the Roman Governor Pontius Pilate and King Herod were both in Jerusalem that week, instead of in their mansions in Caesarea and Tiberius, respectively. They were in Jerusalem to help keep the peace.

You will recall that the very first Passover was in fact the night of the tenth plague that God brought upon Egypt due to Pharaoh's refusal to let His people go. On that fateful night, God had told the Israelites to sacrifice a spotless lamb, and stain the top and sides of their doorframes with its blood (Exodus 12:21-22). No one was to leave their home until morning. Then the Lord sent an angel of death to pass through the land and to strike down any firstborn son who was not in a home with blood on the doorframe. He would "pass over" the households that had blood on the doorframe (Exodus 12:23). The blood of the lamb is what saved the Israelites from death. It was not the Israelites' ancestry or good standing as God's people that saved them, it was the blood of the lamb. And through the blood of the lamb, God enabled the Israelites to be delivered from the bondage of slavery.

As the Jews prepared to commemorate their deliverance through the blood of a lamb, the Lamb of God sat there in their midst teaching from the Scripture. The people were blind to who He was, and unaware of what He was about to do. Don't forget, the cross did not "happen" to Jesus. The cross was an appointment for Jesus, not an accident. The cross had been determined even before time began. And there was Jesus, fully aware of what was about to unfold – calmly, clearly and courageously teaching the people the Truth of God.

The religious leaders had long seen Jesus as a threat to their power and had debated what should be done about Him. The people were blinded to who Jesus was to a great extent because their religious leaders refused to see Jesus for who He was. It wasn't so much that their eyes were blind as it was that their hearts were hardened. And His demonstration in the Temple a few days earlier was the "final straw" – He had now cast aspersion on their lucrative financial enterprise. They had already determined that He needed to die, the question was how they could pull it off. The crowds loved Jesus. More and more were coming to Him. Jesus was a threat, but if they inflamed the crowd by seizing Him, the tide would turn against them and they would be stripped of their power and their control. The religious leaders knew that they could not apprehend Jesus in the Temple in the midst of the crowds. So they withdrew to the house of Caiaphas, the high priest (Matthew 26:3-4), to ponder, debate and discuss their options among themselves. Surely there was a way to rid themselves of Jesus!

i am mindful that some of these very men in their younger days were more than likely among the leading priests and teachers that King Herod the Great had consulted to ascertain the birthplace of the Messiah (Matthew 2:4-5) thirty or so years earlier. Even then, though they were able to provide information for the wise men to locate Jesus, they were disinterested themselves from trying to locate Him. They showed no signs of a heart seeking after the promised Messiah. As a matter of fact, through the information they provided, they had assisted Herod in his attempt to kill the Messiah by having all the little boys under two years of age who lived in and around Bethlehem killed. And i am pretty confident that they had connected those dots somewhere along the line – between that baby boy born in Bethlehem and this same Jesus. Somehow, they had failed the first time. They were determined not to fail again!

What a contrast – the swirling hatred in their hearts as they connived and conspired to kill Jesus – and the calmness, gentleness and steadfastness of Jesus as He prepared to be crucified. It brings to mind the contrast between the fruit of the flesh and the fruit of the Spirit that Paul wrote about:

"When you follow the desires of your sinful nature, the results are very clear: sexual immorality, impurity, lustful pleasures, idolatry, sorcery, hostility, quarreling, jealousy, outbursts of anger, selfish ambition, dissension, division, envy, drunkenness, wild parties, and other sins like these. Let me tell you again, as I have before, that anyone living that sort of life will not inherit the Kingdom of God.

But the Holy Spirit produces this kind of fruit in our lives: love, joy, peace, patience, kindness, goodness, faithfulness, gentleness, and self-control. There is no law against these things!"

(Galatians 5:19-23).

The irony is that, as the religious leaders prepared to celebrate the holiest festival of their religious lives, they paid great attention to cleansing their homes but never gave a thought to cleansing their hearts. In the midst of a commemoration of the saving of firstborn sons, they were conspiring to kill a firstborn Son. And the very meal they were preparing to eat pointed to the very One they were preparing to kill.

As you take up the cross, walk in the fruit of His Spirit, walk in the steadfastness of His mission and keep your eyes on Him. Don't be concerned about what the enemy may be conspiring, rather, keep your ears and your heart attuned to what He is saying to you and what He is teaching you. He knows the plans He has for you.

* * *

26

WHEREVER THE GOSPEL IS PREACHED

Meanwhile, Jesus was in Bethany at the home of Simon, a man who had previously had leprosy. While He was eating, a woman came in with a beautiful alabaster jar of expensive perfume and poured it over His head. The disciples were indignant when they saw this. "What a waste!" they said. "It could have been sold for a high price and the money given to the poor." But Jesus, aware of this, replied, "Why criticize this woman for doing such a good thing to Me? You will always have the poor among you, but you will not always have Me. She has poured this perfume on Me to prepare My body for burial. I tell you the truth, wherever the Good News is preached throughout the world, this woman's deed will be remembered and discussed."
Matthew 26:6-13

* * *

Earlier in the week, while Jesus and His disciples were still spending their evenings in Bethany, Jesus was at the home of Simon. Simon previously had leprosy, and it is highly probable that he was healed by Jesus. It was through that miracle of healing that they probably became friends. In fact, he could have been the leper that Jesus healed as recorded in Matthew 8:1-4. This account in Matthew 26, combined with the parallel accounts in Mark 14:1-9 and John 12:1-8, would tend to indicate that Simon's home was also the home of Lazarus, Martha and Mary, which would tend to imply that Simon – the former leper – whom Jesus healed – is the one who John called Lazarus, the one who Jesus raised from the dead – John 11). That being true would mean that in many respects,

Simon/Lazarus had twice been dead to his sisters. The first time they were separated from him by leprosy. Lepers were forced to live in isolation away from everyone else in a "sentence" of death. And the second time, he had truly been dead and in the grave for four days.

So, on this night, Jesus and His disciples were hosted for dinner by the family – Simon/Lazarus (the host, reclining at the table – John 12:2), Martha (serving, as always – John 12:2), and Mary (again coming to the feet of Jesus – John 12:3). While Jesus, His disciples and His host were eating, Mary *"came in with a beautiful alabaster jar of expensive perfume and poured it over His head."* Then she proceeded to anoint *"Jesus' feet with it, wiping His feet with her hair"*, and *"the house was filled with the fragrance"* (John 12:3). If i am correct about Simon and Lazarus being the same person, i want you to think about the thanksgiving that was overflowing in the hearts of that family. They had a deep love for Jesus, and He had a deep love for them. He called them His "friends". Simon/Lazarus was expressing his thanksgiving by hosting and supping with his "Friend", enjoying intimate conversation and fellowship. Martha was expressing her thanksgiving through her love language – serving, and doing so with excellence.

Then, in walked Mary – expressing her thanksgiving, her love and her worship – by anointing Jesus' head and feet with expensive perfume. She was taking the same care that would typically have been reserved for a deceased loved one in preparation for burial. Only Jesus knew that, in fact, that was what Mary was doing. Not another person in that room – including Mary – knew that in just a matter of days Jesus' body would be buried in a tomb. Even when Jesus made that statement to the disciples, they did not yet understand. And here was Mary presenting worship to her Lord in the best way she knew how, overflowing with love and adoration. Later the apostle John would describe the vision of what worship will look like in heaven in the Book of Revelation. I would venture that this expression of worship by Mary was the closest he saw on this side of heaven to that heavenly vision.

And yet, in the midst of pure, authentic worship, the naysayers came out – criticizing her excess and her impropriety. Though their criticisms were couched in a "godly", "we-care-about-the-poor" way; they were actually godless. When Judas said – *"What a waste; it could have been sold for a high price and the money given to the poor"* – he was really revealing the condition of his cold heart. He revealed a heart that was unable to express true worship. On a quick side road – over the years, i have frequently heard church members expressing criticism of the way others worship – whether it be through the style of their music, expressions through the raising of hands, or the like. Regrettably, most often, the criticism has been more of a commentary of the critic's lack of heart for authentic worship. Mary was worshiping authentically with her whole heart.

Unfortunately, a number of the disciples were taken in by Judas' false piety and echoed his concerns. This needs to be a reminder to us to be discerning in all things before we lend our support. Take the question to Jesus first, before you join in. Listen to what He has to say about the matter, before you cast any aspersion. In this instance, they would have clearly heard Jesus calling out Judas for his errant thinking. As a matter of fact, Jesus went on to declare that little else from that evening would be remembered, but "*wherever the Good News is preached throughout the world, this woman's deed will be remembered and discussed.*"

Matthew has actually backtracked in his chronology to include this event at this point in his Gospel account. And i have inserted it out of order as well. The event actually occurred before Jesus' triumphal entry into Jerusalem. But Matthew inserted it here. At the same time, he is describing how the religious leaders are plotting how to execute Jesus. They fear a bad reaction from the crowd even more than they fear Jesus. So, they are having difficulty in coming up with an answer. What they needed was someone from within His inner circle that could help them with their plan.

On that night at the home of Simon/Lazarus, Judas became that man. Don't misunderstand me, Jesus had always known that Judas would betray him – but the Father's timing was just days away. This event and the rebuke from Jesus were all it took in Judas' heart to set his betrayal in motion. Even this pure expression of worship would be used by the Father to accomplish His plan of redemption.

As you take up the cross, remember these three lessons from the dinner that night:

- worship your Lord authentically, with a pure heart like Mary,
- take every word of criticism before the Lord to discern what is pure and what is true, before you act on it, and

- trust the Father with every detail. Nothing occurs in isolation – He is working all things together for His glory and our good!

Take it from the woman whose deed will be remembered wherever the Good News is preached!

* * *

27

THE TRAITOR'S CONSENT

Then Satan entered into Judas Iscariot, who was one of the twelve disciples, and he went to the leading priests and captains of the Temple guard to discuss the best way to betray Jesus to them. They were delighted, and they promised to give him money. So he agreed and began looking for an opportunity to betray Jesus, so they could arrest Him when the crowds weren't around.
Luke 22:3-6

* * *

Don't lose sight of the fact that Judas didn't set out on his journey to follow Jesus with betrayal on his mind. He followed Jesus because he truly believed that Jesus was the promised Messiah. He "believed" in Jesus. He was an "early adopter" and supporter, and he wanted to get in on the "ground floor" of Jesus' eventual rise to power. It is important to understand, at the outset, that Judas never envisioned that he would betray Jesus. Rather, Judas envisioned that he would be a part of His trusted circle – maybe not as close as Peter, James and John, but certainly close behind. After all, he was the keeper of the treasury for Jesus and the disciples. Judas believed that Jesus had seen his financial skills and abilities, and valued him as a member of His leadership team when the day arrived for His reign as King. Judas "trusted" that Jesus would enable him to be successful and achieve his desires of life – position, possessions and power. Therefore, in the short-term, he was willing to sacrifice all of those things. He was willing to wander the Judean wilderness with Jesus with the rest of the disciples. From his perspective, it was a good investment that would pay off in the end.

. . .

But as time went on and Judas witnessed one miracle after another, he was becoming impatient for the day that Jesus would declare Himself. At first, his impatience was subtle and subdued, but that night that Jesus allowed Mary to waste that expensive perfume and pour it over his head and feet, he couldn't contain his exasperation. If Jesus was going to rise to power, He needed to be more discerning in the best ways to utilize financial resources. He needed to call upon His trusty advisors – like Judas – to give Him counsel. He couldn't just leave it up to the riff-raff to make their own decisions. Those funds could have been invested much more wisely – and Judas could probably have done so in a way that also enabled him to derive some amount of personal gain for himself as well. But that would never happen if Jesus was going to allow things to occur in such an "unconstrained" way.

What's more, Jesus entered into Jerusalem with the people shouting His accolades in every corner of the city. This was the largest crowd that had ever been in Jerusalem at one time. Many, if not most, of them had come to see Jesus. If there was ever a time for Jesus to declare Himself, this was it! And yet, Jesus was showing no sign that He was moving in that direction, and Judas became more and more frustrated. At that moment, blinded by his own selfish ambition, he decided to take things into his own hands. Over the prior years, his ambition had been just the foothold that Satan needed to occupy Judas' thoughts, but his decision to "take things into his own hands" opened the door for Satan to take full control. And let's not forget – Satan is a crafty liar! We can only imagine the convincing "self-talk" that Satan was speaking into his ear to encourage him in his folly.

Judas had witnessed the failed attempts of the religious leaders to entrap Jesus. Time and again, he had seen Jesus outsmart them, out-maneuver them, and outwit them at every turn. The religious leaders were just the pawns that he required for his plan to force Jesus to show His hand. The leaders wanted to arrest Jesus, so if Judas could help them do that, Jesus would have to declare His authority and establish His Kingdom. That would be the game-changer – Jesus would be declared King – and Judas would finally achieve all that he had been working toward. And this was the time. This was the week! So off he went to find his "unlikely" allies, to convince them to go along with his plan.

. . .

As Jesus would later declare, *"Why didn't you arrest me in the Temple? I was there every day"* (Luke 22:53). But the religious leaders were afraid of the reaction of the crowd. They knew that they could not take action in the light. They knew that whatever they did, it had to be done clandestinely and in the cover of darkness. (Just a quick reminder for you and me: Satan never works in the light. Darkness is his greatest ally! As a matter of fact, Jesus said the night He was arrested, *"This is your moment, the time when the power of darkness reigns"* (Luke 22:53b).) So imagine the delight of the religious leaders when one of Jesus' own disciples approached them to discuss the best way for Jesus to be arrested. These unwitting allies all savored their own craftiness.

To seal the deal, the religious leaders agreed to pay Judas thirty pieces of silver. Lest we think Judas betrayed Jesus for the money, let's be clear. Thirty pieces of silver was NOT a lot of money. Hebrew culture did not place a high value on slaves – and in that day, the value of a slave was thirty pieces of silver (Exodus 21:32). Judas was too ambitious to have betrayed Jesus for such a paltry sum. And the religious leaders were too self-aggrandizing to stoop to paying a high bounty for One they disdained so greatly. The thirty pieces of silver was much like the "ten dollars and other good and valuable consideration" used in legal agreements today. It merely implied that both parties had entered into an agreement that was mutually advantageous. And the religious leaders and Judas saw this agreement as "mutually advantageous". So the promise was sealed – and all that remained was to now watch and wait for the right time.

But again, there is great irony even in that presumptuous statement – because the religious leaders and Judas NEVER controlled the timing. The timing always was in the Father's hands – and the religious leaders' and Judas' traitorous agreement was always a part of His all-knowing plan. So, you ask, did God cause Judas to betray Jesus? Did the Father place it in the hearts of the religious leaders to conspire against His own Son? The answer to both questions is a resounding "NO"! But God knew what was in their hearts. And He knew what was in the heart of Satan and his feeble attempt to destroy the Son. And He permitted them all to exercise their own free will in order to fulfill His redemptive plan. Please forgive my repetition in saying this, but the cross did not "happen to" Jesus. He and the Father love us so much that He was a willing participant. It was the Father's plan. The plan didn't hinge on Judas' choice to betray Jesus. The Father and the Son knew it was in his heart long before he did.

. . .

As you take up the cross, make sure you have emptied your heart of any selfish ambition. Because the cross He would have you carry – and anything and everything you may encounter by taking it – is not about you – it's all about God's redemptive and perfect plan for His glory!

* * *

28

JUST AS HE HAD TOLD THEM

Now the Festival of Unleavened Bread arrived, when the Passover lamb is sacrificed. Jesus sent Peter and John ahead and said, "Go and prepare the Passover meal, so we can eat it together." "Where do you want us to prepare it?" they asked Him. He replied, "As soon as you enter Jerusalem, a man carrying a pitcher of water will meet you. Follow him. At the house he enters, say to the owner, 'The Teacher asks: Where is the guest room where I can eat the Passover meal with My disciples?' He will take you upstairs to a large room that is already set up. That is where you should prepare our meal." They went off to the city and found everything just as Jesus had said, and they prepared the Passover meal there.
Luke 22:7-13

* * *

It was the fifth day of the week – Thursday – the 14th day of Nissan on the Hebrew calendar. The Passover Festival began at dusk with the Passover meal and continued for seven days, as it still does. In preparation for the festival, all leavening (or Chametz) was removed from the households of the Jews. Leaven symbolized corruption, or sin, thus, for the seven days of Passover, Jews were to only eat unleavened bread (Exodus 12:15). Often any Chametz remaining in the household the day before Passover was removed and destroyed by burning. That morning in Jerusalem the pungent odor of burning Chametz would have permeated the air in and around the city. Every household was completing their preparations.

. . .

The preparations were so important to Jesus that He sent His two most trusted disciples – Peter (the one upon whom He would build His church – Matthew 16:18) and John (the one to whom He would entrust the care of His mother – John 19:26-27). Notice that when Jesus instructed them to go and prepare the meal, they wisely asked Him for His specific instruction. Both of these men would have known what preparations were required under the Law. Both of them had traveled to Jerusalem many times before for the observance of Passover. Both of these men were leaders. It would have been very easy for them to receive instruction from Jesus to "go" and then head off to do what they believed would be the right thing to do. How often do we attempt to go off and do God's work in our way? How often do we fail to ask the Lord the "how" question? How often do we make our own plan and ask Jesus to bless it instead of asking Him His plan so we can join Him in His activity? Gratefully, Peter and John asked. And Jesus had all the details already worked out. i wonder how much time and energy Peter and John would have needlessly spent if they had failed to ask. As you take up the cross that Jesus has called you to carry, don't forget to continue to ask Him the "how" question. Peter may have had his shortcomings as the day progressed, but he started the day well by wisely asking Jesus "how".

Just as Jesus had arranged for the donkey and its colt to be available for His entry into the city at the beginning of the week, it appears that Jesus had made prior arrangements for the Passover meal. Apparently, the last time He was in Jerusalem for the Feast of Dedication in the winter (John 10:22), He had taken time to make these arrangements. Remember, the record crowd in Jerusalem would have made it very difficult to find a room in the city – but Jesus had already taken care of that detail. He had left nothing out of His planning, as reflected by the detailed instructions that He gave Peter and John. As they entered Jerusalem:

1. There would be a man waiting to meet them.
2. He would know who they were (in a crowd of two million no less!).
3. He would be carrying a pitcher of water so that he could be identified by them.
4. They were to follow him.
5. As he entered the house, they were to follow him in and speak to the owner.
6. They were to ask on behalf of the "Teacher" where the room was that they would be using for the meal.

7. The owner would take them to the room that had been reserved and was of sufficient size for all of them to gather.
8. It was there that Peter and John were to make preparations for the meal so that everything would be ready when Jesus and the other disciples arrived.

Bear in mind that Jesus knew He would be betrayed and arrested that night. He knew it that morning when He gave Peter and John these instructions, and He knew it back in the fall when He made these arrangements. He wasn't distracted by what was about to occur. To the contrary, His planning and preparation was complete to the most "minor" detail – because nothing in God's providential plan is minor! Don't lose sight that our God is God over all the details. There is nothing in our path – or in our lives – that escapes His notice – or that escapes His foreknowledge.

Imagine if you knew exactly what the stock market was going to do tomorrow. You could buy or sell today and tomorrow in a way that would maximize your financial gain because it would all be mapped out for you. You would know the exact time and manner to execute your strategy – and there would be no guessing involved – no matter how informed the guessing might be. Well, we serve a God and follow a Master who knows exactly what tomorrow holds – and His designs are much greater than anything that will happen in the stock market! He has a perfect plan and path for us – including the most minor detail, if we will but ask, heed and follow His plan!

The meal typically was conducted in a family home or, as pilgrims gathered in Jerusalem, in a room set aside for that purpose with a gathering of family members or friends. There would have been a table large enough for Jesus and His disciples to gather around. There would be pillows for everyone to be seated on the floor in a reclining position. The menu would have included an unleavened flatbread called "matzo", bitter herbs called "maror", dipping bowls of salt water, and red wine to drink (symbolizing the lamb's shed blood). The Gospel accounts do not reference other elements that may have also become a part of a Passover meal, so i will not include them here. It is however very possible that other elements were a part of their meal that night. Peter and John were charged with the responsibility to make sure that everything was in place, and they found everything as Jesus told them it would be.

• • •

The same Lord who directed the angel of death to "pass over" the homes whose door posts were stained with the blood of the lamb, and who directed the people through Moses to observe the Passover each year was now going to lead His disciples through one last remembrance. And the Lamb of God made certain that every detail was in place – just as He had told them.

As you take up the cross to follow Him, everything will be ready – every detail that is needed will be in place – to accomplish His plan and purpose. Trust Him and heed His word – just as He has told you.

* * *

29

THE HOUR HAS COME

When the hour had come, He reclined at the table, and the apostles with Him.
Luke 22:14 (NASB)

* * *

God's timing is perfect. He is eternal. He is not constrained by such things as time or space. He created it all. Time is as much His creation as we are. He can turn it backward, as we see recorded in 2 Kings 20:9-11. He could have just as easily turned it forward, as we see in the same passage. He can make time stand still, as we see recorded in Joshua 10:12-13. He does everything according to His own timing. He chose to create heaven and earth, and all of its inhabitants within six days. He put the rotation of the earth, the sun and the moon in motion to create through each rotation a day in time. He determined that each orbit of the earth around the sun would equate to one year with four seasons. He created time, as He did all of His creation, for His purpose and to bring Him glory. And nothing and no one can frustrate His plan, His purpose, or His timing.

God created man, and from him woman, to worship Him. He created them as man and woman in order to procreate and multiply into a multitude of people who would worship Him. And He knew, even before creating that first man and woman, and choosing to give them a free will, that they would sin against Him. Therefore He also knew before He created them – and before He created time – that He would need to make a way for His creation to be redeemed. As a result, everything – including time – was created by Him with His plan in mind.

The apostle Paul writes, *"But when the fullness of the time came, God sent forth His Son…"* (Galatians 4:4 NASB). The "fullness of time" means the timing was as it should be. There are many who have tried to answer the question as to why Jesus came to earth as a baby at the moment He did. Some have pointed to the unification of the world under Roman rule. Prior to the Romans, the Greeks had set the stage with a common trade language. Others have pointed to the growing existence of even pagan worship that emphasized the need for blood sacrifice. But the problem with all of that is that it is man's feeble attempt to understand God's wisdom. The reality is that only God knows the reason for why that time was His perfect time for the Son to be born, and it was! God ordered every millisecond leading up to it, and He ordered every moment from His birth to this moment in the upper room. Repeatedly throughout the Gospels, we have seen the religious leaders making feeble attempts to arrest Jesus or stone Him, and He just disappeared before their eyes. And what was the reason that Jesus continued to give? His hour had not yet come (John 7:30). And, by the way, God has ordered every millisecond leading up to Jesus' return as well. And as Jesus said, *"no one knows the day or hour when these things will happen, not even the angels in heaven or the Son Himself. Only the Father knows"* (Matthew 24:36). But on that night in the upper room at the beginning of Passover, the hour had come.

Hold onto this truth about time and timing. We have a tendency to grow impatient as we "wait" on God for answers to our prayers. We like to place deadlines on God – those we deem to be real based upon influences outside of our control, as well as deadlines that we sometimes contrive to "test" God. Remember He controls the timing – and He knows His purpose for His "seeming" delay. He will accomplish His purpose in His time. Here is what God Himself has said, as recorded by the prophet Isaiah:

"I am God, and there is none like me. Only I can tell you the future before it even happens. Everything I plan will come to pass, for I do whatever I wish" (Isaiah 46:9-10).

And He will do so according to His perfect timing!

Jesus was reclining at the table. This was the moment of peace and calm before the storm. It is very similar to the night Jesus was sleeping in the boat in the midst of the storm. Jesus knew all that was about to unfold, and yet there He reclined. You and i would have been at the very least anxious, if not outright panicked. But as the Son of God, He knew that nothing was about to occur that was not in accordance with the Father's plan. And as the Son of Man, He knew that the next almost-twenty-four-hours were going to require tremendous physical strength and endurance. So He availed Himself to the rest that the Father now provided.

Grasp this truth! In the midst of your journey, as you take up the cross, there will be moments of rest in the midst of, or in preparation for, great activity. Don't rest when you are to be active, and don't be active when you are to be resting. But avail yourself to the time of rest that the Father has provided. Unlike Jesus, we don't know what is ahead – but the Father does – and He is providing this time to renew your strength to endure.

That brings us to what i believe is the most important truth of this particular verse. His apostles were there surrounding Him. He was in their midst. They were enjoying the intimacy of His presence. At the most critical twenty-four-hour period in human history – and most likely heavenly history – Jesus was right there with His own. And He was preparing to pour into them, nurture them and encourage them. He knew of what they had need. He knew that the very foundation of their belief in Him was about to be shaken. He knew the tragedy and despair they would experience. But He also knew the victory they would witness and experience on the other side of their pain. So He was going to spend every moment He possibly could with them to enable them to walk through the hours ahead.

We need to take confidence in the reality that no matter what lies ahead, the Master is right there with us. And He will not leave us or forsake us – not ever! He knows the victory on the other side of the pain. i don't know what the hour may be for you, or for me. It will look different for each one of us. But i do know that as we follow Him, an hour will come when we are to enter into something in our path that He has permitted for His purpose and His glory. In that hour, trust Him in the timing, rest in the intimacy of His presence and know that He is walking with you every step of the way!

* * *

30

YOU WILL NEVER EVER WASH MY FEET

Jesus knew that the Father had given Him authority over everything and that He had come from God and would return to God. So He got up from the table, took off His robe, wrapped a towel around His waist, and poured water into a basin. Then He began to wash the disciples' feet, drying them with the towel He had around Him. When Jesus came to Simon Peter, Peter said to Him, "Lord, are You going to wash my feet?" Jesus replied, "You don't understand now what I am doing, but someday you will." "No," Peter protested, "You will never ever wash my feet!" Jesus replied, "Unless I wash you, you won't belong to Me." Simon Peter exclaimed, "Then wash my hands and head as well, Lord, not just my feet!" Jesus replied, "A person who has bathed all over does not need to wash, except for the feet, to be entirely clean. And you disciples are clean, but not all of you." For Jesus knew who would betray Him. That is what He meant when He said, "Not all of you are clean." After washing their feet, He put on His robe again and sat down and asked, "Do you understand what I was doing? You call Me 'Teacher' and 'Lord,' and you are right, because that's what I am. And since I, your Lord and Teacher, have washed your feet, you ought to wash each other's feet. I have given you an example to follow. Do as I have done to you. I tell you the truth, slaves are not greater than their master. Nor is the messenger more important than the one who sends the message. Now that you know these things, God will bless you for doing them.

John 13:3-17

* * *

There is absolutely no one who has ever walked on this earth who has had more authority, more majesty and more adoration due Him than

Jesus Christ. Every ruler who has ever lived, the most wealthy, the most powerful, and the most famous all fall short of His glory and His authority. The Father had sent Him, and He would return to the Father.

i grew up in Palm Beach County, Florida. It has been said that the island of Palm Beach is home to ten percent of America's wealth. It is the island of the rich and famous. Our current U. S. President has a home there. Whenever he is in town, traffic is rerouted on land, sea and air. i would not even venture to guess how many people are in his entourage and service to make sure his every need is met, and every comfort is provided. i don't say that critically of the President, nor do i disparage in any way the other residents of the town and the way they are served. i mention them solely as a point of comparison. Jesus, who has authority over every one of them – and every one of us – and is worthy of all praise, all worship, all respect, and all reverence, got up from the table, took off His robe and wrapped a towel around His waist like a servant. There are a very few of us who would ever do that – and none of us are the King of Kings.

But this wasn't the first or the last time that our Lord gave no regard to His divine privilege. The apostle Paul writes:

"Though He was God, He did not think of equality with God as something to cling to. Instead, He gave up His divine privileges; He took the humble position of a slave and was born as a human being. When He appeared in human form, He humbled himself in obedience to God and died a criminal's death on a cross" (Philippians 2:6-8).

Then Jesus kneeled before each of His disciples, washed their dirty feet, and dried them with the towel He was wearing around His waist. Let that picture sink in! His humility. His selflessness. And He is the Almighty God. Now – think about whose feet He is washing. One of the men will vehemently deny that he even knows Him before the night is out. One of them will doubt that He could possibly have resurrected from the grave, in just a few short days. And if that's not enough, one of them will betray Him and provide the means for Him to be arrested that very night. And all of those who remain, except one, will scatter when He is arrested and will not follow Him to the cross. There is not a lot that is praiseworthy about these men over the next few days. These are Jesus' closest friends – and all but one will abandon Him. And yet, Jesus, who knew everything that would transpire, and knew everything about them, washed their feet.

. . .

Scripture only records how Peter reacted. We don't know what the others said or did, if anything. I can't help but wonder what was going through the mind of Judas as Jesus was washing his feet. Or Thomas, the skeptic. Or John, the beloved. (It's interesting to me that John did not include any personal commentary about the experience.)

But we do know what Peter did. "All or nothing Peter" never hesitates to be the first one to speak up (until later that night) and he is always the one jumping in with both feet. When he sees what Jesus is about to do to him, he protests – *"You will never ever wash my feet!"* Peter probably had the clearest understanding of who Jesus was (which made his denial later that night even more devastating for him). So, to him, to have the Son of God abase Himself to such a degree would have been so inappropriate. Rather, he was probably thinking, *"Lord, I need to wash Your feet. And I'm embarrassed that I didn't even think of it!"* But then when Jesus tells him, *"Unless I wash you, you won't belong to Me"*, in true Peter-form He says, "Then Lord, wash all of me!"

After Jesus had washed all of their feet, He put His robe back on and returned to His place reclining at the table. As their Almighty God, He washed their feet. As their Lord and Teacher, He used the experience to teach them an important Kingdom principle. He is the Master; they – and we – are the slaves. He is the King; they – and we – are the messengers. As He has done, we are to do likewise. If He served, we are to serve. If He abased Himself for the sake of the Kingdom, we are to abase ourselves for the sake of the Kingdom. If He gave all for us, we are to give all for Him.

i would expect that if Jesus walked up to any one of us right now and knelt down to wash our feet, our response may be very similar to Peter – "Oh no Jesus, You will never ever wash my feet." But would that response be driven, like Peter, by our understanding of His Majesty, or would it be driven by our unwillingness to wash the feet of others. Who has the Master placed before you to wash their feet? It may be literal, or it may be to minister to a difficult need. As He has done, we are to do likewise. And just like Jesus told the disciples that night, *"Now that you know these things, you must do them. And the Father will bless you for doing them."* But allow me to add a caution. Don't do them in order to receive a blessing. Do them because our Master and Teacher did. Do them because our Almighty God did. Do them because it is Him who we take up the cross to follow!

* * *

31

THE PASSOVER SUPPER

Jesus said, "I have been very eager to eat this Passover meal with you before My suffering begins. For I tell you now that I won't eat this meal again until its meaning is fulfilled in the Kingdom of God." Then He took a cup of wine and gave thanks to God for it. Then He said, "Take this and share it among yourselves. For I will not drink wine again until the Kingdom of God has come." He took some bread and gave thanks to God for it. Then He broke it in pieces and gave it to the disciples, saying, "This is My body, which is given for you. Do this in remembrance of Me." After supper He took another cup of wine and said, "This cup is the new covenant between God and His people—an agreement confirmed with My blood, which is poured out as a sacrifice for you."

Luke 22:15-20

* * *

Luke records that Jesus was "very eager" to eat this Passover meal with His disciples. But Luke doesn't record whether or not the disciples were "eager" to eat this meal with Jesus. Obviously, Jesus had a perspective that the disciples did not. Jesus knew the suffering He was about to endure. He knew that the very meaning of the meal did not only look back to "that night" in Egypt when the angel of death "passed over" and the covenant that God had made with His chosen people, but from this moment on, the meal of remembrance would now be looking forward to the fulfillment of God's Kingdom under the new covenant.

What were the disciples thinking as they gathered around that table? Were some of them caught up in the tradition of the Passover meal without much thought about its deeper meaning? Were they going through the motions on "autopilot" as they walked through the very familiar components of the meal? Were some of them still processing what Jesus had just done in washing their feet? Were they so preoccupied with their thoughts that they really weren't considering the deeper meaning of what Jesus was telling them at the moment? Or were some – specifically Judas Iscariot – thinking only about what he was about to do – and considering how he might inconspicuously slip out of the room?

The Passover meal incorporated significant traditional elements, reflecting God's covenant with His chosen people, and we have no reason to believe that Jesus would not have incorporated them into their evening:

- First, the supper would have begun with a prayer of thanksgiving for God's deliverance through the Exodus from Egypt and the heritage He had given to His chosen people.
- Next, they would have eaten raw vegetables dipped in salt water, as a reminder of the tears of gratitude shed by their enslaved ancestors.
- Then they would have broken bread – the "matzah" – an unleavened bread symbolizing the haste and urgency with which the people exited from Egypt (not having the time to allow the bread to rise).
- They would have eaten "maror" – the bitter herb – as a reminder of the bitterness of the slavery endured by their ancestors.
- They would have reclined at the table during the meal as a reminder that they were a free people, and no longer standing as servants or slaves in bondage.
- They would have eaten roasted meat, probably roast lamb, as a reminder of the lamb that was sacrificed for their deliverance.
- Throughout the evening four cups of wine would have been passed, each cup traditionally representing the specific promises of God in Exodus 6:6-8 under the old covenant, which were respectively:
- I will free you from slavery (the first cup at the start of the meal),
- I will redeem you (the second cup during the meal),
- I will be your God and you will be My people (the third cup of redemption after the meal), and
- I will bring you into the land I have promised (the final cup at the conclusion of the meal).

But on that night Jesus unveiled the new covenant between God and all people.

First, Jesus shared that He would *"not drink wine again until the Kingdom of God has come."* Under the old covenant, the lamb was shed for the deliverance of God's chosen people. But under the new covenant, Jesus as the Passover Lamb was to be slain to ransom people from every language, tribe and nation. When He says, "the Kingdom of God has come", He is speaking of that time upon His return when the multitudes of all peoples are reached and gathered, and His Kingdom is established.

Second, He presented the bread as His body which would be given freely – not taken – and broken as the ransom for all people. The Father had sent Him as the Lamb of God to be offered as the once and for all sacrifice for the forgiveness of sin.

Third, as He presented the final cup, He said, *"This cup is the new covenant between God and His people—an agreement confirmed with My blood, which is poured out as a sacrifice for you."* In essence that new covenant, as opposed to the old covenant above, is:

Through My blood which is poured out, I make the way so that

- All people can be freed from the slavery of sin,
- All people can be redeemed from the consequence of sin,
- All people can be restored into a relationship with their God and they will be His people, and
- All people can enter into the Kingdom of God.

And in so doing, Jesus instituted His Supper of Remembrance that we might gather to remember what He has done and the covenant He has made through the breaking of His body and the shedding of His blood. The apostle Paul would later write:

"On the night when He was betrayed, the Lord Jesus took some bread and gave thanks to God for it. Then He broke it in pieces and said, "This is My body, which is given for you. Do this in remembrance of Me." In the same way, He took the

cup of wine after supper, saying, "This cup is the new covenant between God and His people — an agreement confirmed with My blood. Do this in remembrance of Me as often as you drink it." For every time you eat this bread and drink this cup, you are announcing the Lord's death until He comes again"
(1 Corinthians 11:23-26).

As we gather to do so, we are to do so in remembrance of Him. So, as you take up the cross to follow Him, what are you thinking about as you gather around that table? Are you possibly distracted like the disciples were? Are you caught up in the tradition of the Lord's Supper without giving much thought to its meaning? Are you going through the motions on "autopilot" as you partake of the elements of the Supper? Are you preoccupied with thoughts on other matters, and not considering the meaning of what Jesus has done? Or, like Judas Iscariot, are you thinking about other things you need to do? Do not ever allow your observance of the Lord's Supper to become routine or perfunctory. We have an advantage that the disciples did not have that night. The disciples did not know what was about to unfold, but we do know the price that Jesus paid. Remember the covenant that was made between the Almighty God and you through the broken body and shed blood of our Savior. Do so in remembrance of Him!

* * *

32

A BETRAYAL AND A DENIAL FORETOLD

Now Jesus was deeply troubled, and He exclaimed, "I tell you the truth, one of you will betray Me!" The disciples looked at each other, wondering whom He could mean. The disciple Jesus loved was sitting next to Jesus at the table. Simon Peter motioned to him to ask, "Who's He talking about?" So that disciple leaned over to Jesus and asked, "Lord, who is it?" Jesus responded, "It is the one to whom I give the bread I dip in the bowl." And when He had dipped it, He gave it to Judas, son of Simon Iscariot. When Judas had eaten the bread, Satan entered into him. Then Jesus told him, "Hurry and do what you're going to do." None of the others at the table knew what Jesus meant. Since Judas was their treasurer, some thought Jesus was telling him to go and pay for the food or to give some money to the poor. So Judas left at once, going out into the night. As soon as Judas left the room, Jesus said, "The time has come for the Son of Man to enter into His glory, and God will be glorified because of Him. And since God receives glory because of the Son, He will give His own glory to the Son, and He will do so at once. Dear children, I will be with you only a little longer. And as I told the Jewish leaders, you will search for Me, but you can't come where I am going. So now I am giving you a new commandment: Love each other. Just as I have loved you, you should love each other. Your love for one another will prove to the world that you are My disciples." Simon Peter asked, "Lord, where are you going?" And Jesus replied, "You can't go with Me now, but you will follow Me later." "But why can't I come now, Lord?" he asked. "I'm ready to die for you." Jesus answered, "Die for Me? I tell you the truth, Peter — before the rooster crows tomorrow morning, you will deny three times that you even know Me."

John 13:21-38

* * *

As we have said multiple times, the events unfolding that night were not happening "to" Jesus. This plan of redemption had been set forth by the Father before the beginning of time. Jesus had always known what was going to occur. Jesus knew when He called Judas Iscariot to follow Him, that he would betray Him. For there to be a cross, there needed to be an arrest. For there to be an arrest, there needed to be a betrayal. For there to be a betrayal, there needed to be a betrayer. Judas did not betray Jesus because God put it in his heart. Satan put it in his heart. But God knew Satan would do it, and God knew Judas would make that choice.

But for all of that foreknowledge, Judas' action still caused Jesus to be deeply troubled. i don't believe, at that moment, that He was troubled about the betrayal; i believe He was troubled about Judas. Jesus loved Judas. Jesus had walked together with all of His disciples for over three years. They had walked together intimately. They laughed together. They cried together. Jesus poured His life into each of those men – even Judas. Yes, He knew that Judas was about to betray Him. But He also knew that, soon after, Judas would hang himself. And most importantly, He knew that Judas would spend eternity in the torment of hell. As Peter would later write, the Lord "*does not want anyone to be destroyed, but wants everyone to repent*" (2 Peter 3:9). "Everyone" includes Judas. In spite of what Judas was preparing to do, Jesus never "gave up" on him, or stopped loving him. That was Judas' choice, not Jesus' choice. Jesus extended His love, even when it was not returned. As we take up the cross, we are to do the same.

Four other observations regarding this passage: First, notice that Jesus treated Judas as the guest of honor. It would have been the custom for the host of a special feast to take a piece of bread, dip it in sauce and present it to the guest of honor. Jesus was not giving the piece of bread to Judas solely to signify to John who the traitor was. He was extending honor and grace to Judas even up to the last moment. Jesus extended His grace, even when it was not returned. As we take up the cross, we are to do the same.

Second, by turning away from his Lord, Judas opened his heart to Satan. It is a reminder to each of us that there is no place of neutrality. If we do not turn to Jesus, we are, in fact, turning to Satan. There is no middle ground. Just ask Judas. As we take up the cross, let's make sure that our heart remains turned toward Jesus.

. . .

Third, when Jesus declared to the disciples that one of them would betray Him, John records that *"the disciples looked at each other, wondering whom He could mean."* But what is telling is that apparently only Peter and John took the initiative to ask Jesus who the traitor was. That would indicate that each one thought it might be the other, or each one thought it might be himself. But apparently, except for John and perhaps Peter, no one suspected Judas when he got up to leave. So, each of the other disciples apparently believed that any one of them was capable of betraying their Lord, including himself. That needs to be a sobering reminder to each one of us. Those who at that time had the most intimate relationship with the Savior did not see themselves as being incapable of betraying Him. Before we rush to passing judgement on Judas, we too need to take a thorough examination of our own hearts, lest we fall into the same pit. Each and every one of us is capable of betraying our Savior by our word, our action or our inaction. Don't think that you're beyond betraying Jesus. It has been said that we are all one step away from stupid! And stupid is a character issue; it is not a knowledge issue. It is only by His grace and by the power of His Holy Spirit that we can possibly remain faithful to the end. Don't take that for granted. The disciples knew they were vulnerable, and so are we. As we take up the cross, let's make sure that we walk circumspectly.

And lastly, at the end of this passage, we have a very practical example of this same truth. Jesus tells Peter that he will deny Him before the night is out. This comes on the heels of Peter declaring that He will follow Jesus anywhere – even to death. Peter believed he was incapable of such a thing. After all, he is Peter, the one on whom Jesus said He would build His church. He's Peter, the leader of the other disciples. He's Peter, the first to boldly declare Jesus to be the Christ, the Son of the Living God. He's Peter, one of Jesus' most intimate followers and friends. And he's Peter, the one who before the sun rises would do exactly what Jesus told him – he would betray his Lord.

Take heart that we have a resource that the disciples did not have that night. If you are a follower of Christ, His Holy Spirit lives within you to empower you to walk according to His Spirit, evidencing His character – His love, His grace and His righteousness. As you take up the cross, make sure you stay close to Jesus, filled with His Spirit.

* * *

33

WHO IS GREATEST?

Then they began to argue among themselves about who would be the greatest among them. Jesus told them, "In this world the kings and great men lord it over their people, yet they are called 'friends of the people.' But among you it will be different. Those who are the greatest among you should take the lowest rank, and the leader should be like a servant. Who is more important, the one who sits at the table or the one who serves? The one who sits at the table, of course. But not here! For I am among you as one who serves. You have stayed with Me in My time of trial. And just as My Father has granted Me a Kingdom, I now grant you the right to eat and drink at My table in My Kingdom. And you will sit on thrones, judging the twelve tribes of Israel."

Luke 22:24-30

* * *

Jesus had just washed their feet. He had just declared that one of them was going to betray Him. And yet, all the disciples could seemingly think about was their position in the Kingdom. This wasn't the first time. It had occurred several times before (Mark 9:33-37 and Luke 9:46-48). Even the mother of James and John had asked the question to Jesus (Matthew 20:20-28). But no matter how many times Jesus answered them, they kept coming back to the same question.

Now bear in mind, they had all given up their homes and their careers to follow Jesus. By this time, they truly believed Jesus was the Messiah, and that He would come into His Kingdom. And they wanted to know –

"what's in it for me?" We have served faithfully. Aren't we assured positions of honor in the Kingdom?

Perhaps the discussion arose as they were discussing which disciple was going to betray Jesus. Or perhaps it arose as they discussed the seating arrangements around the table. Jesus had just given Judas the piece of bread dipped in sauce that was befitting the guest of honor. Then Jesus had apparently sent him off on an important mission. Perhaps Judas would have the greatest position in the Kingdom. Whatever prompted the discussion, it ensued.

There actually is an appropriate context for this discussion that Jesus would bring them back to toward the end of this passage. But the way the discussion started was just flat out soulish! It was framed in the way the world would look at position, instead of a Kingdom point of view. Jesus again brought them back to the reality that in the Kingdom, *"those who are the greatest among you should take the lowest rank, and the leader should be like a servant."* Notice that He said, *"like a servant"*. That indicates that we are not just to serve, but we are to serve in the posture of humility of a servant and with the selflessness of a servant. Instead of the greatest being "the big man" sitting in the seat of honor, it is the servant humbly serving all those in the room. Jesus was again totally redefining "greatness". He wasn't telling them not to be great – or – that they wouldn't have positions of greatness in the Kingdom, He was redefining what that meant!

In the day of the apostles, as well as in our day (because it has not changed), greatness is defined by position, power, influence, wealth and recognition. It is an elevation of self. It is an "all about me" focus and goal. It's the game of Monopoly, and whoever has the most wealth at the end of the game wins. But Jesus was telling them that self, or selfish ambition, is the enemy of servanthood. It is the exact opposite of greatness in the Kingdom.

Jesus said, *"I am among you as one who serves."* He is our model. He who deserved the greatest that the world possibly could have offered, served. He who was worthy of all accolades and honor was a servant of all. He who was worthy of all comfort and adoration, endured trials and aspersions for the sake of the gospel, and served. He who endured loneliness and being misunderstood – all for the sake of the gospel – served. He who gave even His own life for us – and for the sake of the gospel – served. He who is the greatest in the Kingdom is the Servant of all, and he or she who would be honored in the Kingdom must likewise be a servant of all.

It's interesting that Jesus did not rebuke them regarding the question of position in the Kingdom. He only rebuked them for their worldly perspective. In spite of their weaknesses and failures, Jesus extended grace and affirmed them for having stayed with Him until the end (though they didn't realize the "end" had come). Jesus knew that He was entrusting these remaining eleven disciples with the "keys of the Kingdom". He was entrusting them with His mandate and commission to make disciples of all peoples. They were to be bridges through whom His Holy Spirit would work to draw all peoples unto Himself. They had a significant role in the Kingdom. And just as the master had entrusted his servants with talents to invest for the sake of the master's business, Jesus was entrusting these men with "talents" to be invested for the sake of the Kingdom. He assured them here that – just like the returning master had said to his faithful servants – if they were faithful with what He entrusted to them, they would receive positions of honor in the Kingdom. As a matter of fact, He told the apostles that they would *"eat and drink at My table in My Kingdom. And you will sit on thrones, judging the twelve tribes of Israel."*

We, too, have been entrusted with the "keys of the Kingdom". We, too, have been commissioned to make disciples of all peoples. We are to be His ambassadors of reconciliation (2 Corinthians 5:20) – the bridges through whom His Holy Spirit works, as He draws peoples unto Himself. And when Jesus returns there will be an accounting that we will need to make to Him, of what we have done with that which He has entrusted us.

Let me hasten to add at this point, lest there be any confusion, we are not earning our "place" in heaven. Our place in heaven has been extended to us through the grace of God, sealed by the shed blood of the Son of God, and has been received by faith through the forgiveness of God. There is nothing we can do to merit or earn our place in heaven, We do however "earn" our "position" in heaven. We will be rewarded for faithful stewardship of the time, talent and treasures with which God has entrusted us for His Kingdom purpose. Our motivation is not the "position" we will receive. Our motivation is out of love for our Master, and a God-given desire to honor Him and obey Him. It is our expression of worship unto Him. And yes, just like the master in the parable, He will reward His faithful servants.

• • •

So, the question for us as we take up the cross and follow Jesus is not, "Who will be the greatest in the Kingdom?" The question for us in this hour must be, "How can i be the greatest He has called me to be for His Kingdom?" Oswald Chambers put it another way – "How can I be My Utmost For His Highest?" And that will only occur if we follow Him as faithful servants of the Servant.

* * *

34

A NEW COMMANDMENT

Dear children, I will be with you only a little longer. And as I told the Jewish leaders, you will search for Me, but you can't come where I am going. So now I am giving you a new commandment: Love each other. Just as I have loved you, you should love each other. Your love for one another will prove to the world that you are My disciples."
John 13:33-35

* * *

As we will see over the next eight chapters of this book, God used John in his Gospel to reveal in detail all of what Jesus taught His disciples that night just before He was betrayed (John 13 – 16). Remember, the Gospel of John is not primarily a chronological account of Jesus' life and ministry here on earth. The focus of the Gospel of John is the deity of Christ and the glory of God as revealed through the Son. So, he takes his time to walk us through the rich teachings of Jesus on the very last night He was with His disciples before He went to the cross. The teachings of that night fall into the category of "last words", those truths He wanted His disciples to remember if they forgot everything else. So, pull up close, and let's not miss a word. Jesus said, "I am going…" and *"you can't come where I am going"* – at least for now. *"So now I am giving you a new commandment…."*

"…Love each other." They had already heard Jesus say, earlier in the week, that the greatest commandment is to *"love the Lord your God with all your*

heart, all your soul, and all your mind", and the second greatest is to *"love your neighbor as yourself"* (Matthew 22:37-39). Now He says that He is giving them a new commandment to *"love each other."* Love God. Love Your neighbor. Love each other. Why did Jesus feel it was important to add that third statement? Isn't loving each other a part of loving your neighbor? Earlier in His ministry, His mother Mary and His half-brothers had come looking for Jesus, and He said, looking at His disciples gathered around Him, *"whoever does the will of God, he is My brother and sister and mother"* (Mark 3:35 NASB). Jesus was communicating that His followers were not only family to Him, but also to one another. So that when He said, "love God, love your neighbor and love each other", He was saying, "yes, love your neighbor, and make sure you don't leave out loving your family of brothers and sisters in Me." Jesus knew that sometimes we can be more loving and giving to our neighbors around us than we are to our immediate family beside us. He knew that sometimes we can be loving neighbors and still be a feuding family. Sometimes we can be more forgiving of others than we can be of immediate family members – whether it be our nuclear family or our family in Christ. i will confess that some of my greatest disappointments and some of my greatest hurts have occurred at the hands of church family members. Too often new church plants are a result of church splits instead of good mission strategy. And those splits have most often occurred within church families that forgot – or failed to – love each other.

Tertullian was a theologian in the early church (A.D. 155 – A.D. 240). He wrote that the Roman government was disturbed by the early church. So, they sent spies to infiltrate and observe worship gatherings. They came back to their Roman leaders with a report that was something like this: "These Christians are very strange people. They speak of One by the name of Jesus, who is absent, but who they expect to return soon. And my, look at how they love one another, and are ready to die for each other." Jesus said, *"There is no greater love than to lay down one's life for one's friends"* (John 15:13). And the early church took Him seriously. We are to love each other!

"…Like I have loved you." The apostle Paul writes, *"Love is patient and kind. Love is not jealous or boastful or proud or rude. It does not demand its own way. It is not irritable, and it keeps no record of being wronged. It does not rejoice about injustice but rejoices whenever the truth wins out. Love never gives up, never loses faith, is always hopeful, and endures through every circumstance"* (1 Corinthians 13:4-7). Paul was writing to a church. He was describing the love of Christ – and the love that they – and we – are to have for one

another. It is a love that is selfless. It is a love that is unconditional. It is a love that doesn't give up.

And, it is a love that *"...proves that you are My disciples."* It's interesting that Jesus didn't say that it would be their doctrine that proved that they were His disciples. He didn't even say it would be their service or their mission that distinguished them as being His disciples – though in reality, love for one another will in fact drive our service and our mission. He didn't say it would be the eloquence of their speech. He didn't say it would be the orderliness or beauty of their worship experiences. He said it would be their – our – love for one another. So, we have got to ask the question: Do we love each other in a way that proves we are followers and disciples of Jesus? The "proof" is in our love – or lack thereof. As those not within the body of Christ encounter us, are they overwhelmed, like those Roman spies were, by our love for one another? Or do they witness division, criticism, gossip or enmity?

Why was Jesus giving a "new commandment"? Because He was birthing something new. He was birthing His church. He was instructing the apostles who would be the first shepherds of His church. He was instructing those to whom He was giving the assignment to go forth and make disciples. But before He talked about how they were to do that, He told them that they had to love each other. Before He told them to baptize new believers, He told them that they had to love each other. Before He went to the cross and expressed His ultimate love for them – and for us – He told them to follow His lead and love each other. Before they – or us – could take up the cross and follow Him, there must be a love – His love – for one another.

i am convinced that if we truly would be followers of Jesus and be people who take up the cross and follow Him, then everything He is calling us to be and to do can be encapsulated in these simple truths:

Love God. Love our neighbors. Love each other.

* * *

35

A WORD OF COMFORT

"Don't let your hearts be troubled. Trust in God, and trust also in Me. There is more than enough room in My Father's home. If this were not so, would I have told you that I am going to prepare a place for you? When everything is ready, I will come and get you, so that you will always be with Me where I am. And you know the way to where I am going." "No, we don't know, Lord," Thomas said. "We have no idea where You are going, so how can we know the way?" Jesus told him, "I am the way, the truth, and the life. No one can come to the Father except through Me."

John 14:1-6

* * *

Jesus and the disciples were still in that upper room. He had just told them He must leave them, and that they could not come with Him – at least for now. Remember, they had no idea what was going to happen later that night. There was still a part of them that was waiting for Jesus to declare Himself as the Messiah and establish His Kingdom. A few minutes earlier, He had told them that one of them was going to betray Him and now He has said that He's going away. To put it mildly, they were troubled. They couldn't understand what was happening. None of this looked anything like the way they thought their time with Jesus would end. They had been thinking about positions in the Kingdom – and now Jesus was telling them that He was leaving. Do you hear their confusion and anxiety?

. . .

Thus, Jesus spoke words of comfort and encouragement to them. *"Don't let your hearts be troubled. Trust in God, and trust also in Me."* Jesus was saying, "You know Me. You know Me better than anyone else knows Me. You know I am trustworthy. You know that the Father sent Me. And you know You can trust Him as well. So, whatever happens, don't be troubled. The Father and I have this. And We are worthy of your trust!"

"Besides, where I am going there is more than enough room for each one of you. I am going to make the way for your arrival. I am going to make preparations for you. If I don't go, you won't be able to follow. But if I go, then, after everything is ready, I will be able to come and get you when the time is right. Then, from then on, we will always be together. You will be where I am. I will be where you are. We will never again be separated. And you know where that is. It's the Father's house. And you know the way!" Jesus was speaking words of assurance. He was speaking truth that they could hold onto in the midst of tumultuous times.

This passage is often quoted during funeral services. The loss of a loved one is a tumultuous time. We're grieving the loss of one who has gone. We are experiencing sorrow, knowing we will not see them again on this side of eternity. We miss them. We ache for them. The certainty that their life brought to ours is gone. We can no longer call upon him or her for advice, for counsel, for encouragement, or for comfort. Our life has just been turned upside down. And in the midst of all that hurt, upheaval and uncertainty, we need an anchor. We need a truth we can hold onto. We need someone or something that we can hold onto with complete confidence and trust. So it was at that moment with the disciples.

At that point, Thomas spoke up. He may have been the one speaking, but i would venture that his question was also on the minds of others in that room. Remember, they were troubled and uncertain. They were seeking certainty. They were seeking truth they could understand, and truth they could hold on to. And i am so glad he asked. Because he asked, we know the answer!

Thomas said, "Lord, we really don't know where You are going. We have no idea! We've never been there. We've never seen it. (Remember, Thomas was one who needed to see in order to believe!) So how can we possibly know the way?

. . .

Jesus, in essence, replied, "Thomas, you know the way. You know the way because you know Me – and I am the way! Whatever confusion you experience, whatever trouble you encounter, whatever sorrow or pain you are walking through – I am the way! My way leads through all the mess, all the pain and all the confusion. My way leads to the Father's house. My way leads to the place where there is no pain and there is no suffering. My way leads to that place where we will forever and always be together."

"Thomas, I am THE Way. I am not a way; I am the only way. Don't be duped into trying another way, or make the mistake of trying to follow your own way. I am the only way. Only My way leads to the Father's house. Other ways may seem right in your own human thinking, but those ways will take you where you don't want to go. Like you said, you've never seen the Father's house. But I have! You don't know the way there. But I do! And I'm the only one that does. Trust Me, Thomas – and all – I am THE WAY!"

"And Thomas, I am THE TRUTH! I am not a truth. My word is absolute. My word is without error. My truth does not change based upon season or whim. It is not situational. It is not relative. It is absolute! You will never know the truth of any situation, or trial, or circumstance until you hear from Me. I existed before the beginning of time. My truth has been the same from before the beginning, and will remain beyond the end of time. My truth is ageless. My truth is matchless. And my truth is beyond reproach. If you need an answer, I am the One to ask. I am the only One to ask! Trust Me, Thomas – and all – I am THE TRUTH!"

"Lastly, Thomas, I am THE LIFE! In Me, through Me and by Me have all things been created. All life comes from Me. Tomorrow on a cross and in three days from now when I step forth out of that tomb, I will carry the keys to death and hell. I will have conquered death once and for all. I am the Creator of life and the Defeater of death. Through Me – and Me alone – you can experience life – abundant life – life to the max! Only through Me can you escape the chains of sin and death. Only through Me can you experience unfettered life. I am the only One who can make that promise. Trust Me, Thomas – and all – I am THE LIFE!"

"And no one comes to the Father except through Me!" I and the Father are one. If you have seen Me, you have seen the Father. For this is how the

Father loved the world, He gave His one and only Son, so that everyone who believes in Him will not perish but have eternal life." There is no plan "B". I am the only way to the Father.

"Trust Me, Thomas – and all – as you take up the cross to follow Me, I alone am the Way. I alone am the Truth. I alone am the Life. Follow Me."

* * *

36

A WORD OF ONENESS

"If you had really known Me, you would know who My Father is. From now on, you do know Him and have seen Him!" Philip said, "Lord, show us the Father, and we will be satisfied." Jesus replied, "Have I been with you all this time, Philip, and yet you still don't know who I am? Anyone who has seen Me has seen the Father! So why are you asking Me to show Him to you? Don't you believe that I am in the Father and the Father is in Me? The words I speak are not My own, but My Father who lives in Me does His work through Me. Just believe that I am in the Father and the Father is in Me. Or at least believe because of the work you have seen Me do. I tell you the truth, anyone who believes in Me will do the same works I have done, and even greater works, because I am going to be with the Father. You can ask for anything in My name, and I will do it, so that the Son can bring glory to the Father. Yes, ask Me for anything in My name, and I will do it! If you love Me, obey My commandments."
John 14:7-15

* * *

Don't lose sight of the fact that the focus of John's Gospel is that we would see, discover and know Jesus as the Son of the Living God. John desired that we see Jesus in the fullness of His glory as God incarnate. Jesus' desire for His disciples – and for us – is that each of us would see the glory of the Father and come to know the Father through Him. He's just told the disciples that He is going to His Father's house to make a way for them – and us – to join Him. So, He seizes this moment to remind them that if they REALLY know Him, they know the Father.

. . .

Throughout the Gospels, Philip was bringing people to Jesus. As soon as Jesus had found him (John 1:43), he had immediately gone off to find Nathanael and bring him to Jesus (John 1:45). And he had been bringing people ever since, including the Greek pilgrims who were seeking Jesus earlier that week (John 12:20-22). So, Philip responds to Jesus with a heart-felt desire and ambition to see the Father. He says, "Lord, you don't need to take us to Him. We KNOW that You are His Son. Simply show Him to us, so we can get a glimpse of Him like Moses did, and we will be satisfied." Just like the Greeks had said to him, "We would see Jesus", he is now saying to Jesus, "We would see the Father!" And just like the Greeks knew that Philip could help them to see Jesus, Philip knew that Jesus was able to show him the Father.

Can you think of a greater desire than "we would see the Father"? Each of us have worthy goals, but can you think of a higher goal than the desire to see the glory of God! i don't believe that Jesus' response to him was one of consternation. i believe He was now patiently helping Philip – and that entire group – truly begin to understand that, in seeing Jesus, they had seen the Father.

The Merriam-Webster dictionary defines "oneness" as being "the quality or state or fact of being one: such as singleness, integrity, wholeness, harmony, sameness, identity, unity and union." Jesus would have Philip and all the disciples – and us – know that He and the Father are One – in every aspect of that definition of oneness. Jesus would have us all know that He and the Father are One in appearance. "If you've seen Me, you've seen the Father." "Everything that I am, and everything that I do is a reflection of the Father."

"The words I speak are not My own." The Father and the Son can never say anything that is contrary to one another. The Son only speaks the words of the Father. And that Word endures. It is true. It is honest. It is certain. It is without error. The very Word of the Father became flesh in the Person of His Son (John 1:14) and that very Word is unfailing love and faithfulness. If we have heard the Son, we have heard the Father.

"My Father who lives in Me does His work through Me." Every miracle and every action, including Christ's crucifixion and resurrection, were according to the Father's plan and the Father's timetable. Each act and action were a work of the Father through the Son, and a work of the Son in

the Father – for the two of Them are One – in appearance, in word, and in work.

But then Jesus went on to say, *"anyone who believes in Me will do the same works I have done, and even greater works."* Those who believe in the Son are one with Him. When He says, "believes", He's not talking about mere mental assent. He's not simply describing some intellectual exercise; He is talking about a belief that involves our whole heart, soul and mind. It is a surrendering of our life to Him in the way that the apostle Paul describes as:

"I have been crucified with Christ; and it is no longer I who live, but Christ lives in me; and the life which I now live in the flesh I live by faith in the Son of God, who loved me and gave Himself up for me"
(Galatians 2:20 NASB).

We are one with Him in the work. We are no longer focused in our work, rather, we are focused in joining Him in His work – responding to His activity and His invitation. In so doing, we are able to see Him accomplishing *"even greater works"*, because it is the work of His Holy Spirit in us and through us. Again, as Paul writes:

"The Spirit of God, who raised Jesus from the dead, lives in you. And just as God raised Christ Jesus from the dead, He will give life to your mortal bodies by this same Spirit living within you"
(Romans 8:11).

And we are one with Him in bringing glory to the Father through prayer. He said, *"You can ask for anything in My name, and I will do it, so that the Son can bring glory to the Father. Yes, ask Me for anything in My name, and I will do it!"* Even if we don't know what to pray, His Holy Spirit within us will guide us in prayer:

"...the Holy Spirit helps us in our weakness. For example, we don't know what God wants us to pray for. But the Holy Spirit prays for us with groanings that cannot be expressed in words. And the Father who knows all hearts knows what the Spirit is saying, for the Spirit pleads for us believers in harmony with God's own will"
(Romans 8:26-27).

We are joined together with Him in prayer as one – His Holy Spirit within us and the Son of God sitting on the right hand of the Father interceding for us.

And lastly, we are one with Him in love through obedience. Jesus said, *"If you love Me, obey My commandments."* As we saw in the last chapter, the world around us will know we are His disciples by the love we have for each other. And the world will also know we are His disciples because we obey Him. Don't misunderstand – we're not His because we obey Him, rather, we obey Him because we are His. Our obedience is simply an expression of love – it's not an expression of law. Our son's wife refers to us as her mother and father – in love – not, in law. It is a reminder to all of us that our bond comes through love, not through law. Thus, it is with Jesus. We are one with Him through our obedience because it expresses our love for Him – in light of the fact that He first loved us – with a love that included the cross.

That night in the upper room, Jesus wanted them to fully understand His oneness with the Father, and their oneness with Him. And today, at this moment, as we take up the cross and follow Him, He would have us fully understand as well.

* * *

37

THE HELPER IS COMING

"And I will ask the Father, and He will give you another Advocate, who will never leave you. He is the Holy Spirit, who leads into all truth. The world cannot receive Him, because it isn't looking for Him and doesn't recognize Him. But you know Him, because He lives with you now and later will be in you. No, I will not abandon you as orphans.... When the Father sends the Advocate as My representative — that is, the Holy Spirit — He will teach you everything and will remind you of everything I have told you. I am leaving you with a gift — peace of mind and heart. And the peace I give is a gift the world cannot give. So don't be troubled or afraid. Remember what I told you: I am going away, but I will come back to you again.... Come, let's be going."

John 14:16-31

* * *

Throughout the Gospels, we see the weakness and foibles of the disciples. We see them cry out in fear even when Jesus is in their midst. We see them doubt Jesus. We see them deny Jesus. We see them scatter in fear. We see them easily distracted from the mission of Jesus. We see them argue with one another. We see petty rivalries break out between them. We see them blinded by their own emotion. We see them make bone-headed mistakes. They are really a lot like us, aren't they? But the thing that we need to remember is that throughout the time of the Gospels – until Acts 2:4 – they were not equipped in the way that we are (if we are followers of Jesus). Oh sure, they walked with Jesus. They knew Him intimately. They were eye-witnesses to the miracles He performed. They heard His teaching first hand – and what's more, He would often further explain His teachings privately to them. And yet, they were lacking one very important gift. Though the Holy Spirit had been at work in the world, He was not in them. They had the benefit of the teaching of Jesus, and the application of Jesus, but they did not have the benefit of the empowerment of the Holy Spirit dwelling within them.

i have often thought that, though the Sermon on the Mount (Matthew 5 – 7) was the greatest and most beautiful sermon ever preached, apart from the salvation of Jesus and the empowerment of the Holy Spirit, it is the greatest indictment against us all. Because, apart from His saving grace and the filling of His Spirit, there is no way we can walk in the truths of that message. We don't have it within us. And neither did the disciples… until the Day of Pentecost!

But, on this night, in the upper room, before they left to go to the Garden of Gethsemane on the Mount of Olives, Jesus made them a promise. He told them that, though He was going away, the Father would send another – an Advocate (NLT) – a Comforter (KJV) – a Helper (NASB) – a Counselor (HCSB) – the Holy Spirit (CEV). And once He came to dwell within them, He would never leave them. Jesus needed to leave them to sit at the right hand of the Father. But until He returns, the Father would send One who would not go away. He would be with them and in them – and with us and in us – 24/7. His role was – and is – to lead them – and us – in all truth. The Spirit of God would have the capacity to speak to them – and us – through the Word of God with such clarity and accuracy that they – and we – would know the Truth of God. His role was – and is – to be a guide in all truth.

Jesus said, *"The world cannot receive Him, because it isn't looking for Him and doesn't recognize Him."* The world cannot receive Him because first they must believe in Jesus Christ as Savior and Lord. Until that occurs, the world isn't even looking for Him, because He can only be seen through spiritual eyes. And it doesn't recognize Him because He can only be seen and worshiped in spirit and truth. The Holy Spirit is the Teacher to lead us and guide us into truth. Without Him, the Bible is a book of history and a book of facts. Without Him, we will stutter and trip and fall just like the disciples even did that night.

And Jesus assured them that they would know Him, *"because He lives with you now and later will be in you."* The Spirit could not be in them then, because Jesus needed to return to the Father before His Spirit could come to dwell within them. It is through the indwelling of the Spirit of Christ that the character of Christ – the fruit of the Spirit of Christ – love, joy, peace, patience, kindness, goodness, faithfulness, gentleness, self-control (Galatians 5:22-23) – can be made manifest within us and through us. It is the indwelling Spirit of Christ who takes the Word of God to thoroughly prepare and equip us for every good work (2 Timothy 3:16-17).

Jesus promised that He would not *"abandon* {them} *as orphans"* – without comfort, without help, without an advocate. They would not be left to their own devices or their own defenses. They would not be left with the task that Jesus was giving them without the Resource required to carry it out. They would not be left to find their own way. They would not be left powerless against Satan and the ways of the world. The Father would send the Advocate as the Son's Representative. And He will teach them – and us – all things, reminding them – and us – of all things that Jesus has taught.

Then Jesus gave them the gift of peace. By peace, He meant so much more than just the absence of war or distress. He meant wholeness, completeness, joy, contentment. In the world, peace is something that is hoped for or worked for, but for the follower of Christ, peace is a gift of God received by faith. In the world, peace is enjoyed in the absence of trouble, but in the life of a follower of Christ, peace is experienced in spite of trouble. It is the peace that Jesus modeled as He slept in the boat in the midst of the storm. It is the peace that He modeled even that night in the upper room knowing He would be arrested, beaten and crucified all within the next 18 – 24 hours. He then reminded them that, though He was going away, He would come back again. But now it was time for them to be going.

That same reminder is given to us. Jesus has given us that gift of peace – peace that is not dependent on our circumstances, but peace that can overshadow our circumstances and give us comfort and hope. Peace that can even sleep in the midst of a storm. And He gave it not only as a promise, He sealed the promise by sending His Spirit. Jesus is coming back! But in the meantime, as you take up the cross, walk in the fullness of His Spirit. He still has more for you to do. And until He returns, walk in His perfect peace. *"Come, let's be going."*

* * *

38

A WALK THROUGH A VINEYARD

"I am the true grapevine, and My Father is the gardener. He cuts off every branch of Mine that doesn't produce fruit, and He prunes the branches that do bear fruit so they will produce even more. You have already been pruned and purified by the message I have given you. Remain in Me, and I will remain in you. For a branch cannot produce fruit if it is severed from the vine, and you cannot be fruitful unless you remain in Me. Yes, I am the vine; you are the branches. Those who remain in Me, and I in them, will produce much fruit. For apart from Me you can do nothing. Anyone who does not remain in Me is thrown away like a useless branch and withers. Such branches are gathered into a pile to be burned. But if you remain in Me and My words remain in you, you may ask for anything you want, and it will be granted! When you produce much fruit, you are My true disciples. This brings great glory to My Father."

John 15:1-8

* * *

Jesus and the disciples were now headed from the upper room to the Garden of Gethsemane. More than likely, they were walking through a vineyard in the Kidron Valley. It would have been a full moon, so they would have been able to clearly see all that was around them. So, Jesus used the vineyard as an illustration of a foundational truth.

As i write this, i am reminded of a trek that i and a few friends made through a city in China. Some of the members of our group were from the US, and some lived in that city. Our Chinese friends were giving us a guided tour of some of their favorite sites. Along the way, we stopped at an art shop that had beautiful, colorful sketches hanging on the walls. And most of the sketches included a wise saying that was also penned on the canvas. We came upon one that was a beautiful drawing of a grapevine with clusters of grapes. i asked one of our friends to translate the words that were inscribed beside the drawing. She read, *"I am the Vine, you are the branches; he who abides in Me and I in him, bears much fruit, but without Me you can do nothing."* She was speaking the exact same words that Jesus said to His disciples in that vineyard that night. She was reading this important truth – the essence of what Jesus wanted His disciples to remember in the hours, days and years to follow. He wanted them to remember who He was, who they were and what their purpose was.

A number of us in the group had heard that verse before. But some of our friends were reading that verse for the very first time. They wanted to know where the saying came from and who said it. Having never read it before, or seen a Bible, or studied about Jesus, they proceeded to tell the rest of us that this saying was about a relationship between two people – one was the vine and the other was the branch. They perceived that the branch's purpose was in the vine and that apart from the vine, the branch was incapable of doing anything! Our friends clearly understood the truth of what Jesus was saying – the very first time they ever heard it! The owner of the shop had been quietly listening in the background. Having heard our friends' comments, she pulled out her Bible, and together we had the opportunity to show our friends where the saying was written. Later, having given each of our friends a Bible, we encouraged them to read more about Jesus – who He is and what He has said. But, as i said, folks, they got it – the first time – they understood this simple truth that Jesus is the Vine, and as His followers, we are the branches. All our friends needed to know now was, who this Jesus is.

That night in the vineyard, the disciples knew who Jesus was. You and i know who Jesus is. The question is, do we truly understand the truth He was sharing? Like our Chinese friends said, it is all about a relationship between two people – each one of us, in a relationship with the Person of Jesus Christ. He is the VINE. It is in Him and through Him that all we need for life and nourishment flows. It is through Him that we have life – life that is abundant and fruitful. We are the BRANCHES. Jesus has made the way for us to be grafted into His Vine – by accepting Him and trusting Him to be our Savior and LORD. The branch apart from the vine is dead, and so are we if we are apart from Him. Our branch is drying up and decaying. But through Jesus' death, burial and resurrection, He made the way for us to have life – to be grafted into the Vine and, through Him, to have everlasting, abundant life.

And Jesus, right at the beginning, told His disciples that this was the Father's plan. The Father is the VINEDRESSER. He sent the Vine, He prepared the way for the branches to be grafted and He even selected the branches – so that through the branches, the Vine could produce fruit. Fruit that remains – inner fruit and outward fruit. Fruit that is full and sweet. And the Vinedresser tenderly cares for His branches so that they produce the fullest crop possible. When the branches fall into the dirt, the Vinedresser doesn't throw them away or abandon them. He lifts them up and cleans them off and helps them to flourish again so that they can bear fruit. So it is with you and i. God didn't graft us onto the Vine so that we might grow and become beautiful branches. He grafted us onto the Vine so that through us He can bear fruit. And the Vinedresser lovingly does in our lives all that He needs to do to maximize the crop.

As we understand our relationship (as the branch) to Jesus (the Vine) and to the Father (the Vinedresser), there are three principles that our LORD would teach us regarding the work He is doing through all of our lives, in order to bear fruit that is full and sweet.

First, if your life consistently bears no fruit, God will intervene to discipline you. Branches that are covered in dirt won't bear fruit. Air and light can't get in. The branch sags. No fruit develops. Our sin is just like that dirt. It prevents the Light of God's Word from shining in and through our lives. It keeps us from getting the nourishment we need. It causes our lives to "sag". But, because God loves us and desires His best for us, and desires to cleanse us and free us from sin so that we can live a more abundant life for His glory, He disciplines us. Not to punish us, but to move us from barrenness toward fruitfulness. Allow God's discipline to train you and cleanse you; not only to escape sin but also to grow you in maturity. Allow Him through His discipline to take you not just from minus ten to zero but from minus ten to plus ten. Don't resist His discipline; respond to it – and in so doing allow Him to take you to a new level of fruitfulness.

Second, if your life bears some fruit, God will intervene to prune you so that you bear more fruit. The Father's strategy for coaxing a greater harvest out of His branches is not the one we would prefer. His plan is to prune, which means to thin, to reduce or to cut-off. The Vinedresser's secret for more … is less. In the process of pruning, He will cut away immature commitments and lesser priorities to make room for more growth. The vinedresser removes the growth that is preventing the sun from reaching into the area where fruit should form. So it is with the Father. He will prune away the areas of our lives that are preventing the S-O-N from reaching in and producing fruit.

We so easily get caught up in appearances – how we look and what we have. We're more concerned with how we as branches look. But the branch's purpose isn't to look good, or even feel good. The branch's purpose is to bear fruit. Our Father, the Vinedresser, will prune away anything that is keeping us from bearing more fruit. Pruning is about our values and our personal identity. When Jesus told His friends what it would cost to follow Him, many turned back. Yet the impact of those who didn't turn back is still shaking the world. His artful pruning is not just "taking away"; He is faithfully "making room" to add strength, productivity and spiritual power in our lives, so that through our lives, He can shake the world.

Lastly, God does not want us to do more for Him, He wants us to be more with Him. He is inviting us to abide more deeply in Him. Abiding isn't a suggestion, it's a command! Abiding doesn't come naturally, it's a choice and an action that we must take. It means placing our complete trust and faith in Him. It means seeking, longing for, thirsting for, waiting for, seeing, knowing, loving, hearing and responding to … His Person. Abiding is the connection to the Vine. It is the place through which all of the life nutrients flow and the fruit is produced. The amount of fruit isn't dependent on the size of the branch, it is dependent on the size of the connection – and what flows from the vine through the branch as a result of the connection. And the harvest that results brings great joy – and great glory – to the Vinedresser.

Yes, our Chinese friends were right on target. It comes down to a relationship with a person – the Person of the Vine – Jesus! As you take up the cross, don't only FOLLOW Him, make sure you ABIDE in Him.

* * *

39

HE CALLS US FRIENDS

"I have loved you even as the Father has loved Me. Remain in My love. When you obey My commandments, you remain in My love, just as I obey My Father's commandments and remain in His love. I have told you these things so that you will be filled with My joy. Yes, your joy will overflow! This is My commandment: Love each other in the same way I have loved you. There is no greater love than to lay down one's life for one's friends. You are My friends if you do what I command. I no longer call you slaves, because a master doesn't confide in his slaves. Now you are My friends, since I have told you everything the Father told Me. You didn't choose Me. I chose you. I appointed you to go and produce lasting fruit, so that the Father will give you whatever you ask for, using My name.... If the world hates you, remember that it hated Me first. The world would love you as one of its own if you belonged to it, but you are no longer part of the world. I chose you to come out of the world, so it hates you. Do you remember what I told you? 'A slave is not greater than the master.' Since they persecuted Me, naturally they will persecute you.... They will do all this to you because of Me, for they have rejected the One who sent Me. They would not be guilty if I had not come and spoken to them. But now they have no excuse for their sin. Anyone who hates Me also hates My Father. If I hadn't done such miraculous signs among them that no one else could do, they would not be guilty. But as it is, they have seen everything I did, yet they still hate Me and My Father. This fulfills what is written in their Scriptures: 'They hated Me without cause.'"

John 15:9-25

* * *

Jesus and the disciples were still en route to the Garden of Gethsemane. As they walked, Jesus declared to them that they were His friends. Yes, He was still their Master, but they were no longer slaves. They were His friends.

When God was setting in motion His plan to raise up a chosen people through whom He would bring glory to His Name, He sought out a friend. And that friend was Abraham (2 Chronicles 20:7; Isaiah 41:8; James 2:23). God chose Abraham and appointed him (Genesis 12:1). He wasn't God's friend on his own merits. Abraham was a liar and a deceiver (Genesis 12:18-19; Genesis 20:2). He was a sinner, chosen solely by God's grace. But God confided in him and told him His plan (Genesis 12:2-3). God chose to save Abraham's nephew Lot, and his family, simply because His friend Abraham asked Him to do so (Genesis 18:22-33). God chose a friend through whom He would bless "all the families of the earth" (Genesis 12:3).

God was now preparing to do a new work. He was preparing to enter into a new covenant through which all the peoples of the earth would be blessed. It would not be a covenant of Law sealed through the shed blood of sacrificial lambs, it would be a covenant of Grace sealed through the shed blood of the Sacrificial Lamb – His one and only Son. Thus, God had again chosen friends through whom He would carry out this new work. These were friends with whom He had confided. These were friends who He had chosen – one by one. These were friends into whom He had poured His life. These were friends for whom He was about to die. These were friends to whom He had just promised to send a Helper.

Abraham did not choose to be God's friend; God chose Abraham. The disciples did not choose to be Jesus' friends; Jesus chose them. He appointed them to go and produce fruit. He appointed them to go and make disciples. He appointed them to go and spread the Good News.

Did you ever wonder why God needed a chosen people to declare His glory to the nations? Why did He need Abraham to be the friend through whom He raised up a chosen people? He is God. He could have chosen a much more efficient way to make His Name known and declare His glory to the nations. But for some reason He chose to use a people who became more known for their grumbling, complaining and stiff-necked ways than for their faithfulness to God. There were some bright lights in the bunch – Moses, Joseph, David, Daniel, Isaiah, Hosea – but even these men had times in their lives when they fell short of the glory of God. And yet, that was the Father's plan. They were the people through whom He would send His Son.

But Jesus had now come. So why did God still need a people – a new people, if you will – to declare His gospel to the nations? Why did He need this "ragtag" bunch of uneducated men to be His friends to further His plan? Jesus could have returned from the grave, declared Himself the Messiah, immediately established His Kingdom on earth and reigned from then forevermore. He could have presented His majesty and declared His truth far more effectively and eloquently than this fraternity of fishermen, tax collectors and sinners. Well, at least they had spent three years under His teaching. Therefore, they had some qualification for Him to call them "friends".

But His pronouncement of them as friends didn't stop with those eleven men. Notice He prefaced His statement by saying, *"You are My friends if you do what I command."* Then He went on to say, *"This is My commandment: Love each other in the same way I have loved you."* That means that if we do what He has commanded, we, too, are His friends. If we love each other in the same way He has loved us, we are His friends. As we abide in His Word, He has told us *"everything the Father told {Him}"*, and therefore He calls us friends – not by our choosing, but by His. And as His friends, He has chosen us to be a people through whom He makes His Name known. We are His friends for His purpose. He is building His Kingdom according to His design, and He has chosen us to be a part of that work as His friends.

Jesus went on to tell the apostles two important truths that they needed to know if they were going to continue as His friends – and those truths apply to us as His friends as well. First, He said, *"I appointed you to go and produce lasting fruit, so that the Father will give you whatever you ask for, using My name."* As we continue in the Master's mission of producing fruit, we must be fully reliant on the Father – just as Jesus was. Therefore, if we would be about His task in His way, we must continually be bringing the work before Him. We must know what the Father would have us do. In order to know, we must continually be asking Him. And Jesus has promised that whatever we ask according to His will, in His Name, the Father will grant. We can walk confidently knowing that, just as the Father ordered the steps of the Son, He will order our steps, and He will provide everything that is needed to accomplish His plan and His activity to bear fruit. As a "friend" of Jesus, the Father will provide us with all that is needed, so we can walk with a bold confidence.

The second truth, however, is not quite as reassuring. He promised that if we follow Him as His friends the world will hate us. The world hated Jesus, so it only makes sense that the world will hate us as well. The world rejected Jesus and hated Him "without cause". Jesus said, *"The world would love you as one of its own if you belonged to it, but you are no longer part of the world. I chose you to come out of the world, so it hates you. Do you remember what I told you? 'A slave is not greater than the master.' Since they persecuted Me, naturally they will persecute you...."* No one wants to be hated. But the reality is that if we are not being hated by the world, the world is not seeing us as friends and followers of Jesus. If they hated the Master, they will hate His followers. But let's be careful to make sure that if we are experiencing the hatred of the world, it is because we are faithfully following Jesus and NOT just being obnoxious sinners. i fear that too much of the "hatred" being directed toward Christians today is not due to our "Christlikeness", but rather due to our sinful worldliness. Let's make sure we know the difference.

One last point before we close this chapter. Though Abraham, Moses and David were all referred to by God as being His friends, they never referred to God as their Friend. He is Jehovah God. He is our Savior, our Lord and our Master. He isn't – and never will be – one of the boys. Though He sees us as His friends, it is not a reciprocal friendship. The same John who reclined next to Jesus that night in the upper room (John 13:23) would in later years fall at His feet as a dead man (Revelation 1:17) when he saw Him in His glory. Let's be careful that we do not allow our position in Christ as His friends to blind us to the majesty of Who He is and the reverence that is due Him.

Yes, as you take up the cross, remember, He has called you friend!

* * *

40

THE SORROW WON'T LAST

"In a little while you won't see Me anymore. But a little while after that, you will see Me again." Some of the disciples asked each other, "What does He mean when He says, 'In a little while you won't see Me, but then you will see Me,' and 'I am going to the Father'? And what does He mean by 'a little while'? We don't understand." Jesus realized they wanted to ask Him about it, so He said, "Are you asking yourselves what I meant? I said in a little while you won't see Me, but a little while after that you will see Me again. I tell you the truth, you will weep and mourn over what is going to happen to Me, but the world will rejoice. You will grieve, but your grief will suddenly turn to wonderful joy. It will be like a woman suffering the pains of labor. When her child is born, her anguish gives way to joy because she has brought a new baby into the world. So you have sorrow now, but I will see you again; then you will rejoice, and no one can rob you of that joy."

John 16:16-22

* * *

Jesus continued to speak words of encouragement and truth to His disciples as they walked from the upper room to the Garden to pray. Already that night, Jesus had used the traditional observance of Passover to teach His disciples new truth. And His teaching did not cease when they left the upper room, it continued throughout their journey. Allow me to make a quick observation before we get into the passage. Notice that Jesus does not waste a moment or a motion. Nothing with Jesus is perfunctory. No moment of traditional "religious" reflection passes without Jesus using it in our lives to open our eyes and hearts to

His truth. No journey we take is solely about the journey. Jesus uses every moment of the journey to reveal His truth about Himself and about ourselves. His reflections along the way are not purposed to scold us or defeat us. His words to us throughout the journey are intended to lead us to a greater understanding of Him, as He draws us closer to Him. Jesus knew what was ahead for His disciples. He continued to use this time to prepare them. He knows what is ahead for us, and He is using this time in our respective journeys with Him to prepare us.

i wonder how attentive the disciples were to all Jesus was saying. Were they even listening? Remember, they didn't know what was about to happen, so they didn't realize that these were some of His last words to them. They were tired – it had been a long day – and a long week. They were anxious – not because they had an idea of what was ahead, but because Jesus' words to them were portending times of uncertainty. As a result, their anxiety was distracting them from hearing all of what Jesus had to say. Since they didn't know what was about to occur, they didn't have context for what He was saying. We experience those same challenges as we take up the cross to follow Jesus. We can become tired – or anxious – or lack understanding because we don't know what's ahead. In the midst of the journey, hold onto the truth that Jesus is always preparing us for what lies in our road ahead. He knows exactly what we will have need of. So, lean into Him. Listen attentively and – if you are able – journal what Jesus tells you through His Word. That simple act of journaling will help you remember His promise – His truth – when the time comes.

Jesus was teaching them important truths about joy and sorrow. He knew that, in just a few hours, He would be arrested and the disciples would scatter in fear. He knew He would be crucified the next day and they would grieve over His death and be fearful about their own lives. He wanted them to know that *"in a little while you won't see Me anymore. But a little while after that, you will see Me again."* Though He would die, and His enemies would rejoice in thinking that they had been victorious, He, in three days' time, would rise again and return as the Victor. He wanted them to hold to His promise even when everything looked dark. He wanted them to remember that the journey would not end in death, it would end in resurrection. Thus, they could be confident that though they might sorrow for a season, "joy would come in the morning" (Psalm 30:5).

But Jesus' promise was not only regarding His three days in the tomb. This promise looked to the days that would pass before He returned to establish His Kingdom on earth. Those days too would pass, just like His days in the tomb. In the meantime, the Father would send His Spirit to indwell, to comfort, to encourage and equip as they – and we – walk through those days. But, though they – and we – would experience sorrow – and for some, hatred, ridicule and persecution – those days too would come to an end – and they would end in joy. Just as He promised to rise again from the grave, He promised to return again, and they – and we – must walk in the joy of His promise. Though we look back on His resurrection from the tomb with sight as a historical fact, we too look forward to His return with the same eyes of faith as the disciples who He was encouraging that night.

But His promise of joy in the midst of sorrow went even further. He likened the pain that we will endure throughout these days until He returns – or until we are with Him – as those of *"a woman suffering the pains of labor. When her child is born, her anguish gives way to joy because she has brought a new baby into the world."* Pain is a part of the process. It can't be avoided. But the pain will not endure indefinitely. It will be transformed into joy. Jesus was not minimizing pain, suffering or sorrow. He acknowledged its reality. But He was assuring them – and us – that it will not last. It will endure – perhaps for a season – but then it will be gone. Our pain will not be replaced by joy, it will be transformed into joy! And when it is, that joy will remain for eternity. Pain and sorrow are real – but they are finite. They will end. But the joy that comes "in the morning" will endure.

If you are a follower of Jesus and are walking through sorrow, or have tears in your eyes, be assured that this is not the end. He has promised joy – joy that will endure for eternity! In that day, our joy in His presence will exceed and overshadow any sorrow we may have experienced in our lives on this side. Remember, we may have sorrow now, *"but I will see you again; then you will rejoice, and no one can rob you of that joy."*

* * *

41

OUR LORD'S PRAYER

"At that time, you won't need to ask Me for anything. I tell you the truth, you will ask the Father directly, and He will grant your request because you use My name. You haven't done this before. Ask, using My name, and you will receive, and you will have abundant joy.... I'm not saying I will ask the Father on your behalf, for the Father Himself loves you dearly because you love Me and believe that I came from God."

After saying all these things, Jesus looked up to heaven and said, "Father, the hour has come. Glorify your Son so He can give glory back to you.... My prayer is not for the world, but for those You have given Me, because they belong to You. ... Now protect them by the power of Your name so that they will be united just as We are.... Now I am coming to You. I told them many things while I was with them in this world so they would be filled with My joy.... I'm not asking You to take them out of the world, but to keep them safe from the evil one.... Make them holy by Your truth; teach them Your word, which is truth.... I am praying not only for these disciples but also for all who will ever believe in Me through their message. I pray that they will all be one, just as You and I are one—as You are in Me, Father, and I am in You. And may they be in Us so that the world will believe You sent Me.... Father, I want these whom You have given Me to be with Me where I am.... I have revealed You to them, and I will continue to do so. Then Your love for Me will be in them, and I will be in them."

Selected verses from John 16:23-27
and John 17:1-26

* * *

As Jesus and the disciples concluded their final steps to the Garden of Gethsemane, Jesus gave them one more word of instruction on how they were to pray. The instruction He gave them is very familiar to us – many of us have been hearing it for most of our lives. But for the disciples, it was unfamiliar. It was a "new way" to pray – prayer that would lead to joy, prayer that would be offered in power, and prayer that would reveal God's glory.

Jesus told them that they should always direct their prayer to the Father. He told them that they would not need to ask Him (Jesus) for anything; rather, they should make all of their requests to the Father. And the Father, who loves them – and us – because of our love for the Son, will answer those requests. It is worthy to repeat that Jesus emphasized that they were not to pray to Him, expecting Him to pass their requests on to the Father. He clearly told them – and us – to pray to the Father – in Jesus' Name (that was the "new part"). Praying in Jesus' Name doesn't mean a simple tag at the end of our prayer. It means we are asking and walking according to the will of the Son. He had just taught them that their love for the Son would be expressed through their abiding in Him and their obedience to Him. John would later go on to write, "*And we are confident that He* (the Father) *hears us whenever we ask for anything that pleases Him* (the Son). *And since we know He* (the Father) *hears us when we make our requests, we also know that He* (the Father) *will give us what we ask for*" (1 John 5:14-15). And as we pray to the Father, Jesus will be interceding on our behalf. Paul wrote to the believers in Rome: "*Christ Jesus is He who died, yes, rather who was raised, who is at the right hand of God, who also intercedes for us*" (Romans 8:34 NASB). Therefore, as His disciples – both those then and we now – abide in Him and obey Him, we can boldly and confidently approach the Father's throne, knowing the access that we are granted to Him through the Son, and knowing that the Son is interceding on our behalf. We have the "inside track" through prayer, because of the Son, to the Father!

And Jesus' intercession on our behalf began that night in the Garden. As Jesus now arrived at the Garden, He transitioned from speaking with His disciples to speaking with His Father. This is not the passage in Scripture that is typically entitled "The Lord's Prayer", as i have entitled this chapter. Rather, we looked at that passage (Luke 11:1-4) as we explored the lesson that Jesus gave His disciples in prayer in chapter 49 of ***Walking With The Master***. And though Mark records that Peter, James and John fell asleep while Jesus was praying (Mark 14:32-42), apparently John was alert for enough of the time that He was able to hear a portion of our

Lord's prayer to the Father. And, as a result, He was able to share it with us here.

First, Jesus acknowledged that the hour had come – the hour for which the Father had sent Him to earth. Jesus prayed that the Father would glorify the Son through all that was about to transpire so that the Father, in turn, would be glorified through the Son. Jesus never sought glory for Himself alone. He and the Father are One. The Father was revealed through the Son, and the Father was glorified through the Son. Remember, Jesus is 100% God and 100% man. He prayed that the Father would glorify Him as the Son of God, so that He (Jesus) would endure to the end and glorify the Father as the Son of Man. He knew all that He was about to bear on our behalf and in obedience to the Father. Jesus was about to go to battle with sin and death – two powerful foes. Satan was amassing all of the resources he could muster in an attempt to defeat Jesus. In the heavenly realm, Jesus was embarking on the greatest spiritual battle that ever was. And He asked His Father to glorify Him, so that sin and death would be defeated, and the Father would be glorified.

Second, Jesus prayed for His disciples. He prayed for their protection. He prayed for their unity – for their oneness together in Christ. He prayed that they would be filled with joy. He prayed that they would be delivered from the attempts of the evil one to attack them. He prayed that they would be set apart and sanctified in all truth. He prayed that as they went out in obedience to His command as His ambassadors, that they would not only go out in His Name, but also, that they would be clothed in His righteousness and His holiness. Jesus saw all that laid in their paths ahead – in the immediate days – but also, in the weeks, months and years ahead. He prayed that they would run the race with endurance and finish well.

Third, Jesus prayed for *"all who will ever believe in Me through their message."* If you are a follower of Jesus, He prayed for you! He prayed for our oneness in Him. He prayed that the Son and the Father would be revealed through our lives – not only through our words, but also through our actions. He prayed that our lives would be characterized to the world around us through our love for one another, and the Father's love expressed through us to the world around us. In so praying, He was praying that our lives would never be reflective of bigotry, hatred, uncaringness or selfish ambition. He prayed that our very thoughts, attitudes, words and actions would radiate the Father's love.

• • •

He prayed that we would walk in fellowship with Him – that we would "be with Him". And that fellowship is not only for the hereafter, it is for the here and now. He was praying that we wouldn't walk according to a set of rules and regulations, like the religious leaders of His day. Rather, He prayed we would walk each and every moment in intimate fellowship and relationship with Him – not only in our prayer closets – but throughout every moment of our everyday lives.

And He prayed that we would behold His glory – the glory as the Only Begotten of the Father. We would see His glory as the Baby in the manger – as the Feeder of the five thousand – as the Savior on the cross – as the Risen Lord emerging from the tomb – and as the Coming King who will return to judge the earth. We would see His glory as the King of Kings and the Lord of Lords.

Long before we knew Him, He knew us. Long before we chose Him, He chose us. Long before we began to follow Him, He interceded for us. And He still does! As you take up the cross to follow Him, walk in the boldness and the confidence – and the love – that He prays for us.

* * *

42

DON'T LET TEMPTATION OVERPOWER YOU

Then, accompanied by the disciples, Jesus left the upstairs room and went as usual to the Mount of Olives. There He told them, "Pray that you will not give in to temptation." He walked away, about a stone's throw, and knelt down and prayed, "Father, if You are willing, please take this cup of suffering away from Me. Yet I want Your will to be done, not Mine." Then an angel from heaven appeared and strengthened Him. He prayed more fervently, and He was in such agony of spirit that His sweat fell to the ground like great drops of blood. At last He stood up again and returned to the disciples, only to find them asleep, exhausted from grief. "Why are you sleeping?" He asked them. "Get up and pray, so that you will not give in to temptation."

Luke 22:39-46

* * *

Before Jesus withdrew to a place where He could spend time with the Father in prayer there in the Garden of Gethsemane on the Mount Olives, He instructed His disciples to *"pray that you will not give in to temptation"*. He left eight of His disciples in one place in the Garden, then Peter, James and John (Mark 14:32-33) in another, as He then went just a stone's throw away to pray to the Father.

As we saw in the last chapter, Jesus used this time to pray for Himself, His disciples, and all of those who would follow Him in the future. He prayed that each one of us would not give in to temptation, and He instructed His disciples to join with Him in that prayer. Matthew in his account of these events (Matthew 26:36-46) records that three times Jesus returned to the disciples and found them sleeping. It was late. It had been a long day. It had been a very long week. The disciples were exhausted. They were grieving over the foreboding words that Jesus had spoken to them that night. And they had no grasp of what was taking place that night in the Garden.

Take a moment in the hush of Gethsemane and listen. Hear the sobbing of Jesus' soul. Hear the falling drops of His blood. There in the Garden at the base of an olive tree, just a few yards away, kneeling low in agonizing prayer, is the Savior praying for you and for me as He prepares to take on our humanity and our sin.

You see, the battle of Calvary was actually being fought right there in Gethsemane, and the victory of Calvary was won that night in Gethsemane. Jesus knew that His time in the hands of His accusers and persecutors would be momentary in the scope of eternity and limited in the hands of the Father. He wasn't agonizing over the humiliation and abuse, or the shame and pain of the cross. He also knew full well that He would rise from the grave, and death would be defeated. He wasn't agonizing over death.

His agony came from the reality that He knew that He would be made sin for us. He, who knew no sin, would carry the full weight of our depraved, despicable and decadent sin. Every immoral, self-serving, evil, disobedient act and action that had ever been committed and would ever be committed was being placed on Him. We cannot imagine the weight of that burden, nor the cost of our sin. And the result of sin is separation from God. For all time and eternity, Jesus had never been separated from the Father. And now in this selfless act, not only was He carrying the weight of our sin, He was also bearing the agony of a time that He would be separated from the Father. Remember, He and the Father are One. When He most needed the connection with the Father, He would be separated from Him. Separation from the Father was the great agony of the cross. It wasn't the physical pain over which Jesus agonized; it was that deep spiritual pain.

And it wasn't the physical pain that Satan was tempting Him to avoid either; it was that spiritual pain. You remember that Satan had been defeated in his attempts to tempt Jesus after those forty days in the wilderness as recorded in Matthew 4:1-11 (***Walking With The Master,*** *chapter* 7). But on this night, he returned, in a "last ditch" effort to tempt Jesus once and for all. The tempter came to once again offer Jesus the crown without the cross. We will never really know or fully comprehend the full weight of Jesus' pain. We will never know or understand the full weight of that temptation or the agony that He endured. We will never fully understand the bitterness of that cup of suffering. There is a rare physical phenomenon known as "hematidrosis", in which, under great emotional stress, the tiny blood vessels rupture in the sweat glands and produce a mixture of blood and sweat. Such was the agony – and the temptation – that our Savior endured.

Then just as the angels ministered to Jesus after Satan tempted Him in the desert, they also came to minister to Him after Satan tempted Him in the Garden. The angels could not die for our sins, but they could strengthen our Savior as He courageously accepted the cup of suffering. The famous Scottish pastor and writer, Dr. George Morrison, said, *"Every life has its Gethsemane, and every Gethsemane has its angel."*

Remember, Jesus was not only praying to the Father about what He would endure over the next twenty-four hours. He was not only praying that the Father would glorify the Son so that the Father would be glorified through the Son. He was also praying for His disciples. He knew they would be tempted – to scatter – to deny Him – to hide in fear. He knew that their worlds would be turned upside down – and they would feel as if they had no place to turn and no one to whom they could turn. He knew they were entering into the most difficult days of their lives. And He agonized for them. He desired that they would pray to the Father that they would not give in to temptation. He had just promised them that if they prayed according to His will that the Father would hear and answer their prayer. But instead of praying, they slept. Three times He told them, and three times they responded by sleeping. So, when the enemy came, they were unprepared. As a result, they scattered. They denied Him (at least we know Peter did). They hid in fear.

As we take up the cross, there are two truths we need to hold onto out of this passage. The first is the depth of our Father's and our Savior's love for us and the magnitude of the agony that He endured for our salvation, even knowing that multitudes would reject His free gift and would never embrace His saving love. The second is our need to pray that we not give in to temptation. Temptation remains at our doors – in different forms. As Jesus taught us to pray to the Father, "don't let us yield to temptation, but rescue us from the evil one" (Matthew 6:13). The Father is ready, waiting and able to answer that prayer. He has angels standing by to minister to our needs. All Jesus has told us to do is ask! Let's not be found sleeping.

* * *

43

A BETRAYAL, AN ARREST, AND A HEALING

But even as Jesus said this, a crowd approached, led by Judas, one of the twelve disciples. Judas walked over to Jesus to greet Him with a kiss. But Jesus said, "Judas, would you betray the Son of Man with a kiss?" When the other disciples saw what was about to happen, they exclaimed, "Lord, should we fight? We brought the swords!" And one of them struck at the high priest's slave, slashing off his right ear. But Jesus said, "No more of this." And He touched the man's ear and healed him. Then Jesus spoke to the leading priests, the captains of the Temple guard, and the elders who had come for Him. "Am I some dangerous revolutionary," He asked, "that you come with swords and clubs to arrest Me? Why didn't you arrest Me in the Temple? I was there every day. But this is your moment, the time when the power of darkness reigns."

Luke 22:47-53

* * *

The hour had come. Even while Jesus was still speaking to His disciples, the crowd approached. John tells us that Judas came with a Roman cohort of six hundred men (John 18:3), plus the leading priests and elders from the Temple, as well as the captains of the Temple guard (Luke 22:52). They came with their lanterns, torches and weapons. Humanly speaking, it would have been a very overwhelming sight for Jesus and the eleven disciples. Why such a large crowd to arrest Jesus? Did they fear He would run away or hide in the Garden? If you have visited the Garden and that portion of the Mount of Olives, you know that that portion of land is not very large. Even in the dark, it would have been very difficult for anyone to hide in the terrain. Did they expect Jesus to resist arrest? Did they fear He would perform a miracle and again slip from their grasp? Remember, their previous attempts had been unsuccessful, and the religious leaders were not going to take any chances. What they didn't realize was that their previous attempts had not been in alignment with the Father's timing – but this was His time. Remember, Jesus had intentionally established a "routine pattern" that week. He had been spending each night on the Mount of Olives since Tuesday so that Judas would know exactly where He and the remaining disciples would be.

Why did Judas need to identify Jesus for the soldiers? Again, the religious leaders were taking every precaution. Don't lose sight of the fact that as the Son of Man, Jesus took on an appearance of those that He came to live among. Recall that on the Mount of Transfiguration (Matthew 17:1-9), Jesus took on a very different appearance as the Son of God. And when John sees Him as the Son of God in Revelation (1:17), he falls at His feet as dead. As the Son of God, Jesus clearly stands out above the crowd. But when He first came – to pay the penalty for our sins – He took on our appearance, that of a humble servant. In their "craftiness", the religious leaders – and Judas – didn't want the Roman soldiers to make a mistake and arrest the wrong man.

Why did Judas "greet" Jesus with a kiss? It was customary for disciples to greet their teachers with a loving and respectful kiss. However, this kiss was anything but loving and respectful, it was the basest kind of hypocrisy and treachery. That's what betrayal is. The writer of Proverbs says it well: *"You can trust a friend who corrects you, but kisses from an enemy are nothing but lies"* (Proverbs 27:6 CEV).

But let's also look at the disciples' response. Earlier in the Gospels, when Jesus sent out His disciples to proclaim the Good News, He had instructed them not to take anything with them, even though they would be "lambs among wolves" (Luke 10:3-4). He was teaching them that the Father would provide all the resources that were needed, and they had seen Him faithfully do so. But on this night, they would have resources in hand, and they would have the choice to make as to which resources they would depend upon – those of the Father or those of the world.

Luke records that when Jesus and the disciples were leaving the upper room earlier that night, He had told them, *"'take your money and a traveler's bag. And if you don't have a sword, sell your cloak and buy one! For the time has come for this prophecy about Me to be fulfilled: 'He was counted among the rebels.' Yes, everything written about Me by the prophets will come true.' 'Look, Lord,' they replied, 'we have two swords among us.' 'That's enough,' He said"* (Luke 22:36-38). Just as Isaiah had prophesied in Isaiah 53:12, Jesus would be counted among the rebels. And that night, Jesus knew that His disciples would respond to the ways of the world by acting like the world – just like we often do. He knew they would attempt to enter into battle using the weapons of the world, and then when that failed, they would flee. So, two swords were more than enough to prove the point. Apparently, one of those swords was in Peter's possession.

The saying, "never bring a knife to a gun fight", means that one should bring the appropriate weapon for the fight. The battle that night in the Garden was a spiritual battle. Peter chose the wrong weapon – a sword made of metal. He should have chosen the right sword – the Word of God (Ephesians 6:17). And not only did Peter choose the wrong weapon, he also failed to look to his Master. He asked, *"Lord, should we fight?"* But instead of waiting to hear from the One who was able to calm the storm, He just plowed ahead to do what He thought was right in his own eyes. Peter was backing up the boastful words he had uttered in the Upper Room (Luke 22:33) and on the way to the Garden (Matthew 26:33-35). Peter had been sleeping when he should have been praying, talking when he should have been listening, and boasting when he should have been fearing. (How often have we done that?) And now, his impetuous actions led to his cutting off the right ear of Malchus, a servant to the high priest (John 18:10, 26). Let that be a reminder to us that most often our impetuous ways will lead to further hurt and destruction. Peter was right to ask Jesus the question – but he should have waited for the answer!

How did Jesus respond? When faced with actions of malice, Jesus responded with grace. He showed grace to Peter by rebuking his sin and repairing the harm that he had done. He showed grace to Malchus by healing his ear. He showed grace to the mob by willingly yielding Himself to them. And He showed grace to us by submitting to each step of the journey to Calvary.

This was the Master's last miraculous act before the cross. He could have summoned twelve legions of angels to protect Himself and His disciples (Matthew 26:53). But instead, He chose to inconspicuously heal the ear of an obscure servant. It is very probable with all that was taking place that the only ones who knew that Malchus was injured were Malchus, Peter and Jesus. And yet, in the midst of all of the turmoil, Jesus never withheld His healing grace.

Then Jesus rebuked the priests, the captains and the elders for waiting for the cover of darkness. They thought the darkness gave them advantage. But the reality was that nothing – not even evil – would be able to do anything that the Father was not permitting them to do. The Father's redemptive purpose would not be thwarted – even by the evil intent that these men displayed. That is an important lesson for us to hold onto. If the power of darkness is reigning, it is only because the Light of the world has permitted it for His greater redemptive purpose. The world will betray you. Evil will endeavor to bind you. But the Master's grace and purpose will prevail. Trust Him! Look to Him! And wait for His answer. It will come!

* * *

44

WHO WAS STANDING BEFORE THE HIGH PRIEST?

So the soldiers, their commanding officer, and the Temple guards arrested Jesus and tied Him up. First, they took Him to Annas, since he was the father-in-law of Caiaphas, the high priest at that time. Caiaphas was the one who had told the other Jewish leaders, "It's better that one man should die for the people…." Inside, the high priest began asking Jesus about His followers and what He had been teaching them. Jesus replied, "Everyone knows what I teach. I have preached regularly in the synagogues and the Temple, where the people gather. I have not spoken in secret. Why are you asking Me this question? Ask those who heard Me. They know what I said." Then one of the Temple guards standing nearby slapped Jesus across the face. "Is that the way to answer the high priest?" he demanded. Jesus replied, "If I said anything wrong, you must prove it. But if I'm speaking the truth, why are you beating Me?" Then Annas bound Jesus and sent Him to Caiaphas, the high priest.

John 18:12-14, 19-24

* * *

They arrested the Almighty Son of God! They tied up the Creator of the universe using materials He had created! Can you think of anything more preposterous? They thought they had authority over Him! Can you think of anything more presumptuous? Can you think of anything more absurd than placing God on trial? But can you think of anything more amazing than the fact that He willingly allowed Himself to be subjected to this humiliation – for me – and for you?

. . .

John is the only Gospel writer that includes this detail that after they arrested Jesus in the Garden, they first took Him to the home of Annas. Annas was not the current high priest. He was the father-in-law of the current high priest, Caiaphas. He had been the high priest prior to his son-in-law. But he currently did not hold that position. Therefore, he had no legal standing under Mosaic Law in this proceeding. And yet, his home was the first place the guards and soldiers brought Jesus. Why would they have brought Jesus here, and not taken Him directly before Caiaphas?

You will recall that in chapter 3 we looked at Jesus' cleansing of the temple. That had only occurred three days before this. And you may recall that we discussed the fact that Annas was the overseer of all of the financial enterprises that were profiting from the buying and selling taking place within the Temple. Annas saw Jesus' actions as a direct attack on himself, his position, his authority and on his financial livelihood. Though Annas by no means acted alone, he was without question one of, if not the leader of, the principal plotters behind the arrest and crucifixion of Jesus. I believe his purpose for having Jesus brought to him first was two-fold. First, i believe in his arrogance, he wanted Jesus to know that he – Annas – was in charge, and that though Jesus may have been in control the day He cleansed the Temple, today was Annas' day. And he had the arrogance to think he was now getting the last word. Second, Annas is considered, even in secular history, to have been crafty and clever. As one of the main architects of this plot to have Jesus crucified, he doubtless believed that he was the best qualified to "catch" Jesus in saying something that could be used against Him in the planned trial.

John also carefully inserted the notation that it was Caiaphas who had said, *"It's better that one man should die for the people…."*. Caiaphas made that statement after Jesus had raised Lazarus from the dead (John 11:50). And in doing so, he was saying that Jesus must die so that the Romans would not take away the privileges of the Jewish nation – and particularly the privileges of its religious leaders. John inserted this statement as a reminder that the religious leaders had already predetermined that Jesus was to die – and that the trial that was about to unfold was nothing but a mockery – a diabolical plot – conceived in the minds of the likes of Annas and Caiaphas, and birthed from the heart of Satan. And Caiaphas and Annas were truly very likeminded. They both believed that Jesus' death would lead to their salvation. But the salvation they were seeking was the salvation of their power, their positions and their profits. These were the "high priests" who stood before Jesus!

• • •

It's amazing to me that Annas had the audacity to ask Jesus to tell him what He had been teaching. Jesus had been speaking publicly for over three years and had repeatedly taught in the very Temple where Annas oversaw his enterprise. As we've already said, Annas was looking for Jesus to say something that could be used against him in the trial. But Annas could have done that while Jesus was speaking in the Temple. It is possible that Annas had never taken the time to listen to Jesus personally. Perhaps he had relied on the accounts of other religious leaders and couldn't be bothered to listen to Jesus himself. Listening would have interfered with his Temple enterprise. He wouldn't permit truth to stand in the way of his personal religious business.

In chapter 25, we looked at the fact that some of the older religious leaders in this day would have, in their younger days, likely been some of the leading priests and teachers that King Herod the Great had consulted to ascertain the birthplace of the Messiah (Matthew 2:4-5) thirty or so years earlier. Annas most definitely would have been one of them. They – and he – showed no signs of a heart seeking after the promised Messiah. As a matter of fact, through the information they provided, they had assisted Herod in his attempt to kill the Messiah by having all the little boys under two years of age who lived in and around Bethlehem killed. Again, i am pretty confident that Annas had connected those dots somewhere along the line – between that baby boy born in Bethlehem and this same Jesus. Somehow, they had failed the first time. He was determined not to fail again!

Bear in mind that everything that was now being done to Jesus was illegal under Mosaic law:

1. Annas was no longer the high priest. He had no legal authority to detain or question Jesus.
2. There was no witness of Jesus having done anything that violated the Law. And the Law required that there be witnesses before an arrest took place.
3. No trial was ever to begin at night. (They had arrested Jesus under the cover of darkness to avoid the watchful eyes of the crowds.)
4. No trial was ever to begin and end on the same day.
5. No prisoner was ever to be struck in any way unless proven guilty.

But to me, the greatest irony of this passage is the reality that truly there is only one High Priest in this account, and His Name is Jesus. He alone is the High Priest (Hebrews 4:14). And as He was brought before each one that night, beginning with Annas, the reality is that they were standing before Him – indicted by their own sin. Caiaphas and Annas (the "high priests") sought to sacrifice Jesus' life for their own selfish salvation. But Jesus – the true High Priest – had come to offer Himself as the Sacrifice for many (Matthew 20:28) – through whom many would be saved.

This plot may have been hatched in the minds of Annas and Caiaphas (the high priests), and been birthed from the heart of the deceiver (Satan), but it was allowed to unfold only because it was permitted by the Father. It was the Father's redemptive plan and it required no one less than the High Priest Himself, the Son of the Living God.

As we take up the cross to follow Jesus, we, too, will encounter attempts to falsely accuse and decry the works of God. Follow the lead of the One who has stood in that place – and through it all brought glory to the Father. Because He is your High Priest and His work, His will and His Word will prevail!

* * *

45

THE ROOSTER CROWED

Simon Peter followed Jesus, as did another of the disciples. That other disciple was acquainted with the high priest, so he was allowed to enter the high priest's courtyard with Jesus. Peter had to stay outside the gate. Then the disciple who knew the high priest spoke to the woman watching at the gate, and she let Peter in. The woman asked Peter, "You're not one of that man's disciples, are you?" "No," he said, "I am not." Because it was cold, the household servants and the guards had made a charcoal fire. They stood around it, warming themselves, and Peter stood with them, warming himself.... Meanwhile, as Simon Peter was standing by the fire warming himself, they asked him again, "You're not one of His disciples, are you?" He denied it, saying, "No, I am not." But one of the household slaves of the high priest, a relative of the man whose ear Peter had cut off, asked, "Didn't I see you out there in the olive grove with Jesus?" Again, Peter denied it. And immediately a rooster crowed.

John 18:15-18, 25-27

* * *

When John writes, *"another of the disciples"* and *"that other disciple"*, he is, as you know, referring to himself. We have previously looked at the fact that John was apparently well-known in the circles of the religious leaders. You will recall that it was probably John that orchestrated the conversation that took place between Nicodemus and Jesus (John 3), and he was the only disciple present when the conversation took place. And here we see that he has no difficulty entering the high priest's courtyard, nor does the servant watching at the gate question his request to grant Peter access through the gate. It is quite possible that John's family had position and influence in the community. That being the case, we have no idea why his brother, James, hadn't joined he and Peter, but apparently, he had chosen to scatter with the other disciples. Perhaps, as the eldest son, he had gone to alert their mother, who was also a part of the entourage that followed Jesus. Regardless, John was able to provide Peter with access.

John, because of his standing, was able to gain access nearer to where the questioning of Jesus was taking place. It doesn't appear that anyone confronted him about being a disciple of Jesus, though the leaders most assuredly would have known that to be the case. It could have been because of his position in their society, but, more likely, i would venture that at that moment the religious leaders were more focused on their plans regarding Jesus than they were on His followers. So, it appears that no one confronted John.

But that was not the case with Peter. Instead of standing with the "high and mighty" of society, Peter was warming his hands with the household servants and guards around the fire. He had no position, and they had no pretense. The first questioner was the servant woman to whom John had made his request to allow Peter to enter. Again, she, like the others there, knew John was a disciple of Jesus. Other translations, include the word "too" or "also" in her question, evidencing her understanding about John. And since Peter hadn't entered further into the courtyard with John, but had stayed with the servants, there was an opportunity for her to question him further. Bear in mind she wasn't one of the accusers, she was merely an inquisitive servant. i personally think she was using the question more as a conversation starter than as leveling an accusatory challenge. It's quite possible she just wanted to know more about this Jesus that she had heard of, or perhaps seen, and who better to ask than one of His disciples? But rather than seeing it as an opportunity to tell her about Jesus, in the midst of the chaos and confusion over all that was taking place, he denied that he was a follower.

But remember, Peter was the "de facto" leader of the other disciples. He was always conspicuously seen with Jesus when He was teaching or performing miracles. So, others of the servants and guards had to have seen him with Jesus in days past. As they talked among themselves, they became certain that he was one of the disciples. So, again someone asked him. Like before, it wasn't accusatory; it was an honest inquiry. But again, the disciple who always spoke out boldly when others stood silent was tongue-tied by fear.

The third question to Peter came from a slightly different perspective. This was a relative of Malchus, the servant whose ear Peter had cut off, but Jesus had healed. This relative was apparently in the crowd when they arrested Jesus, so this question was asked with a different motivation. Possibly this person was preparing to accuse Peter of cutting off Malchus' ear. Or, more than likely, the story of how Jesus had healed his ear was now being repeated among the servants, and this servant wanted to hear more about it from someone who was standing right there. Regardless, it was another opportunity for Peter to bear witness to the grace and mercy of Jesus. But instead, He adamantly denied even knowing Jesus! Three opportunities to bear witness – all refused and denied.

Therein is the reminder to each one of us. As we take up the cross and follow Jesus, He will grant us many opportunities to bear witness about Him and His gospel of grace and mercy. Prayerfully, we will be walking in a way that distinguishes us as one of His followers. As a result, He will grant us with occasions to respond to the same type of questions that were being directed to Peter. How will we respond? Will we seize the moment and the opportunity to bear witness and bring glory to God, or will we become tongue-tied by fear or anxiety and avoid the conversation? Yes, Peter denied Jesus, but, when we fail to seize the opportunity to bear witness, so do we.

Earlier that night, Peter had boastfully declared to Jesus that he was willing to die with Him (Luke 22:33), to which Jesus replied that Peter would deny Him three times before the rooster crowed the very next morning (Luke 22:34). i am certain that Peter neither believed nor received what Jesus said to him. At the moment of Jesus' statement, he could not conceive that he would ever deny Jesus.

But now, the rooster crowed. Peter remembered Jesus' words. And Matthew, Mark and Luke record Peter's personal testimony that *"he left the courtyard, weeping bitterly"* (Luke 22:62).

What's that i hear? Is it the rooster crowing? Have we been faithful to the

Master's call to make disciples and bear witness of His gospel? If so, continue to ask for His grace and mercy to stay the course in His mission. If not, allow the tears of repentance to flow and His Spirit to fill you with the boldness to share His truth. Because the rooster didn't just crow for Peter, it crows for us as well.

* * *

46

A TRAITOR'S REMORSE

Very early in the morning the leading priests and the elders of the people met again to lay plans for putting Jesus to death. Then they bound Him, led Him away, and took Him to Pilate, the Roman governor. When Judas, who had betrayed Him, realized that Jesus had been condemned to die, he was filled with remorse. So, he took the thirty pieces of silver back to the leading priests and the elders. "I have sinned," he declared, "for I have betrayed an innocent man." "What do we care?" they retorted. "That's your problem." Then Judas threw the silver coins down in the Temple and went out and hanged himself. The leading priests picked up the coins. "It wouldn't be right to put this money in the Temple treasury," they said, "since it was payment for murder." After some discussion they finally decided to buy the potter's field, and they made it into a cemetery for foreigners. That is why the field is still called the Field of Blood. This fulfilled the prophecy of Jeremiah that says,

"They took the thirty pieces of silver— the price at which he was valued by the people of Israel, and purchased the potter's field, as the Lord directed."

Matthew 27:1-10

* * *

Apparently, John and Peter weren't the only disciples of Jesus at the home of Caiaphas that early morning. While Peter had been with the servants denying Jesus, Judas Iscariot had been standing near the religious leaders continuing in his betrayal of Jesus. He was standing close and watching carefully. He fully expected Jesus at any moment to say "enough!" and declare Himself the Messiah and establish His authority over everyone in the room. This was the moment for which Judas had been waiting. His three years of following Jesus were now going to pay off. These religious leaders who had treated Judas with disdain were about to have the tables turned. Jesus was about to establish His Kingdom. Judas was about to step into his position of authority. And these religious leaders were moments away from having their authority stripped away. Judas was certain of how this was all going to end. Surely Jesus would be appreciative of how Judas had helped prompt the moment. And perhaps that had been Jesus' plan all along. Judas would have plenty of opportunity to talk through this with Jesus once He declared Himself. That's how blinded Judas had become by his own sin.

Then Caiaphas, Annas, and the entire high council said to Jesus, *"Tell us, are You the Messiah?" But He replied, "If I tell you, you won't believe Me. And if I ask you a question, you won't answer. But from now on the Son of Man will be seated in the place of power at God's right hand." They all shouted, "So, are You claiming to be the Son of God?" And He replied, "You say that I am." "Why do we need other witnesses?" they said. "We ourselves heard Him say it"* (Luke 22:67-71). Judas couldn't believe his ears. Jesus was not taking control of the situation (or so Judas thought). Instead of declaring Himself, Jesus was allowing Himself to be bound, and the religious leaders were taking Him to Pilate to be crucified. And Jesus was going willingly. Judas became filled with confusion, which quickly turned to the realization that Jesus had been condemned to die. And he – Judas – had been the one who betrayed Jesus. At that moment, the scales that had blinded him from seeing his own treachery and deceit fell from his eyes. He realized that he had been complicit in the plot to murder Jesus – the Messiah. Matthew records that he became filled with remorse. Regrettably, he did not become filled with repentance. Repentance would have led to forgiveness of his sin. Repentance would have led to restoration of his relationship with Christ, and through Christ with the Father. But instead he fell short and stopped with remorse. The Oxford Dictionary defines remorse as "deep regret or guilt for a wrong committed". It is a guilt and regret that is inconsolable. Remorse can become so great that one "drowns" in their guilt, shame and regret. Remorse left unattended leads to death. Repentance, on the other hand, though it begins with a sincere regret or remorse is, in fact, a turning point – a turning to God for forgiveness, receiving His forgiveness and walking according to His righteousness. Repentance leads to life – a life that is free of the bondage of remorse.

But Judas never made that turn. He verbalized his sin to the religious leaders, but he never sought the forgiveness of God. And if we had any question about the heart condition of the religious leaders, their response of *"What do we care? That's your problem"* leaves no doubt that they were anything but men of God. Thus, Judas' remorse led to death – physically. He immediately went out and hung himself. But his remorse also led to death – eternally. Having never repented and sought forgiveness, he died eternally separated from God.

So, let's wrap this chapter up with two closing points. First, could Judas have been forgiven by God? He betrayed the Son of God. You can't get any worse than that! But the fact of the matter is that even Judas could have been forgiven by God. That man whose name is now synonymous with betrayal could have experienced the forgiveness of the Heavenly Father and – even the One he betrayed – Jesus. Scripture tells us *"if we confess our sins to Him, He is faithful and just to forgive us our sins and to cleanse us from all wickedness"* (1 John 1:9). All wickedness. Even Judas' wickedness.

Earlier this week, i met a man by the name of Leon. Leon has spent 38 years in prison for doing some very evil things. But in the midst of that time in prison, God brought someone across his path who shared the gospel with him. He told Leon about repentance and God's merciful forgiveness extended by His grace through the shed blood of His Son. And Leon repented, asked God to forgive Him, and surrendered His life to Christ. Since then the Lord has used Leon to share that Good News with many men – young and old – who are on that same path he was on. God is using Leon as an ambassador of His gospel and His grace. God can forgive a repentant sinner like Leon. God can forgive a repentant sinner like Ken. God would have forgiven a repentant sinner like Judas – if he would have only repented and sought the forgiveness of God.

That leads me to the second point. As you take up the cross and follow Jesus, He will bring people across your path who are drowning in their remorse. They feel shame, guilt and regret for what they have done, but they are content to just wallow in their remorse. They prefer to medicate their remorse with everything and anything that lessens the pain, but they stop short of the only remedy. Years ago, i had the blessing to know Dr. Henry Brandt, a renowned Christian psychologist. Dr. Brandt wrote a book that was originally entitled, "When You're Tired Of Treating The Symptoms And You're Ready For A Cure, Give Me A Call"[1]. (You can imagine the challenge of fitting that title on the book cover!) But there's a lot of truth in that statement. When you stop short at remorse, you just want to treat the symptoms. Only repentance leads to the cure. We have the cure – it is the Good News of the gospel. Let's be faithful to share it widely – because there are too many "Judases" lost in their remorse.

[1] Re-released as "The Heart of the Problem: How to Stop Coping and Find the Cure for Your Struggles" by Dr. Henry Brandt and Dr. Kerry L. Skinner (2015)

* * *

47

THE PREFECT'S PART

Then the entire council took Jesus to Pilate, the Roman governor. They began to state their case: "This man has been leading our people astray by telling them not to pay their taxes to the Roman government and by claiming He is the Messiah, a king." So Pilate asked Him, "Are You the king of the Jews?" Jesus replied, "You have said it." Pilate turned to the leading priests and to the crowd and said, "I find nothing wrong with this Man!" Then they became insistent. "But He is causing riots by His teaching wherever He goes—all over Judea, from Galilee to Jerusalem!" "Oh, is He a Galilean?" Pilate asked. When they said that He was, Pilate sent Him to Herod Antipas, because Galilee was under Herod's jurisdiction, and Herod happened to be in Jerusalem at the time.

Luke 23:1-7

* * *

After the death of the Roman client King Herod the Great, the Herodian kingdom was divided into three parts, each ruled by one of his three sons. His son Herod Archelaus was subsequently deemed incompetent by the Roman emperor Augustus and a succession of prefects was put in place to govern that province. Prefects were military men who would typically only govern a portion of larger provinces. Pontius Pilate was the fifth prefect (or governor) of the Roman province of Judea. Herod the Great's other two sons – Herod Antipas and Philip – were still in power at the time of this account. Herod Antipas ruled over the provinces of Galilee and Perea, and Philip ruled over the territories north and east of the Jordan River. In essence, Pilate, Philip and Herod Antipas were equals in their accountability before Rome, and were careful to honor one another's authority.

As we already discussed in chapter 25, large crowds gathered in Jerusalem always caused the Roman rulers to be anxious about possible uprisings, and the record crowd gathered for this Passover made them even more so. Accordingly, Pilate and Herod Antipas were already both in Jerusalem that week to help keep the peace, instead of at their mansions in Caesarea and Tiberius, respectively.

Both rulers were familiar with the ministry of Jesus. They were well aware of His growing popularity among the people. Pilate, being a military leader with the responsibility of keeping peace and order, had kept track of Jesus' movements and actions through his centurions and soldiers. You will recall that Herod Antipas had executed John the Baptist. He, too, kept close tabs on Jesus' movements. Galilee had become Jesus' home and where He had spent the majority of His time during the three years of His ministry. They both were aware of the growing crowds that followed Him. But neither ruler appeared to be concerned that Jesus was a threat to their rule. We have no record that Jesus ever visited either of the cities in which these men lived. Let's be clear, if either of these rulers thought Jesus was a threat to Roman rule, they would have immediately arrested Him long before this.

The religious leaders made three claims about Jesus to Pilate:

1. He was telling the people not to pay their taxes.
2. He was claiming to be king, in a plan to overthrow Roman rule.
3. He was inciting the people to riot.

As we know, all of these claims were false. And Pilate knew all of these claims were false. As i've already said, if he had thought for a moment that any of these claims were true, he would have long before arrested Jesus. He knew the real motivation of these religious leaders. He knew they were threatened by His popularity. He saw this as a religious dispute.

Pilate didn't much care for the religious leaders. He knew their disdain for his religious beliefs, and he held theirs in equal regard. As prefect, his primary role was to keep law and order utilizing a small auxiliary force of approximately 3,000 locally recruited soldiers, to collect the imperial taxes due Rome and oversee limited judicial functions. Beyond that, the local municipal council – the Sanhedrin – under the leadership of the high priest – Caiaphas – was to attend to all other administrative matters. Pilate clearly saw this as an administrative matter, and did not want to get drawn into one of their religious debates. He could find no reason for Jesus to even be brought before him, let alone find any guilt in Jesus.

But he also could not permit an uprising of the people under his watch. The crowd had amassed to about two million people. The soldiers at his disposal could not contain that crowd if a riot broke out. Obviously, the religious leaders were not going to take "no" for an answer, and the crowd that was with them was beginning to become animated. As he continued to look for a way to keep himself out of a matter that he did not believe was his to adjudicate and, at the same time, not incite this crowd that could easily be stirred, he was presented with an opportunity. Since Jesus was a Galilean, this was Herod's problem! He welcomed the opportunity to "pass the buck" – at least for the moment.

So, what was the prefect's part in all of this? To answer that, we need to remember that Jesus was never the victim of human decisions. He wasn't the victim of the corrupt disciple who betrayed Him. He wasn't the victim of the corrupt high priests who orchestrated His arrest. He wasn't the victim of the Sanhedrin who condemned Him. Nor was He the victim of Herod or Pilate, who ultimately had Him executed. He was God's chosen Lamb in His redemptive plan. God had determined before the beginning of time that He would die as the atonement for our sin. But nonetheless, each of these corrupt and tragic characters do play a very particular role in the murder of the Son of God. They cannot escape their personal responsibility.

The better way to put it is to say that none of them really determined the destiny of Jesus. But what they did with Jesus determined their own destiny. None of them really condemned Jesus, but each of them condemned himself. In reality, it wasn't Jesus that was on trial. It was them who were on trial, and they all damned themselves.

There is a defining moment in everyone's life. Everyone ultimately has to decide what they will do with Jesus. You can't "pass the buck". You can't "wash your hands of it". Even no decision is a decision. God had a plan, but Pilate had a choice. God knew the choice Pilate would make, but He didn't cause Pilate to make it. *"The Lord is not slow about His promise, as some count slowness, but is patient toward you, not wishing for any to perish but for all to come to repentance"* (2 Peter 3:9). He is not wishing for any to perish – Judas, Annas, Caiaphas, Herod, Pilate, Ken, or you – but wants all to come to repentance.

The prefect's part was not to condemn an innocent Man; his part was to follow Jesus. He chose the wrong part. Many of you know that my life verse is from the apostle Paul's admonition to the Colossian church: *"So we tell others about Christ, warning everyone and teaching everyone with all the wisdom God has given us. We want to present them to God, perfect in their relationship to Christ. That's why I work and struggle so hard, depending on Christ's mighty power that works within me"* (Colossians 1:28-29). If we would take up the cross and follow Jesus, we are to warn and teach everyone – that includes the Judases, the Annases, the Caiaphases, the Herods and the Pilates – everyone. Let us be faithful to do "our part", trusting the Holy Spirit to prompt them to do "their part".

* * *

48

A KING'S MOCKERY

Herod was delighted at the opportunity to see Jesus, because he had heard about Him and had been hoping for a long time to see Him perform a miracle. He asked Jesus question after question, but Jesus refused to answer. Meanwhile, the leading priests and the teachers of religious law stood there shouting their accusations. Then Herod and his soldiers began mocking and ridiculing Jesus. Finally, they put a royal robe on Him and sent Him back to Pilate. (Herod and Pilate, who had been enemies before, became friends that day.)
Luke 23:8-12

* * *

Herod Antipas would have been a young man of 17 or 18 years of age when Jesus was born. He would have been an understudy of his father, King Herod the Great, when the wise men arrived from the east seeking the birthplace of The King (Matthew 2:1-8). He would have witnessed how his father directed the wise men, and how he responded when the wise men failed to return with news of the "baby's" location (Matthew 2:16-18).

Over thirty years had passed since that time, and Herod the Great had long been dead. Herod Antipas, now as ruler over Galilee and Perea, began to hear about the ministry and miracles being performed by Jesus in Galilee. It would be interesting to know if Herod ever connected the Baby who the wise men sought with the Miracle Worker who he was now hearing about. Luke writes, *"When Herod Antipas, the ruler of Galilee, heard about everything Jesus was doing, he was puzzled. Some were saying that John the Baptist had been raised from the dead. Others thought Jesus was Elijah or one of the other prophets risen from the dead. 'I beheaded John,' Herod said, 'so who is this man about whom I hear such stories?' And he kept trying to see Him"* (Luke 9:7-9). John the Baptist had not performed any miracles, but Herod allowed for that possibility if he had, in fact, been raised from the dead. Having had John beheaded, Herod's conscience was no doubt convicting him. Had God sent John back from the dead to judge him? Herod wanted to see Jesus, but his pride would never permit him to travel into the countryside to seek Him out. And Jesus did not make it a point to mingle with the "high and mighty" of society. As i mentioned in the last chapter, there is no record that Jesus ever visited the city of Tiberius, where Herod's palace was situated. Therefore, their paths did not cross.

One year earlier, while Jesus was in Perea, the religious leaders had wanted to get Him back into Judea where they could watch Him more closely and entrap Him. So, the Pharisees attempted to frighten Jesus back to Judea. As Luke writes, *"At that time some Pharisees said to Him, 'Get away from here if you want to live! Herod Antipas wants to kill You!' Jesus replied, 'Go tell that fox that I will keep on casting out demons and healing people today and tomorrow; and the third day I will accomplish My purpose. Yes, today, tomorrow, and the next day I must proceed on My way. For it wouldn't do for a prophet of God to be killed except in Jerusalem!'"* (Luke 13:31-33). There is no record that Herod was truly seeking to kill Jesus. That was an attempted ploy by the Pharisees. However, Jesus rightly knew that Herod was a fox. [A quick word of context: In that day, Jews did not perceive foxes to be crafty or clever, rather they viewed them as being inferior vermin. Great men were "lions"; lesser men were "foxes". Brilliant men were "lions"; inept men were "foxes".] Herod had demonstrated his baseness as a leader in divorcing his first wife, in lusting after his step-daughter and in having John the Baptist beheaded. In referring to Herod as a fox, not only was He declaring that Herod held no true power over Him, but He was also belittling the Pharisees for their feeble threat.

Now, several weeks later, in the Father's timing, Jesus is brought before Herod, and he is "delighted" at the opportunity to finally see Jesus perform a miracle. Obviously, Herod does not view Jesus as a threat – as his father had once viewed Jesus when He was a baby. Herod viewed Jesus more as a curiosity – a performer. That should give us great insight into both his political and spiritual worldviews. Thus, he begins to ask a series of questions, intended to elicit a miraculous act from Jesus. But to his consternation, Jesus remains silent. Jesus is not there to "perform" for

Herod. Neither is He there to "prove" Himself to Herod. Herod does not seek truth, he seeks entertainment. Allow me to pause on that important truth. Jesus never came to provide entertainment to a curious crowd; He came to provide truth to – and make the way for – honest seekers. We would do well to remember that the gospel is never to be viewed as entertainment, with our focus being on the creativity or skillful execution of our presentation. The gospel is uncompromising in truth and is to be rightly communicated in word and in action.

The priests and teachers, who had earlier been unsuccessful in manipulating Jesus with their idle threats, now turned their attention to manipulating Herod with their false accusations. And Herod – being a fox, instead of a lion – was as easily swayed by them as he had been by his wife, Herodias (Mark 6:17). Instead of truly seeking truth, or attempting to stand on truth, Herod was more concerned with the public opinion being expressed by the priests and teachers. Thus, the fox was easily swayed to join in the mockery and ridicule of the one True King in the room – the Lion of Judah. In an attempt to gain even more approval from the religious leaders, it was probably Herod's idea to have one of his old robes placed on Jesus as a mockery.

But, having been the executor of John the Baptist, "the fox" determined that he would not be responsible for this Man's death, so he craftily defers the matter back to Pilate. Since the leaders in Judea were seeking the death of Jesus in Judea, he deferred the matter to the prefect of Judea. In that action, Herod created a stronger alliance – and gained political capital – with not only the religious leaders, but also with Pilate. It is worthy to note, however, that any capital gained through the mockery of truth is short-lived. Within just a few short years, Herod's favor waned, and he was removed from power by Rome and exiled to Gaul. The adage is true that "he who doesn't stand for something, will fall for anything" – and such was the life of Herod Antipas, the fox.

They mocked Jesus and, in doing so, they mocked Truth and Righteousness. Mockery is defined as "contemptuous language or behavior directed at a particular person or thing"[1]. Scripture tells us that "the king's heart is in the hand of the LORD" (Proverbs 21:1), and so is the heart of those who walk as spiritual leaders among the flock. In mocking Jesus, they were mocking the very authority under whom they were placed in their positions of leadership. They were making a mockery of God's law and the divine authority over them. In their effort to make a mockery of

Jesus, they truly made a mockery of themselves and, in doing so, sealed their eternal fate. They would have been wise to heed the truth that was later penned by the apostle Paul: *"Don't be misled — you cannot mock the justice of God. You will always harvest what you plant. Those who live only to satisfy their own sinful nature will harvest decay and death from that sinful nature. But those who live to please the Spirit will harvest everlasting life from the Spirit"* (Galatians 6:7-8).

Any attempt by a king to mock the King will always result in the king himself being mocked – by death and decay. And that truth holds true for those who aren't kings. So, as we take up the cross to follow our King, let us take care to do so in a way that brings Him honor – and that nothing in our thoughts, attitudes or actions makes a mockery of Him, His Word or His mission.

[1] Oxford English Dictionary

* * *

49

A CRIMINAL'S RELEASE

Then Pilate called together the leading priests and other religious leaders, along with the people, and he announced his verdict. "You brought this man to me, accusing Him of leading a revolt. I have examined Him thoroughly on this point in your presence and find Him innocent. Herod came to the same conclusion and sent Him back to us. Nothing this man has done calls for the death penalty. So, I will have Him flogged, and then I will release Him." Then a mighty roar rose from the crowd, and with one voice they shouted, "Kill Him, and release Barabbas to us!" (Barabbas was in prison for taking part in an insurrection in Jerusalem against the government, and for murder.) Pilate argued with them, because he wanted to release Jesus. But they kept shouting, "Crucify Him! Crucify Him!" For the third time he demanded, "Why? What crime has He committed? I have found no reason to sentence Him to death. So, I will have Him flogged, and then I will release Him." But the mob shouted louder and louder, demanding that Jesus be crucified, and their voices prevailed. So, Pilate sentenced Jesus to die as they demanded. As they had requested, he released Barabbas, the man in prison for insurrection and murder. But he turned Jesus over to them to do as they wished.
Luke 23:13-25

* * *

Pilate was trying to escape making a decision about Jesus – but he could not. He had already announced for a second time that he did not find Jesus guilty of any of the charges the religious leaders had made against Him. Pilate knew that Herod had also not been able to find fault with Jesus. Herod had avoided making a pronouncement by simply mocking Him, putting a robe on Him and sending Him back to Pilate. But

Pilate, try as he might, could not avoid making a decision – and he knew that the fair and just decision was very different from the politically-correct decision being sought by those before him. Pilate knew that a Jewish uprising under his watch would bring a hasty conclusion to his political and military career. He was not prepared to sacrifice his own well-being for this Jew. However, he knew that this Jew was innocent of every charge being made against Him.

The reality is that it was Pilate who was on trial, not Jesus. Jesus was not trying to escape from the decision, but Pilate was. He sought an easy escape. The decision between the release of Barabbas versus Jesus should have been a "no-brainer". A prevailing custom called for the prefect to commute one prisoner's death sentence at Passover. Barabbas was a thief (John 18:40), a murderer and an insurrectionist. Pilate knew that the religious leaders' motivation for seeking the execution of Jesus was their envy of His standing with the ever-growing multitude. But he underestimated the depths to which religion can sink when it goes wrong. To Pilate's surprise, the chief priests and elders were successful in persuading the crowd who stood in front of Pilate to ask for the release of Barabbas. But bear in mind, the Pharisees had put together a crowd of "ringers". The crowd was not representative of the general populace gathered in the city for Passover. This crowd was made up of the religious leaders of the nation. This crowd – or jury, if you will – was by no means impartial or representative of the crowd that had shouted "Hosanna" when Jesus entered Jerusalem a few short days prior. This crowd was made up of the very people who felt threatened by Jesus' ministry. Imagine a judge asking a biased crowd for their decision as to what should be done with a man on trial! He knew Jesus was innocent, and yet, he feared that a riot was about to break out.

He carefully questioned Jesus, and even trembled at His answers. But even the Truth of the Word would not make a difference in his decision. The question came down to what was right versus his own selfish ambition, and his selfish ambition won out. He chose being popular over being right. He chose expediency over character, and compromise over what was just. There is at least one moment in everyone's life where they must stand up for what is right. This was Pilate's moment, and he failed miserably.

Imagine being Barabbas. He had been found guilty by a legal tribunal and had been condemned to death. There was never any question as to his guilt – in the minds of his condemners or in his own mind. He knew that he deserved his sentence of death. He knew that at any moment the Roman soldiers would be coming to take him from his prison cell to the hill of execution outside the city walls to be crucified on a cross. There would be no appeal. There would be no mercy. His sentence had been issued and his fate was sealed. Off in the distance, he heard the crowd shouting his name. It began as a dull roar, but the shouts quickly increased in volume. Then he heard them repeatedly shouting, "Crucify him!" The crowd was obviously shouting for his blood. The time of his execution had arrived. The soldiers arrived at his cell and led him out still bound. But to his surprise, instead of being led to Golgotha under the weight of a cross, he was led to stand before Pilate. There was another Man, also bound, standing there as well. Then the unimaginable took place. The man clothed in unrighteousness who deserved to be crucified for his transgressions was set free, and the Man clothed in righteousness – the One without sin – was undeservedly condemned by Pilate to be crucified. The criminal was released, and the Savior was condemned.

Keep the faces of Pilate and Barabbas both in your mind's eye. They are familiar faces – not only from this Gospel account – but also, they are the faces of many people that we encounter every day. They are the "Pilates" who refuse to make a decision about Jesus. They can find no fault with Him, but they are easily swayed by the crowd. It's not politically correct to decide in favor of Jesus, so the "Pilates" either make no decision, or give into the peer pressure of the crowd. But alas, they are the ones who are condemned to death – condemned by their rejection. And yes, there are also the "Barabbases" – and i am one. Their offenses and unrighteousness have rightly condemned them to death. But, undeservedly, Jesus has paid the price in their stead. Jesus has paid the price for their release.

Don't lose sight of Who the judge was on that day. This was the Father's plan. Jesus was the Judge and the Savior. Pilate was the sinner who rejected Jesus. And let there be no doubt that though it was the Father's plan, Pilate made his own choice. Barabbas was the sinner set free through the crucifixion of Jesus. (Let me hastily add that there is absolutely no indication in Scripture that Barabbas believed in Jesus. So, i am not making a claim that he was saved for eternity that day. However, the events of that day are a great picture of Christ's substitutionary death on the cross for our sins and, in that sense, Barabbas is a picture of those of us who have been set free through the sacrificial death of our Savior.)

. . .

One other picture that begins there in Pilate's court and continues to Calvary is that of Jesus freely and willingly taking up the cross that day. There was no one in that crowd, and there has been no one since that day, that merited His action. There was no one then, and no one since, who merited release or favor. As we take up the cross to follow our Savior, we will encounter many who do not merit our favor or our grace. Don't forget that neither do we, and Jesus extended it anyway. Go, and do likewise.

* * *

50

THEY AREN'T THE ONLY ONES WHO MOCKED JESUS

The soldiers took Jesus into the courtyard of the governor's headquarters (called the Praetorium) and called out the entire regiment. They dressed Him in a purple robe, and they wove thorn branches into a crown and put it on His head. Then they saluted Him and taunted, "Hail! King of the Jews!" And they struck Him on the head with a reed stick, spit on Him, and dropped to their knees in mock worship. When they were finally tired of mocking Him, they took off the purple robe and put His own clothes on Him again. Then they led Him away to be crucified.

Mark 15:16-20

* * *

We live in a world that is a mere shadow of what our Creator intended for it to be. The consequence of sin is so pervasive that it casts its pallor across every facet of our lives. Daily we are bombarded with news reports of acts of brutality perpetrated by one person upon another without any degree of shame or guilt. It has become so common place to the point that our senses have almost become numb to the daily reports. But often something occurs that is so egregious – or so close to home – that we cry out asking why a loving God would ever permit such a thing. Surely if there is a God in heaven, He would not permit these atrocities to occur.

Prior to making his final judgement, Pilate had Jesus scourged in the hopes that would satisfy the blood thirst of the religious leaders and the crowd they had incited to ask for crucifixion. Though he knew that Jesus was without guilt, he still permitted Him to go through the brutality of a Roman scourging. The Roman scourge was a short whip made of two or three leather thongs or ropes connected to a handle. The thongs were knotted with pieces of metal or bones at various intervals, with a hook at the end. The scourge was intended to quickly remove the flesh from the body of the victim stopping just short of death. The Romans were masters of this cruel form of punishment. And this torturous act was Pilate's attempt to free this innocent Man! Such was the state of our Lord when Pilate acquiesced to the religious leaders and turned Jesus over to the soldiers to be crucified.

As we saw in chapter 47, the entire military force under Pilate's command was 3,000 men for all of Judea. They were organized into ten cohorts of 300. One of those cohorts would have been based at the Praetorium. The soldiers were the brute force presence used by Rome to maintain law and order over its subjects. Though many had been locally recruited, they were a constant reminder to the Jewish people of their oppressive Roman ruler. Thus, they were viewed with disdain and disrespect by the Jews. But because they were not Roman citizens, they were also looked down upon by their Roman leaders. The rank and file soldiers were not selected for their good character; they were selected for their sadistic brutality and fighting ability. Most of the time, they were forced to control their growing hatred for the Jewish people and the frustration they felt by not being able to physically express that hatred. It was to this group that Pilate released Jesus – and there were no constraints on their actions, except that they had to deliver him to Golgotha for crucifixion.

We cannot fully comprehend the unbridled brutality, torture and humiliation that was unleashed on Jesus by these 300 men as they sought to satisfy their sadistic appetites. One writer describes a "game" that the Roman soldiers often "played" called "hot hand". The soldiers would each hold up a fist in the face of their victim. Then they would blindfold him, and each soldier would hit him in the face. They would beat their victim until his face was unrecognizable. Then they would remove the blindfold, and the victim was to identify which fist had not hit him. The prisoner was never able to identify the right one, and even if he did, the soldiers wouldn't admit it. So, the blindfold would be put back on him, and the "game" would continue. In the case of Jesus, even the mockery of the robe placed on His shredded flesh and the crown of thorns pressed into His brow were intended to subject Jesus to more brutality and torture.

. . .

But in the midst of it all, our Savior quietly suffered and did not speak out or fight back. By a single command, He could have surrounded Himself with a multitude of angels to protect Himself from the suffering. By a simple thought, He could have reduced the soldiers to a pillar of salt. By a single word, He could have said, "Enough!" and brought it all to an end. But He did not. He allowed Himself to suffer the fullness of the depravity of His fallen creation on our behalf, according to the Father's plan. It was a lesson that Mark's readers would need to learn as they soon faced some of the very same persecution themselves:

"For God called you to do good, even if it means suffering, just as Christ suffered for you. He is your example, and you must follow in His steps. He never sinned, nor ever deceived anyone. He did not retaliate when He was insulted, nor threaten revenge when He suffered. He left His case in the hands of God, who always judges fairly"
(1 Peter 2:21-23).

But even beyond the physical suffering, Jesus allowed Himself to be subjected to the humiliation and ridicule of being spat upon and taunted in mock worship, until they tired of mocking Him. Then after that morning of inhumane suffering, they led Him away to be crucified.

Again, surely if there is a God in heaven, He would not permit these atrocities to occur – even to His Own Son. And yet, He did. He wasn't the author of the brutality. We, as a fallen creation, don't need any help in being brutal. Our sin has fully equipped us for that task. But He permitted it because He had a purpose beyond what anyone could imagine. The religious leaders who thought they were victorious couldn't comprehend it. The Roman soldiers with their insatiable and unconscionable thirst for brutality were blind to it. Even His followers who hid in fear were unable to understand it. It was a dark day, and it was going to get even darker. But our God has told us, *"My thoughts are nothing like your thoughts," says the LORD. "And my ways are far beyond anything you could imagine"* (Isaiah 55:8). Paul would soon write to a group of believers who were being persecuted in Rome, *"And we know that God causes everything to work together for the good of those who love God and are called according to His purpose for them"* (Romans 8:28). And if God causes "everything" to work together, then that includes the brutality that was extended to His Son… to the Roman believers to whom Paul was writing… and to you and me.

. . .

Every action that the Roman soldiers perpetrated upon Jesus was an act of mockery in the face of a Holy God. Every deed of brutality, every word of disrespect, and every unrepentant action was an affront and an offense. And the brutality and the mockery did not end with the Roman soldiers. It has continued through the ages – even to this day. There continue to be governments, religious leaders and even family members who brutalize and mock Jesus through their actions and words inflicted upon brothers and sisters around this globe today who are being persecuted for their faith in Christ. And, in an even more pervasive way, through mockery that continues to be inflicted in ever increasing subtle ways of disregard and dishonor directed toward Jesus.

But one day, that will all stop. One day, our Lord will say, "Enough!" And on that day, He will return – not as a Suffering Savior, but as the King of Kings. Until that day, continue to take up the cross and follow Him, *"even if it means suffering, just as Christ suffered for you."*

* * *

51

HE TOOK UP THE CROSS

A passerby named Simon, who was from Cyrene, was coming in from the countryside just then, and the soldiers forced him to carry Jesus' cross. (Simon was the father of Alexander and Rufus.)
Mark 15:21

* * *

According to Roman law, one who was found guilty and condemned to death was required to carry his cross, or at least the cross beam, to the place of his crucifixion. Jesus left the Praetorium bearing His cross, but along the way the Roman soldiers conscripted Simon the Cyrene to carry Jesus' cross.

Let's ponder the question as to why someone was needed to carry His cross. The obvious explanation is the one that we immediately presume to be correct, and the one we see depicted in dramatizations of His crucifixion. That being, that physically, Jesus could no longer walk under the weight of the cross. Jesus would have been 33 years of age. He had spent most of His life as a carpenter and therefore would have had a muscular physique. Throughout the three-plus years of His ministry, He walked all over the countryside. And earlier that week, He had physically driven the moneychangers out of the Temple. Jesus had been in excellent physical condition. But after the brutal scourging and beatings that Jesus received at the hands of the Roman soldiers that morning, as the Son of Man, He would have been at near-death physically. But don't lose sight that He is also the Son of God. He could have easily called upon supernatural strength to shoulder that cross. Luke records in his Gospel (Luke 23:32) that the two criminals were also led out with Him to be executed. They, too, would have been scourged and beaten that morning, and yet, there is no mention of anyone else carrying their crosses. Though i don't in any way minimize the physical effects of the scourging and the beatings that He bore for my sins – and yours, i do wonder if, according to the Father's plan, there weren't at least two other reasons for someone else to carry His cross.

The first of the two has to do with the reason that Roman law required the cross to be carried. It was to be carried by one who was guilty. Jesus wasn't guilty of anything. Jesus lived a righteous, sinless life. Even the pagan Pilate could not find any guilt in Jesus. Jesus wasn't being crucified because He was guilty. The Father had ordained that the Son would be crucified to bear the iniquity of our sin. It was not for Jesus to carry that cross – it was for a sinner to do so.

At that moment – just the right moment – the Father led Simon the Cyrene to arrive at that place along the way to Golgotha. Simon was a Hellenistic Jew coming to Jerusalem for the observance of Passover. Cyrene was situated in modern-day Libya, on the northern coast of Africa. Settled by the Greeks in 630 B.C. and later infused with a significant Jewish population, Cyrene was the capital of the Roman district of Cyrenaica at the time of Jesus' crucifixion. By then, Cyrene was home to a large number of Greek-speaking, or Hellenistic, Jews. It was possibly some of his Cyrenian "brothers" who had approached Philip earlier in the week (John 12:20-21) about meeting Jesus. Unbeknownst to Simon, the Father had planned for his life to be transformed that day – and the impetus would be that the Roman soldiers would force him to carry Jesus' cross.

i would imagine that Simon's immediate reaction was resentment. Of all of the people on the road at that moment, why were the soldiers singling him out to carry the cross for this Man? Since Simon was just arriving in the city, i don't believe that he immediately knew that this was Jesus who was being led to be crucified. i do believe, that like the other Greeks i mentioned, he had heard of Jesus, but i don't believe that when the soldiers first pulled him out of the crowd that he knew who this Man was. And the soldiers didn't give him a choice. They commanded him to do so, and to refuse would have been fatal for him. So, get this picture in your mind. Jesus is ahead being led by the soldiers to His death, and there was

Simon, following Jesus, carrying the cross. As they continued along the path, Simon would have heard the shouts from the crowd. He would have heard the grief-stricken cries of the women trailing behind (Luke 23:27). And at some point, he realized who this Man was. He heard Jesus turn to the women and say, *"Daughters of Jerusalem, don't weep for Me, but weep for yourselves and for your children"* (Luke 23:28). Jesus then bore witness to what would occur in the end times. Even as He was being led to His death, this Man, Jesus, was speaking as One in authority. Perhaps it was at that moment that Simon believed. Perhaps it was later as he stood to watch at the foot of the cross. Perhaps it was later after he heard that Jesus had risen from the tomb. But at some point, Simon believed in Jesus. Mark is the only Gospel account that records the names of his two sons – Alexander and Rufus. It would appear that Mark is mentioning these two men as familiar names to the church. Remember, Mark was with the apostle Paul in Rome. He would have been a discipler of the believers there in Rome. And Paul references a believer by the name of Rufus in his letter to the church in Rome (Romans 16:13). Very possibly the Rufus that he mentions is Simon's son. He also references the mother of Rufus, so it would appear that the whole family had become followers of Jesus.

You will recall that earlier in His ministry, as recorded in Luke 9:23, Jesus had told those in the crowd, *"If anyone would come after Me, let him deny himself and take up his cross daily and follow Me"* (ESV). Simon gives us a picture of that. Though he didn't at first choose to follow Jesus, at some point he appears to have made that choice. And here, on this day, he is carrying the cross of Jesus and following Him all the way to Calvary. The Father had a path for Simon to follow – and He led him to follow Jesus. The Father had a cross for him to carry – and it was the cross on which our Savior shed His blood for the forgiveness of your sin, and mine.

And today, the Father has a path for us – a path to follow Jesus. And He has a cross for us to carry – a cross that the Father will use as a part of His redemptive plan for His glory. The Roman soldiers gave the task to Simon out of disdain for him and contempt for Jesus, but the Father orchestrated the plan out of His perfect will for Simon and His love for His Son. No matter the cross you are carrying, or the one who has placed it onto your shoulders, the Father has orchestrated it – out of His perfect will for you and His love for His Son. Take up the cross and follow Him!

* * *

52

A PLACE CALLED GOLGOTHA

...He went to the place called Place of the Skull (in Hebrew, Golgotha). There they nailed Him to the cross. Two others were crucified with Him, one on either side, with Jesus between them. And Pilate posted a sign on the cross that read, "Jesus of Nazareth, the King of the Jews." The place where Jesus was crucified was near the city, and the sign was written in Hebrew, Latin, and Greek, so that many people could read it. Then the leading priests objected and said to Pilate, "Change it from 'The King of the Jews' to 'He said, I am King of the Jews.'" Pilate replied, "No, what I have written, I have written." When the soldiers had crucified Jesus, they divided His clothes among the four of them. They also took His robe, but it was seamless, woven in one piece from top to bottom. So, they said, "Rather than tearing it apart, let's throw dice for it." This fulfilled the Scripture that says, "They divided My garments among themselves and threw dice for My clothing." So that is what they did. Standing near the cross were Jesus' mother, and His mother's sister, Mary (the wife of Clopas), and Mary Magdalene. When Jesus saw His mother standing there beside the disciple He loved, He said to her, "Dear woman, here is your son." And He said to this disciple, "Here is your mother." And from then on, this disciple took her into his home.

John 19:17-27

* * *

Golgotha would have been outside the city wall, but near the city. The Romans conducted their executions by crucifixion near a road with high visibility (in this case, leading into Jerusalem). It was a part of the death penalty that the victim would die in the most conspicuous and humiliating way possible. It also reinforced the ironclad rule of Roman law and served as a further deterrent to those who may be considering breaking the law. It was common for the victim's crime to be written on a sign that was hung on the cross – also as a further deterrent. The sign would be written in the three main languages of that region in order to ensure that the maximum number of people were able to read it. It was written in Hebrew, the language of religion. It was written in Latin, the language of law and order. And it was written in Greek, the language of culture and education. In so doing, the Romans were unknowingly proclaiming some of the first written words of the gospel message in ways that people from many tongues and tribes could understand.

Notice the attempt of the religious leaders to have the sign changed. People have been attempting to change the message of the gospel ever since. But, also, notice Pilate's defiance to their request as his feeble attempt to exercise his power despite the way he had allowed them to manipulate him. Accordingly, in an attempt to counteract the message of the sign, "*the leading priests, the teachers of religious law, and the elders mocked Jesus*" by standing nearby and scoffing, "*...so He is the King of Israel, is He? Let Him come down from the cross right now, and we will believe in Him!*" (Matthew 27:41-42). i don't know about you, but as i read those words, other similar words come to mind – "*Then the devil took Him to the holy city, Jerusalem, to the highest point of the Temple, and said, 'If you are the Son of God, jump off!'*" (Matthew 4:5-6). Even in those last moments, the religious leaders were being the conduit of the voice of Satan, as he continued to make every attempt to mock Jesus and tempt Him to step down from the very purpose for which the Father had sent Him.

The soldiers overseeing a crucifixion were permitted to confiscate and share whatever personal belongings their victims had. In this case, all that Jesus possessed was a pair of sandals, a girdle, an outer robe, a head covering and a tunic (which was seamless). Apparently, each of the soldiers took one of the first four items of clothing and they then gambled for the seamless tunic (in fulfillment of Psalm 22:18). i am mindful that we live in a culture that is preoccupied with accumulating "things". But our Savior – who owns the cattle on a thousand hills (Psalm 50:10) – died without possessing one single item. i am not advocating that we are all to take a vow of poverty, but i am mindful that if we are to take up the cross and follow our Savior, He did not walk the way of accumulating possessions. As a matter of fact, He told the rich young man to sell all that He had (Matthew 19:21). Let's make sure that we have our priorities in the right order.

• • •

Jesus, as the Son of Man, was saying goodbye to His mother Mary, because He would rise again as the glorified Christ. He was honoring and completing His responsibility as the firstborn son of His earthly mother. First, He was assuring her salvation. Mary needed to come to faith in Christ just as every believer. Jesus was dying on the cross for the sins of the entire world – and that included Mary. He was making the way for her to be saved. She, then, had to believe, accept and follow Him. Second, through His resurrection, He was clearing her name forever. Her reputation that had suffered the injustice of gossip and innuendo for over thirty-three years would at last be vindicated. Third, as her firstborn son, He was making sure that she would be cared for the remainder of her earthly days. And in order to do so, He turned to His disciple John, whom He loved as a brother.

It is interesting to remember that Mary had other sons – James, Joseph, Jude and Simon (Mark 6:3) as well as daughters. We know that at least James and Jude went on to be followers of Jesus, if not all of His earthly family members. James, as the next oldest son, would have culturally been expected to be given the responsibility by Jesus to care for his widowed mother. We don't know all of the reasons that Jesus did not follow that cultural norm – but here are two things we do know. First, James and the other brothers had not yet believed in Jesus at the time of His crucifixion. They did not believe in Jesus until after His resurrection. Therefore, they were not like-minded, and He could not entrust His mother to anyone who was not. Second, Scripture makes no mention of His brothers being present at His crucifixion. Given the detailed account of who was there, it is reasonable to assume that they were not at the foot of the cross. Also, given the Passover celebration, they, in fact, would have been in Jerusalem, but they obviously chose to not follow Him to the cross. Remember, at that point they had believed that He could be the Messiah, but they did not believe Him to be the Son of God. So, they either stayed away from the cross due to fear of retribution upon His family members, or due to their unbelief since He had failed to declare Himself and establish His Kingdom, or due to their personal embarrassment over the way He had now sullied the family's reputation. So, as His dying request, He entrusted His mother to John's care. (As a footnote, all indications are that John remained in Jerusalem for many years following Christ's resurrection in order to care for Mary, and he did not leave the city until she had died.)

All of this occurred – and more – as our Savior hung on the cross. There are details about His crucifixion that the Gospel writers do not include. The Father Himself caused a veil of darkness to fall across the whole land

(Luke 23:44) while His Son hung on that cross. There was a transaction that took place that day between the Father and the Son. It was a transaction for the sins of the world – which is beyond anything that we can comprehend. The only thing we can do is accept by faith the forgiveness that was appropriated only through the death of Jesus on that cross. Only through His death is the veil of darkness pierced. Only through His death are we enabled to walk in His holy light.

That day on Golgotha must have seemed like a triumph to Satan. He had bruised the heel of the woman's seed as foretold in Genesis 3. It must have seemed like a victory to the religious leaders. The threat to their position and power had been eliminated forever. And to a watching world, it must have seemed like a brutal murder – to many, an injustice. But to the Father, it was the only way His creation would ever be able to cross the sinful divide back to Him.

* * *

53

IT IS FINISHED! OR IS IT?

Jesus knew that His mission was now finished, and to fulfill Scripture He said, "I am thirsty." A jar of sour wine was sitting there, so they soaked a sponge in it, put it on a hyssop branch, and held it up to His lips. When Jesus had tasted it, He said, "It is finished!" Then He bowed His head and gave up His spirit.
John 19:28-30

* * *

Let's not lose sight of the fact that our Savior is as much man as if He was not God at all, and as much God as if He was not man at all. He is both fully divine and fully human. There was never a time when Jesus became God. He has always been God. But Jesus has not always been man. He became man through His incarnational birth in the manger. As the ancient theologian Gregory of Naziansen put it, "Remaining what He was, He became what He was not." The writer of Hebrews writes, "*it was necessary for Him to be made in every respect like us, His brothers and sisters, so that He could be our merciful and faithful High Priest before God. Then He could offer a sacrifice that would take away the sins of the people. Since He Himself has gone through suffering and testing, He is able to help us when we are being tested*" (Hebrews 2:17-18). He became man so that He could die for our sins – so that He could be that unblemished sacrifice. He had to be human in order to pay the penalty for humans. But, as this passage tells us, He didn't cease being human after His crucifixion. He continues as the Son of Man to be a merciful and faithful High Priest. His humanity enables Him to more fully sympathize with us and identify with us. In that moment on the cross when He died, He paid the price once and for all as the sacrifice for the forgiveness of sin. His mission as the perfect Lamb of God was now finished.

His sufferings were now behind Him. He had refused to drink the pain-deadening wine that was always offered to those about to be crucified (Matthew 27:34). Bear in mind, the Roman soldiers did not offer that narcotic out of compassion, they offered it so that the amount of time that a victim suffered the humiliation and brutality of the cross would be lengthened. The excruciating pain accelerated the onset of death. Deadening the pain slowed it down. This would partially explain why the criminals being crucified on either side of Jesus that day were still alive after Jesus died (John 19:31-33). The criminals probably accepted the wine offered by the soldiers. But our Lord was accomplishing so much more on that cross, and He knew that His mind needed to be clear. Thus, He endured the intense excruciating physical pain to its fullest.

There was also a suffering and pain that was far greater than the physical pain that Christ endured. During the three hours of darkness from noon until 3:00PM (Matthew 27:45-49), Jesus felt the full wrath of God, as He carried the full burden of sin, and He experienced complete separation from the Father for the first and only time in His existence. Remember, sin separates us from a Holy God. Jesus was carrying the full burden of sin. That sin separated Him from His Father. We will never fully comprehend the pain and suffering He endured that was caused by that separation and isolation. But He endured that suffering because the Father so loves the world that He sent the Son, and the Son so loves the Father that He endured to the end.

After the sufferings leading up to the cross, and His sufferings on the cross, Jesus was "spent". His physical body was dehydrated and depleted of any moisture. He was parched. He was only able to whisper the words, *"I am thirsty."* One of the soldiers took pity on Jesus and moistened His lips with the cheap sour wine that the soldiers were drinking. We tend to picture that Jesus was hanging many feet up in the air, but the reality is that Jesus' feet were no more than three to four feet off the ground. So, the soldier put the soaked sponge on the end of a branch and reached up and held it to His lips. Even the Messianic prophecy of Psalm 69:21 – *"... they offer me sour wine to satisfy my thirst"* – was fulfilled. That bit of moisture didn't quench Jesus' thirst, but it was all He needed to speak out His last words in triumph, *"It is finished!"*

• • •

Our Lord's sufferings were finished. The prophecies foretelling His incarnation and death were now all fulfilled, including the twenty-eight specifically related to His crucifixion. The sacrifice for our sin was now complete. It was finished! As He bowed His head and gave up His Spirit, "*...the curtain in the sanctuary of the Temple was torn in two, from top to bottom. The earth shook, rocks split apart, and tombs opened*" (Matthew 27:51-52). The earth quaked and the Roman officer, overseeing the crucifixion, declared, "*This Man truly was the Son of God!*" (Matthew 27:54).

Yes, it was finished! Our redemption was made complete. Jesus had met the righteous demands of the holy law. He had paid our sin debt in full. Jesus had completed the work that the Father had given Him to do (John 17:4).

But His work did not stop there. Through His death, "*He entered once for all into the holy places, not by means of the blood of goats and calves but by means of His own blood, thus securing an eternal redemption*" (Hebrews 9:12 ESV). Through His death, He seized the keys of death and the grave (Revelation 1:18). Through His death, He set free the captives of death and the grave (Luke 4:18). Through His death, He set the standard for how we as His followers should live sacrificially (John 15:13). Through His death, He set the stage for the greatest miracle that was to follow (Mark 16:6).

From the day of His incarnational birth to the day of His death on the cross, Jesus was on a mission given to Him by the Father. Even at a young age, He knew that He must be about His Father's business (Luke 2:49). In His last days leading up to the cross, Jesus resolutely set out for Jerusalem (Luke 9:51). Without His death on the cross, there is no mission. Without His shed blood, there is no redemptive work. It is only through His death on the cross that the mission is able to continue. And continue it does. Christ's pain and suffering, and death on the cross is finished, but the mission continues. That's why He has called us to take up the cross and follow Him in being about the Father's mission. It is finished! But the work continues....

* * *

54

LAID IN A TOMB

Now there was a good and righteous man named Joseph. He was a member of the Jewish high council, but he had not agreed with the decision and actions of the other religious leaders. He was from the town of Arimathea in Judea, and he was waiting for the Kingdom of God to come. He went to Pilate and asked for Jesus' body. Then he took the body down from the cross and wrapped it in a long sheet of linen cloth and laid it in a new tomb that had been carved out of rock. This was done late on Friday afternoon, the day of preparation, as the Sabbath was about to begin. As His body was taken away, the women from Galilee followed and saw the tomb where His body was placed. Then they went home and prepared spices and ointments to anoint His body. But by the time they were finished the Sabbath had begun, so they rested as required by the law.

Luke 23:50-56

* * *

Customarily it would have been the responsibility of Jesus' family and friends to arrange for His burial. But remember that this had all unfolded in less than twenty-four hours. No one ever expected Jesus to die that day, so no burial arrangements had been made. Most of His family and close followers had scattered out of fear, and those who remained were just barely coping with what was taking place. They had all traveled to Jerusalem from Galilee and they had very little in the way of money. So, they had nothing at their disposal with which to bury Jesus' body. Luke records that the few family and friends who were there were standing at a distance watching after Jesus died (Luke 23:49). They were experiencing overwhelming grief. Burial may have not yet even crossed their minds. Even if it did, they had no resources. And Sabbath was rapidly approaching. The bodies of the victims of crucifixion were usually left to be eaten by birds or wild animals, or thrown like worthless garbage into the dump and burned. But that would not be the case for the Son of God – His Father had a plan.

Not all of the religious leaders had sought the crucifixion of Jesus. There were at least two voices of reason present when the high council deliberated. Though their voices did not carry the day, they appear to have spoken out (John 7:50-51). One was Nicodemus, from Galilee, and the other was Joseph, from the town of Arimathea in the province of Judea.

Joseph's decision to go to Pilate and request the body of Jesus would not have been popular with Caiaphas, Annas and most of the members of the high council. Though he had apparently argued against their plan to arrest Jesus and have Him sentenced to death, those words of rebellion against the authority of the high council leadership were at least restricted to behind closed doors. But now, this action to go to Pilate was an outward expression of his dissention and would have been considered to be an outright act of betrayal of his Sanhedrin brothers. This action would have been political suicide for Joseph, jeopardizing his position on the Sanhedrin, his influence in the community, and his personal wealth. It would have taken great courage and strength of character for him to go to Pilate to arrange for a suitable burial for the body of Jesus.

The apostle John writes that Nicodemus also assisted in the burial. He brought embalming ointment to assist Joseph in the preparation of Jesus' body for burial (John 19:39-40). But even his action was not done as publicly as that of Joseph. Joseph apparently paid for the linen cloth and provided the newly hewn tomb. The two men needed to act quickly so that Jesus' body could be laid in the tomb before the beginning of Sabbath at dusk. They were resolved to act in a way contrary to the actions of the high council, but they would not violate the laws of Sabbath. You and i would do well to follow the example of these two men. They stepped out boldly and followed Him to His death. We don't follow Him to His death. We serve a risen Savior. Are we as prepared to follow Him no matter the cost?

But let's back up a moment to where Jesus declared, *"It is finished!"* At that moment, Luke records that He also said, *"Father, I entrust My spirit into*

Your hands" (Luke 23:46). Remember, Jesus was as much man as if He was not God at all. That means that at that moment of Jesus' death, His soul and spirit departed from His body – which is the exact same thing that will occur to you and me at the moment of our deaths, if Jesus does not return before then. Joseph and Nicodemus did not lay Jesus in the tomb. He had already departed. They were just laying His dead body in the tomb. Peter tells us that Jesus was very busy while His body was laying in that tomb. In 1 Peter 3:19, we read that Jesus' spirit entered into Hades and proclaimed His victory over Satan and his hosts to the evil spirits that Jesus' half-brother Jude describes in Jude 1:6. And Paul writes in Ephesians 4:8, in fulfillment of the prophecy in Psalm 68:18 – *"You ascended on high, leading a host of captives in Your train…"* (ESV) – that Jesus gathered all the redeemed who had been awaiting His redemption and took them from paradise to their permanent dwelling in heaven. That train into heaven would have included Abraham, David, Joshua, Daniel, the beggar Lazarus, and all those who had been previously justified by faith. Folks, those were some great, "gettin' up" days in the spirit world for those for whom faith had now become sight (2 Corinthians 5:7).

Meanwhile, on the earth, no one, even those closest to Jesus, could fully grasp all that had happened, let alone what was taking place at that moment, or what was about to take place. In the spiritual realm, there was great rejoicing among the saints and great sorrow among the demons. Whereas on earth, there was great rejoicing among the enemies of Jesus, and great sorrow among His family and followers. Though He had foretold that He would rise again, not one of His family or followers seemed to be watching by faith with hopeful anticipation. Interestingly enough, the only ones who seemingly remembered His promise were the religious leaders who petitioned Pilate to post guards at the tomb. And they didn't believe He would rise from the dead, but they were fearful that His followers would remove His body and make that claim (Matthew 27:62-66).

How often do we get caught up in our grief and pain, and lose sight of our Lord's promises? How often do we get so focused on all of the swirling activity around us, and lose sight that the One who has promised is able – and faithful – to accomplish all that He promised He would? How often do we lose sight that even death and the grave can't defeat Him? You might be walking through a period of time right now in your journey that feels just like it did for Mary, for John, for Mary Magdalene, for Peter. All you see and all you feel is pain. The grief and despair are overwhelming. It feels like Jesus is laying in the tomb and there is no hope. Don't believe that lie! Don't even try and figure it all out. You can't! But i'm here to tell you – Jesus isn't laying in that tomb. He is at work on your behalf! And in His time, you will rise out of that circumstance and pain. Trust Him – He who promised is able – and faithful – "*...to do far more abundantly beyond all that we ask or think, according to the power that works within us*" (Ephesians 3:20 NASB).

It's not over!

* * *

55

THEY CAME TO ANOINT HIM

Saturday evening, when the Sabbath ended, Mary Magdalene, Mary the mother of James, and Salome went out and purchased burial spices so they could anoint Jesus' body. Very early on Sunday morning, just at sunrise, they went to the tomb. On the way they were asking each other, "Who will roll away the stone for us from the entrance to the tomb?" But as they arrived, they looked up and saw that the stone, which was very large, had already been rolled aside. When they entered the tomb, they saw a young man clothed in a white robe sitting on the right side. The women were shocked, but the angel said, "Don't be alarmed. You are looking for Jesus of Nazareth, who was crucified. He isn't here! He is risen from the dead! Look, this is where they laid His body. Now go and tell His disciples, including Peter, that Jesus is going ahead of you to Galilee. You will see Him there, just as He told you before He died." The women fled from the tomb, trembling and bewildered, and they said nothing to anyone because they were too frightened.

Mark 16:1-8

* * *

Throughout His earthly ministry, there were a number of women who traveled with Jesus and His disciples. Some were members of His extended family or those of His disciples, such as Salome (the mother of James and John, and the wife of Zebedee) and Mary (the mother of James the Less, and the wife of Clopas). Some of the women had been healed by Jesus, or were those from whom He had cast out evil spirits, including Mary Magdalene (Luke 8:2) and Joanna (the wife of Chuza, the household manager of Herod Antipas – Luke 8:3). These, and many others, *"were contributing from their own resources to support Jesus and His disciples"* (Luke 8:3). Mark lists Mary Magdalene, Mary (the mother of James) and Salome as coming to the tomb that morning. Luke indicates that Joanna was also there. (As a footnote: Luke is the only Gospel writer that includes Joanna, not only at the tomb, but also at other parts of his account. He is also the only Gospel writer that includes details of what occurred in the court when Jesus was brought before Herod Antipas. Given the role of Joanna's husband, she was probably one of Luke's eyewitnesses.) Luke also says that there were other women, so there was at least one other unnamed woman in the group (Luke 24:10).

These women were unable to make the needed preparations for the burial of Jesus' body before sunset on Friday. They just didn't have enough time between the time He died and the time that sunset occurred. Joseph of Arimathea and Nicodemus had been able to make quick arrangements but, before the women realized what was happening, the sun was setting, and Sabbath was beginning. But i hope you see the sovereign hand of God in their delay. The Father's plan was perfect. He had ordained for Joseph and Nicodemus to bury His Son's body, but He had a different assignment for the women. He didn't need for them to be at the tomb when Jesus' body was placed. They were to arrive at the tomb for a totally different purpose!

They apparently were able to prepare some of the spices and ointments on Friday, just before the Sabbath (Luke 23:56). They were then able to purchase those that they still needed and make their final arrangements after dark on Saturday night. But they would need sunlight to do what they needed to do, so they waited until Sunday at sunrise. As the women were walking to the tomb, they realized that the stone would be too heavy for them to roll away in order to gain entry. Remember, this plan was unfolding quickly. They hadn't been able to think through all of the details. Fortunately, the Father had been planning the details for eternity, and He had not forgotten anything!

At this point, let's synchronize the chronology of this account with those in Matthew 28, Luke 24 and John 20. As the women approached the tomb, they saw that the large stone had been rolled away from the entrance. Apparently, Mary Magdalene left the other women to go and alert Peter and John. Meanwhile, the other women entered the tomb and encountered the angels who declared to them that Jesus had risen from the dead. i am not sure what the Greek word is – but apparently the women "freaked out!" They fled from the tomb, trembling and bewildered. Remember, Jesus had tried to prepare them. He had told them He would rise again. But even these, His closest followers, couldn't quite believe it. They had all been there when Jesus called Lazarus to come out of the tomb, but they weren't expecting Jesus to call Himself out of the tomb. Let's be honest – would you have expected it?

Now remember, the night of Jesus' arrest, the disciples had all scattered – except John and Peter. John and Peter had stayed in Jerusalem – they had gone to Caiaphas' home. The rest of the group took off – and probably went to Bethany (where they had been spending the night earlier in the week). Mary Magdalene apparently headed into the city to find Peter and John. The other women apparently headed toward Bethany, where they had probably been staying as well. Mary Magdalene found Peter and John and told them that the stone had been rolled away from the tomb. She was certain that the religious leaders had taken Jesus' body. So, all three of them headed back to the tomb.

We'll pick up on this narrative in the next chapter but, before we do, let's remember what has taken place. Jesus has completed the work that He had to do while His soul and spirit were absent from His physical body. He has completed the work of redemption and He has set the captives free! Jesus had told the Pharisees that He would give them the sign of the prophet Jonah (Matthew 16:4) – He would arise on the third day. He had also told them that if they destroyed "this temple" – His body – He would, in three days, raise it up (John 2:19). He had completed the work that the Father had for Him to do within the timeframe that the Father had set for it to be accomplished. And the Father's timing is perfect!

What has the Father promised you that He will accomplish in and through your life? What has He revealed as a promise from His Word that you are holding by faith, but have not yet experienced by sight? Allow the experience of these women to be a reminder that what He promises, He will accomplish. And He will accomplish it in His timeframe! He won't be late – but He also won't be early. His timing is perfect. And it will probably occur when we are focusing elsewhere on a task that is before us. The women came to anoint the body of Jesus, never expecting that He had risen. Most often His answer will come at a time and in a way that we least expect it. (Incidentally, so will His return. That's why He has told us to stay alert! – 1 Thessalonians 5:6)

. . .

Hold this truth in the light of His resurrection – what He begins, He completes (Philippians 1:6), and what He promises, He fulfills. As Moses said, "*God is not a man, so He does not lie. He is not human, so He does not change His mind. Has He ever spoken and failed to act? Has He ever promised and not carried it through?*" (Numbers 23:19). No, He hasn't! And the empty tomb is proof! Trust Him!

* * *

56

NOW IT'S FINISHED!

Early on Sunday morning, while it was still dark, Mary Magdalene came to the tomb and found that the stone had been rolled away from the entrance. She ran and found Simon Peter and the other disciple, the one whom Jesus loved. She said, "They have taken the Lord's body out of the tomb, and we don't know where they have put Him!" Peter and the other disciple started out for the tomb. They were both running, but the other disciple outran Peter and reached the tomb first. He stooped and looked in and saw the linen wrappings lying there, but he didn't go in. Then Simon Peter arrived and went inside. He also noticed the linen wrappings lying there, while the cloth that had covered Jesus' head was folded up and lying apart from the other wrappings. Then the disciple who had reached the tomb first also went in, and he saw and believed— for until then they still hadn't understood the Scriptures that said Jesus must rise from the dead. Then they went home.

John 20:1-10

* * *

Mary Magdalene was the one from whom Jesus cast out seven demons (Luke 8:2). Some scholars also believe that she was the woman who knelt at the feet of Jesus and anointed His feet with perfume and her tears, wiping them off with her hair (Luke 7:38). She was someone that we all need to aspire to be – someone who was saved by Jesus, and never got over it! She was eternally grateful to her Lord for His salvation.

John is the "other disciple", "the one whom Jesus loved". Throughout his

Gospel account, he always refers to himself in that manner, but any of His disciples could have used that title for themselves. As a matter of fact, each of us should think of ourselves in that way. John wrote, *"We love Him, because He first loved us"* (1 John 4:19 KJV). Each of us is one whom Jesus loves.

John is also a *"friend who sticks closer than a brother"* (Proverbs 18:24). John "stuck" with Peter when Peter desperately needed a friend. Peter ached because of his denial of Jesus. His remorse was overwhelming. But gratefully, he didn't stop with remorse like Judas had. He was repentant for his sin. And he truly sought forgiveness. It would have been easy for John to "write Peter off" in light of his denial of Christ. Too often Christians are known for doing just that – writing off those who have fallen. But John chose to love Peter. He had heeded Jesus' words in the upper room to *"love each other"* (John 13:34). And the Lord used John in His healing work to cleanse and repair Peter's heart.

It is ironic that the religious leaders were concerned about the disciples stealing Jesus' body, and that Mary's first thought was that the religious leaders had taken His body. That thought just added to her grief. So, she let John and Peter run on ahead back to the tomb. She wasn't in any hurry to see an empty tomb. Her thoughts were now even more consumed by her grief.

Peter and John weren't truly expecting the resurrection of Jesus any more than Mary Magdalene was. They probably thought that she had made a mistake in what she saw. Perhaps, she had gone to the wrong tomb. They weren't running to the tomb expecting to find Jesus alive. They were expecting to uncover Mary's error and find His body.

John apparently was the faster runner. He got to the tomb before Peter did (remember Peter was also the older of the two). But John stopped at the doorway looking in. Uninhibited Peter charged past John right into the tomb. There they both saw the linen wrappings neatly rolled up. It was at that moment that John writes, *"he saw and believed"* (John 20:8). John couldn't yet prove that Jesus was risen, but He believed it with all his heart. He believed that Jesus had risen according to the Scriptures, and he believed once and for all that Jesus truly was God in the flesh. The two of them then departed to return to where they had been staying. This time they didn't run. They walked, pondering all that they had just seen.

• • •

About that time, Mary Magdalene arrived back at the tomb. She remained outside weeping. Then *"as she wept, she stooped and looked into the tomb"* for the first time. She saw two angels who asked her why she was weeping. *"They* (the religious leaders) *have taken away my Lord, and I do not know where they have laid Him."* She then turned and saw Jesus standing there. But due to her grief, she did not recognize Him. Thinking He was the gardener she again sought an answer from Him as to where His body was laid. At that moment, Jesus spoke her name and she knew! Having seen Jesus, she believed! And off she went to deliver the good news and His instructions to Peter and John (John 20:11-18).

In the meantime, Jesus appeared to the other women (Mary - the wife of Clopas, Salome, Joanna, and at least one other) who had been at the tomb earlier as they were running to find the other disciples (Matthew 28:8-9). Imagine their reaction. They had not expected to encounter the living Lord Jesus; they had expected to anoint His body. If they were terrified when they saw the angels, can you just imagine how they felt when they saw Jesus? And Jesus said to them, *"Don't be afraid!"* (Matthew 28:10).

The eyes of the "one whom Jesus loved" were opened to the reality of who Jesus was by faith. The woman who had never gotten over what Jesus had done for her, as well as the other women who had been at the tomb, encountered the truth of who Jesus was by sight. Peter and the others continued to contemplate all of these things based upon what these witnesses were telling them. But the day wasn't over! Faith would become sight for many more.

In some respects, as followers of Jesus who are taking up the cross and following Him, we are in the same place as these men and women. We have heard the reports of the witnesses. He has given us His Word. His work on the cross is finished and the tomb is empty! If the work had stopped at the cross, we, as His followers, would be the most pitiable – and the most sorrowful. Because we would be following a dead savior. And a dead savior isn't really a savior at all. He would have set us up to fail. He would have set a standard that we by no means could reach, and He would have failed to make a way whereby we can be saved. As we go through the pain, suffering and death of this life, we would be doing so without hope. But the tomb IS empty. Jesus arose from the dead! Today, we accept that fact and receive that assurance according to the reports of the many witnesses and the authority of Scripture. Like John, our eyes have been opened to that reality by faith. And "the day" isn't over – soon that faith will become sight! We have that hope because we follow a Living Savior who rose from the grave. Salvation in Him is complete. It truly has been finished!

* * *

57

THEIR EYES WERE OPENED

That same day, two of Jesus' followers were walking to the village of Emmaus, seven miles from Jerusalem. As they walked along, they were talking about everything that had happened. As they talked and discussed these things, Jesus Himself suddenly came and began walking with them. But God kept them from recognizing Him. He asked them, "What are you discussing so intently as you walk along?" They stopped short, sadness written across their faces. Then one of them, Clopas, replied, "You must be the only person in Jerusalem who hasn't heard about all the things that have happened there the last few days." "What things?" Jesus asked. "The things that happened to Jesus, the Man from Nazareth," they said. "He was a prophet who did powerful miracles, and He was a mighty teacher in the eyes of God and all the people. But our leading priests and other religious leaders handed Him over to be condemned to death, and they crucified Him. We had hoped He was the Messiah who had come to rescue Israel. This all happened three days ago. "Then some women from our group of His followers were at His tomb early this morning, and they came back with an amazing report. They said His body was missing, and they had seen angels who told them Jesus is alive! Some of our men ran out to see, and sure enough, His body was gone, just as the women had said." ...Then Jesus took them through the writings of Moses and all the prophets, explaining from all the Scriptures the things concerning Himself. ...As they sat down to eat, He took the bread and blessed it. Then He broke it and gave it to them. Suddenly, their eyes were opened, and they recognized Him. And at that moment He disappeared! They said to each other, "Didn't our hearts burn within us as He talked with us on the road and explained the Scriptures to us?" And within the hour they were on their way back to Jerusalem. There they found the eleven disciples and the others who had gathered with them, who said, "The Lord has really risen! He appeared to Peter."

Luke 24:13-35

* * *

Emmaus was a small village seven miles northwest of Jerusalem. Clopas and his companion were downhearted as they made the journey from Jerusalem to Emmaus. Before they left Jerusalem, Clopas' wife (Mary) had told them that, when she and some of the other women had gone to the tomb to anoint Jesus' body that morning, the tomb was empty. (This encounter between Clopas and his wife had apparently taken place before his wife and the other women had personally encountered Jesus along the way.) They had given an amazing report that they had seen angels who said that Jesus was alive. But the women had been somewhat hysterical, so it was difficult to discern what they really had seen or heard. The two men had learned that Peter and John had also been to the tomb, and that, in fact, Jesus' body was gone. But the question still remained – where was the body of Jesus?

Clopas and his traveling companion had both been followers of Jesus. As a matter of fact, Clopas' son (James the Less) was one of Jesus' disciples. After Clopas and his wife (Mary) had spoken, she had headed off with the other women to tell their son and the other disciples what they had seen and heard. But Clopas and his fellow traveler didn't know what to make of it all. They believed Jesus to be a prophet of God who did powerful miracles. And, without question, He was the mightiest teacher they had ever heard. They had believed that He was the Messiah who had come to rescue Israel. But then the leading priests and other religious leaders had handed Him over to be condemned to death, and He had been crucified. Now all their hopes that He was the Messiah had been dashed. His death made no sense. They had faithfully followed Him for three years. What were they to do now? Had they been wrong?

As they walked along, discussing these things, Jesus joined them – though they did not recognize Him. He was a stranger to them. Bear in mind, they weren't looking for Him either. They thought He was dead and gone. They were blinded to who He was by their grief and their doubts. As they continued together, this Stranger graciously began to explain the prophecies regarding the Messiah to them, one by one, with great clarity. When they arrived in Emmaus, they prevailed upon the Stranger to join them for a meal. And as Jesus took the bread and broke it – just as He had many times before as they ate together – their eyes were opened – and they saw Him! Luke writes that *"at that moment He disappeared!"* Within the hour they were on their way back to Jerusalem to tell the others what they had seen and heard.

At some other time that day, after Jesus appeared to Mary Magdalene outside the tomb, He also appeared to Peter. It occurred sometime after Peter and John had visited the empty tomb. And it occurred when he and John were apart from one another. John had believed by faith that Jesus had risen when he saw the empty tomb. Peter hadn't known what to believe. And his belief had been further clouded by his remorse over his denial of Jesus.

It is noteworthy that we do not know any of the details surrounding Jesus' appearance to Peter. We only know that it occurred. Luke and Paul bear witness to their face-to-face meeting (Luke 24:34 and 1 Corinthians 15:5), but the content of their encounter was kept private. There was something that needed to be reconciled between the two of them. It apparently was a two-part conversation. John shares the second part in John 21:15-17. It was a chiding and a word of correction, and we will look at that portion in chapter 60 of this book. But the first part of that conversation was a personal and private transaction of healing that took place between Peter and His Lord. Jesus knew that before correction could take place, healing needed to occur. And that healing needed to occur before Jesus and Peter were together with the other disciples. He knows that in our lives as well. He knows when He needs to rebuke us. He knows when He needs to correct us. And He also knows when He needs to heal us. He knows the "what", the "how" and the "when". And He will take the same care with us that He took with Peter. It's called grace. It's called mercy. It's called love. And we would do well to show that grace, mercy and love to one another.

Jesus knew what Clopas and his companion needed. They needed to have their eyes opened. And He knew what Peter needed. He needed to be forgiven and have his heart healed. And our risen Savior knows of what we have need. May God give us the eyes, the ears and the hearts to receive it.

* * *

58

PEACE BE WITH YOU

That Sunday evening the disciples were meeting behind locked doors because they were afraid of the Jewish leaders. Suddenly, Jesus was standing there among them! "Peace be with you," He said. As He spoke, He showed them the wounds in His hands and His side. They were filled with joy when they saw the Lord! Again, He said, "Peace be with you. As the Father has sent Me, so I am sending you." Then He breathed on them and said, "Receive the Holy Spirit. If you forgive anyone's sins, they are forgiven. If you do not forgive them, they are not forgiven." One of the twelve disciples, Thomas (nicknamed the Twin), was not with the others when Jesus came. They told him, "We have seen the Lord!" But he replied, "I won't believe it unless I see the nail wounds in His hands, put my fingers into them, and place my hand into the wound in His side." Eight days later the disciples were together again, and this time Thomas was with them. The doors were locked; but suddenly, as before, Jesus was standing among them. "Peace be with you," He said. Then He said to Thomas, "Put your finger here, and look at My hands. Put your hand into the wound in My side. Don't be faithless any longer. Believe!" "My Lord and my God!" Thomas exclaimed. Then Jesus told him, "You believe because you have seen Me. Blessed are those who believe without seeing Me."

John 20:19-29

* * *

This is the first time that all of Jesus' disciples are back together since the night of His arrest, with the exception of Judas Iscariot (the betrayer, who is no longer counted among their group, and has himself already committed suicide) and Thomas (the doubter, whose absence from this gathering is a curiosity). They had secretly gathered, and the door to the room was locked. The room was abuzz with the reports. Mary Magdalene had told the group about how Jesus had spoken to her as she stood outside the tomb. John shared how he and Peter had witnessed the empty tomb, and his belief that Jesus truly was the Son of the Living God. Mary, Joanna and Salome relayed their encounter with the angels in the tomb, and then how Jesus had appeared to them on their way to report to the disciples. Then Peter told them that Jesus was alive and had appeared to him earlier in the day. Finally, Clopas and his companion had just returned from Emmaus and were telling *"their story of how Jesus had appeared to them as they were walking along the road"* (Luke 24:35). Luke records that right as they were telling about their encounter with Jesus, He suddenly appeared in the room (Luke 24:36).

The disciples' heads were spinning. They kept hearing these reports from brothers and sisters that they respected, but this was all still hard to believe. How could this possibly be true? Jesus had been subjected to unspeakable brutality and had died on the cross. They had witnessed it, albeit from a distance after they scattered. Could this be a part of the religious leaders' plot to not only murder Jesus, but to defame His teachings and His miracles? Was this all a part of the plan to now draw out His close followers and arrest them as well? At that moment, there was still more fear than faith present in that room.

Then all of a sudden – Jesus appeared – out of nowhere! And the door was locked! i would venture to say that these guys were ready to jump out of their skins! And if we had been there, we would have been ready to do the same. They thought they were seeing a ghost (Luke 24:37). So, it is no wonder that the first words out of Jesus' mouth were *"Peace be with you!"* Be at peace, the One – the only One – who can make sense of it all is now in the room! Jesus calmed their fears and gave them assurance. He ate a piece of broiled fish to assure them that He wasn't a ghost (Luke 24:42-43). He showed them the wounds in His hands, His feet and His side to prove to them that He who was dead was now alive. The work that the Father had given Him to do was now complete. Gradually the disciples' fear and anxiety turned to peace and joy! Allow me to conjecture that, at some point, Jesus' and Peter's eyes knowingly locked for a moment as they saw the rest of the disciples gradually and finally coming to that place of peace. Peter had experienced that same emotional roller coaster earlier that day – and i am certain that his was to an even greater degree.

• • •

Then for a second time, Jesus said to them, *"Peace be with you"*. But this time it wasn't a word of peace for them, it was a word of peace that they were now to go forth and share with a world that desperately needed peace. As the Father had sent Him, He was now sending them (and us)!

Again, we aren't given any explanation as to why Thomas was not in the room that night. John is the only Gospel writer who gives us that report. Surely, Thomas didn't have a more pressing appointment. But later when he did join the other disciples, he refused to accept their testimony. He held to the conviction that since he wasn't there to see it, it must not be true. Thus, he became "Doubting Thomas" – to this day defined as "a skeptic who refuses to believe without direct personal experience." His skepticism and faithlessness robbed him of joy for eight long days before Jesus again appeared in their midst and stood among them, this time including Thomas. Jesus again declared, *"Peace be with you"*, but this time He added a rebuke to Thomas with a truth that we too would do well to embrace – don't believe simply because you see; believe because of Who I am and what I have said" (paraphrase John 20:29).

It would do us well to repeat and rehearse the truths that the disciples learned and experienced on those two occasions:

1. No matter our situation or circumstance, we will always find peace in the presence of our Savior. As the apostle Paul wrote to the church, *"Don't worry about anything; instead, pray about everything. Tell God what you need and thank Him for all He has done. Then you will experience God's peace, which exceeds anything we can understand. His peace will guard your hearts and minds as you live in Christ Jesus"* (Philippians 4:6-7).

2. We have not heard the full truth about any situation until we have heard from Jesus. As you cast your doubts and fear on Him, trust Him for the answers that you need to know – not necessarily all the answers you want to have, but all the answers you need to know. Some of those answers will not come until we are in His presence. But in the meantime, He has promised that *"You are truly My disciples if you remain faithful to My teachings. And you will know the truth, and the truth will set you free"* (John 8:31-32).

3. The peace He gives us – His gospel – is not just for us. He has entrusted

it to us to share it with others. As Jesus said that night, *"As the Father has sent Me, so I am sending you."*

4. Don't believe simply because you see; believe because of Who Jesus is and what He has said.

Peace be with you! *"…Because you belong to Christ Jesus, God will bless you with peace that no one can completely understand. And this peace will control the way you think and feel"* (Philippians 4:7 CEV).

* * *

59

CAST THE NET

Later, Jesus appeared again to the disciples beside the Sea of Galilee. This is how it happened. Several of the disciples were there — Simon Peter, Thomas (nicknamed the Twin), Nathanael from Cana in Galilee, the sons of Zebedee, and two other disciples. Simon Peter said, "I'm going fishing." "We'll come, too," they all said. So, they went out in the boat, but they caught nothing all night. At dawn Jesus was standing on the beach, but the disciples couldn't see who He was. He called out, "Fellows, have you caught any fish?" "No," they replied. Then He said, "Throw out your net on the right-hand side of the boat, and you'll get some!" So, they did, and they couldn't haul in the net because there were so many fish in it. Then the disciple Jesus loved said to Peter, "It's the Lord!" When Simon Peter heard that it was the Lord, he put on his tunic (for he had stripped for work), jumped into the water, and headed to shore. The others stayed with the boat and pulled the loaded net to the shore, for they were only about a hundred yards from shore. When they got there, they found breakfast waiting for them—fish cooking over a charcoal fire, and some bread. "Bring some of the fish you've just caught," Jesus said. So, Simon Peter went aboard and dragged the net to the shore. There were 153 large fish, and yet the net hadn't torn. "Now come and have some breakfast!" Jesus said. None of the disciples dared to ask Him, "Who are You?" They knew it was the Lord. Then Jesus served them the bread and the fish. This was the third time Jesus had appeared to His disciples since He had been raised from the dead.

John 21:1-14

* * *

As we begin this chapter, let's be mindful that this account comes from the Gospel of John. John is the only Gospel writer who includes the incidents described in this twenty-first chapter of His account. John basically concludes His Gospel account at the end of John chapter 20 (John 20:30-31), but then he adds chapter 21 as an epilogue. We would do well to ask "why?" Let's also remember that John's Gospel account is a first-hand account, unlike the other three Gospels. Matthew witnessed much of what He wrote, but His Gospel includes many details that he heard about from others, including Jesus' birth, childhood and more. Mark and Luke both wrote their Gospels exclusively using details provided by others. But John was an eyewitness to most every detail included in his Gospel beginning with John 1:15. From that point forward, very little is second hand. The first fourteen verses of the Gospel of John are his introduction, comprising his summary of the most important truth that he wants his readers to glean from his account – that being that Jesus Christ is the Son of God – a conclusion that he personally did not fully come to until he stepped into the empty tomb (John 20:8). He states it right up front in his Gospel because he wants his readers to hear every detail in that light. And just look at all of the details in John 21:1-14. So, let's look at why John included his epilogue.

During the forty days between His resurrection and His ascension, Jesus appeared and disappeared at will. This is the third time He has appeared to His disciples. Though He had a physical body, it was a resurrected body. He was able to come and go as He pleased – at one moment He was there with His disciples, at another He was with His Father in heaven. Jesus was preparing His disciples for the time that He would no longer be with them continually in bodily form. He was preparing them for the coming of the Spirit and their future ministry assignments. The disciples never knew when He would appear, so they had to remain alert. (Incidentally, we would do well to heed that lesson ourselves!)

After His resurrection, Jesus instructed the disciples to meet Him in Galilee (Matthew 28:7 and Mark 16:7), which is why they were gathered there that day. They apparently had been waiting for a while. Peter, not being one to sit around and wait, decided that he wasn't going to miss a good opportunity to go fishing. He enlisted the other fishermen in the group to join him – Thomas, Nathanael, the brothers James and John, and two others (probably Andrew and Philip). These were the seven who had been fishermen when Jesus first called them to follow Him – and it was "still in their blood". Apparently, Matthew, Simon the Zealot, James the

Less and Thaddeus were the landlubbers and went off to do something else that night – perhaps sleep (it was nighttime). Hopefully, they showed up on the shore at dawn and didn't miss the very special breakfast! (One other side road: note that Thomas was in the boat with the others. i am convinced that he had determined to never again be the one absent from the group when Jesus showed up!)

The events on the boat that night should sound very familiar. Over two years earlier, Peter, Andrew, James and John had been fishing all night and they hadn't caught anything (Luke 5:1-11). Jesus instructed them to go out where it was deeper and cast their nets one more time. You will recall that their nets were so full they began to tear. It was then that Jesus had told them to follow Him. They had followed, and not looked back. And oh, what a two-plus-years journey it had been!

Well this morning, they also had been fishing all night without success. It was now dawn and they were probably getting ready to return to shore. Jesus was standing on the shore. The sun was just coming up, and they were a distance out in the sea, so they couldn't see that it was Jesus. He told them to throw out their net on the right-hand side and they would "get some". Remember, they didn't know it was Jesus – but something told them they needed to cast the net one more time. And just like that time two-plus years earlier, there were so many fish they couldn't haul in the net. As a matter of fact, John includes the detail that they caught 153 large fish. And this time, the net hadn't torn. That familiar memory is all it took to prompt John to say, *"It's the Lord!"* He knew His Lord's ways – and though he couldn't recognize His form and he hadn't recognized His voice, he knew it was Him! And this time, Jesus didn't need to tell Peter to come – hearing from John that it was their Lord, he jumped in the water and headed for Jesus.

This is the last miracle that Jesus performed as a part of His earthly ministry before He ascended to the Father – nets full of fish. It's reminiscent of His first miracle that day in Cana – water pots full of wine. Jesus never did anything halfway. He still doesn't! When Jesus shows up there is abundance – perhaps not always in fish or wine, but in abundant life, abundant joy and abundant mercy. Jesus was preparing to send out His disciples as His ambassadors to be about His mission in the spreading of His gospel and the making of His disciples who would in turn make other disciples. Two-plus years ago, He had called them to follow Him bodily, now He was preparing to tell them to continue to follow Him – though not bodily, but by His Spirit. Jesus' call to us has not been to follow Him bodily; but His call to us has been the same as that morning beside the sea – to follow Him by His Spirit. And one day, when He returns, we'll follow Him in His resurrected body with our resurrected bodies. And oh, by the way – i don't want to miss that "breakfast" – and neither do you!

One other note, along those lines – notice that Jesus already had breakfast prepared, but it wasn't complete until they added some of their catch. There was fruit of their labor by faith that had yet to be added before breakfast was ready. There is fruit of the labor that He has called us to that, by faith, has yet to be added to the "pot" before He returns and calls us to sit down with Him for the marriage supper of the Lamb (Revelation 19:6-9). He's already preparing it, but He is at work in and through our lives to produce fruit that is yet to be added. Cast the net on the right-hand side. There are still fish to be drawn in! There are still many yet to hear!

* * *

60

FEED MY SHEEP

After breakfast Jesus asked Simon Peter, "Simon, son of John, do you love Me more than these?" "Yes, Lord," Peter replied, "you know I love You." "Then feed My lambs," Jesus told him. Jesus repeated the question: "Simon, son of John, do you love Me?" "Yes, Lord," Peter said, "you know I love You." "Then take care of My sheep," Jesus said. A third time He asked him, "Simon, son of John, do you love Me?" Peter was hurt that Jesus asked the question a third time. He said, "Lord, You know everything. You know that I love You." Jesus said, "Then feed My sheep."
John 21:15-17

* * *

In the last chapter, we looked at one of the reasons as to why John had included this epilogue in his Gospel account. The second reason was that there was an unfinished piece of business that we, as readers, needed to know and understand.

On their first meeting, John tells us that Jesus had renamed Simon, the son of John. He was henceforth to be called "Peter", the rock (John 1:42). Jesus had later said that "... *upon this rock I will build My church, and all the powers of hell will not conquer it*" (Matthew 16:18). Jesus was preparing to build His church and He was giving these disciples – and others who they would disciple – the assignment to disciple and lead this new church. Principal among those to whom He was giving that assignment was Simon Peter, the rock… but also, the one who had denied Him. As we already looked at in chapter 57, on the day of His resurrection, Jesus appeared to Peter. It was a personal and a private time of healing and forgiveness for Peter. Peter had sinned against His Lord, and that sin had created a separation between him and Jesus. But gratefully, Jesus' shed blood on the cross covered that sin – as well as so much more. So there needed to be that moment when Peter confessed his sin, sought forgiveness and received it from Jesus. i am certain that Jesus took Peter in His arms as Peter confessed his sin and wept in the embrace of His Lord and His Savior. Jesus already knew his sin. Peter's confession was not for Jesus' sake, it was for Peter's sake. At that moment, Peter was forgiven, and his relationship was reconciled with Jesus. He no longer needed to walk in grief and shame. He had been forgiven. And He had been set free. Jesus was not only faithful to come to Peter like that, He has faithfully come to each and every one of us, on more than one occasion, when we have sinned against Him and sought His forgiveness. Peter knew, as well as anyone, that, *"If we claim we have no sin, we are only fooling ourselves and not living in the truth. But if we confess our sins to Him, He is faithful and just to forgive us our sins and to cleanse us from all wickedness"* (1 John 1:8-9). That confession and the seeking of Christ's forgiveness is a deeply personal matter between us and our Lord. It's not for show. It's not for the crowd. It's between us and Jesus, just like it was between Peter and Jesus. Because Peter had been forgiven, he could boldly declare to the disciples that night in the locked room before Jesus appeared that Jesus was alive! Peter could wholeheartedly, without any degree of guilt or shame, welcome Him into the room that night. He could, without any hesitation, jump into the water and make a beeline for Jesus that morning at the shore. He was forgiven. He had been set free of his sin.

But – there is a public side to our sin – just as there was to Peter's. Peter's denial of Jesus had become well known among the followers. Therefore, Peter's confession and forgiveness needed to be as equally well known. Also, Peter was in a position of leadership within the newly forming church. Thus, He had accountability as a leader. (Incidentally, that is why John had to include it in his Gospel account. It needed to be clear that Peter had confessed his sin and had been forgiven. Otherwise, the church would have been off to a very shaky start.)

One other point, before we look at that conversation between Peter and Jesus. Note that public confession, where it is needed, must follow that time of personal confession and forgiveness, not the other way around.

Public confession bears witness to authentic and sincere confession that has already taken place. It must never be "a show".

Jesus asked, "Peter, *do you love Me more than these?*" Do you love Me above all others? Do you love me in a way that causes your love for everyone else to pale in comparison? (Matthew 10:37). Peter was not expecting Jesus to ask him that question. So, his initial response was along the lines of "of course, I love you, Jesus. How could you think otherwise?" But when Jesus asked him a second time, his response was in greater earnest, wanting to leave no doubt of his love for Jesus. Then, when Jesus asked him a third time, he was greatly hurt. He may have at that point realized that Jesus was asking that question once for each of the three times Peter had denied Jesus. If he in fact made that connection, this third asking of the question hit him the hardest. Had Jesus not truly forgiven him? Peter responded, *"Lord, You know everything. You know that I love You."* Peter wanted to be clear with his answer that he loved Jesus with all of his heart, soul and mind (Matthew 22:37). Why did Jesus ask three times? Peter needed to confess his love for Jesus – and he needed to confess it, not in a perfunctory way, but rather, with his whole heart. And the disciples needed to hear Peter confess his love in that way. There was to be no doubt in anyone's mind as to Peter's love for his Lord.

Then, in response to each of Peter's answers, Jesus replied – "feed My lambs," "take care of My sheep," and "feed My sheep." Jesus was publicly restoring Peter to his apostleship and leadership. He was reminding this fisherman – and the other disciples who were surrounding them – that He was calling them to be shepherds caring for the sheep, protecting the sheep and nurturing the sheep. In fact, they were to be under-shepherds, walking in obedience to Him, under His authority and His leadership as the Good Shepherd (John 10:11), the Great Shepherd (Hebrews 13:20-21), and the Chief Shepherd (1 Peter 5:4). And as an under-shepherd, the most important thing they must do is love Jesus with their whole heart, soul and mind.

Though within the church there is a distinct role and calling as pastor to be the undershepherd of the flock, each one of us to some degree are shepherds. We have all been instructed to make disciples – to be disciples who disciple others. As a discipler we are in fact shepherding – we are caring for those who we are discipling, we are nurturing them, and we are helping to feed them. We, too, would be wise to remember that the most important thing any undershepherd must do is love our Lord with our whole heart, soul and mind.

As Jesus said, *"do you love Me?" "Then feed My sheep."*

* * *

61

OUR TIMES ARE IN HIS HANDS

"I tell you the truth, when you were young, you were able to do as you liked; you dressed yourself and went wherever you wanted to go. But when you are old, you will stretch out your hands, and others will dress you and take you where you don't want to go." Jesus said this to let him know by what kind of death he would glorify God. Then Jesus told him, "Follow Me." Peter turned around and saw behind them the disciple Jesus loved — the one who had leaned over to Jesus during supper and asked, "Lord, who will betray You?" Peter asked Jesus, "What about him, Lord?" Jesus replied, "If I want him to remain alive until I return, what is that to you? As for you, follow Me." So, the rumor spread among the community of believers that this disciple wouldn't die. But that isn't what Jesus said at all. He only said, "If I want him to remain alive until I return, what is that to you?"

John 21:18-23

* * *

Peter had just been restored by Jesus to walk in the way that the Lord was placing before him. He had confessed his undying love for his Savior. And Jesus had just explained that Peter would follow Jesus to his death – a death on the cross. At that point, Jesus said, *"Follow Me."* It wasn't the first time that Jesus had told him to follow Him – and it wouldn't be the last. Jesus would remind him – and encourage him – to follow Him every day until his journey on this earth was completed. This moment may have been the last that Jesus stood in front of Peter physically and told him to "Follow Me", but He would continue to do so through His Spirit. Peter's journey with Jesus was not ending there on the shore of the Sea of Galilee, nor would it end a few days later at the Mount of Olives (Acts 1:1-11) when Jesus ascended into heaven one last time. His journey with Jesus would continue throughout eternity – for a finite period on this side of glory – and for an infinite period on the other side of glory.

Jesus had given Peter, the other disciples and each and every one of us who are His followers an assignment that each one of us is to be about on this side of glory. The assignment was/is to *"tell people about* {Him} *everywhere – in Jerusalem, throughout Judea, in Samaria, and to the ends of the earth"* (Acts 1:8). The assignment to tell was to be accomplished with our actions, as well as with our words – and with our very lives. He said we were/are to be His witnesses, making *"disciples of all the nations, baptizing them in the name of the Father and the Son and the Holy Spirit"* (Matthew 28:19). And Jesus said that the Father had given Him all authority (Matthew 28:18), and that He would send His Holy Spirit to indwell, equip and empower each of His followers to carry out His assignment (Acts 1:8). That is the purpose for which He left Peter and His disciples to continue the work when He ascended into heaven. And that is the purpose for which He has left each of us here after we have entered into a saving relationship with Him. Our lives are not about us, our circumstances and our situations; our lives are about Him, His gospel and His glory. Too often, we become so focused on the former that we lose sight that our purpose is in the latter.

Right after Jesus told Peter how he would die, and that he was to follow Him, Peter turned around and saw John. As he did, he asked Jesus, *"What about him, Lord?"* (referring to John). That question is an example of how easily we can become distracted. Jesus rebuked Peter and reminded him that his job was to follow, not to be focused on the paths of other believers. The writer of Hebrews records that we are to keep *"our eyes on Jesus, on whom our faith depends from start to finish"* (Hebrews 12:2). To be distracted by ourselves, our circumstances or other Christians is to be disobedient to Jesus. And that disobedience will cause us to miss the perfect will of God. We are to keep our eyes of faith on Him – and on Him alone.

Throughout our walk through the Gospels, we have repeatedly seen the way that the Father ordered His Son's steps according to His perfect timing. Not one encounter was "per chance". Not one moment was wasted. Not one circumstance was unexpected by the Father. The Father had known it all from before the beginning of time. And He had ordered the steps of His Son to fulfill His perfect redemptive plan.

. . .

The Father not only ordered the steps of His Son, He has ordered the steps of His Son's followers. He ordered Peter's steps in the work He had prepared for him in the furtherance of His gospel. Peter was the first to preach the Good News on the day of Pentecost when 3,000 believed and were baptized. He was the first to proclaim the gospel to the Gentiles. He suffered persecution, imprisonment, beatings and crucifixion – all for the sake of the gospel (Acts 5:41). John fulfilled his assignment to care for Mary, the mother of Jesus, and then went on to be the leader of the church of Ephesus, was persecuted in Rome by being cast into boiling oil, and then was exiled on the island of Patmos. The paths of each of the disciples were very different. John's brother – James – was the first disciple to be martyred, and John was the last one of that original group to die.

Each of their paths was unique, just as ours are. As we walk in the steps that the Lord has set before each one of us, we will experience very different circumstances. Some will experience extreme persecution. Some will experience severe health challenges. Some will experience painful losses. Some will experience abundant blessing. Some will experience abundant loss.

Whatever the path is that He has set before us, as we take up the cross to follow Jesus, we would do well to remember the words of our Savior to Peter – *"As for you, follow Me."* Our times are in His hands. Our circumstances are in His hands. Our very lives are in His hands. And He has permitted it all. He has ordered our steps through it all. Heed the words of the prophet Isaiah – *"Forget the former things; do not dwell on the past"* – {or even the present!} *"See, I am doing a new thing! Now it springs up; do you not perceive it? I am making a way in the wilderness and streams in the wasteland"* (Isaiah 43:18-19 NIV). Our God is in control – and He who began the good work, *"will continue His work until it is finally finished on the day when Christ Jesus returns"* (Philippians 1:6).

Take up the cross that He has placed before you – and follow Him!

* * *

PLEASE HELP ME BY LEAVING A REVIEW!

i would be very grateful if you would leave a review of this book. Your feedback will be helpful to me in my future writing endeavors and will also assist others as they consider picking up a copy of the book.

To leave a review, go to:
amazon.com/dp/B07N4L76SY

Thanks for your help!

* * *

OTHER BOOKS WRITTEN BY KENNETH A. WINTER

Though the Eyes of a Shepherd

A Novel — **Shimon was a shepherd boy when he first saw the newborn King in a Bethlehem stable.** Join him in his journey as he re-encounters the Lamb of God at the Jordan, and follows the Miracle Worker through the wilderness, the Messiah to the cross, and the Risen Savior from the upper room. Though Shimon is a fictional character, we'll see the pages of the Gospels unfold through his eyes, and **experience a story of redemption – the redemption of a shepherd – and the redemption of each one who chooses to follow the Good Shepherd.**

* * *

Other Books in the *Lessons Learned In The Wilderness* series
Each of the six books in the series contains 61 chapters, which means that the entire series is comprised of 366 chapters — **one chapter for each day of the year.** The chapters have been formatted in a way that you can read one chapter each day or read each book straight through. Whichever way you choose, allow the Master to use the series to encourage and challenge you in the journey that He has designed uniquely for you so that His purpose is fulfilled, and His glory is made known.

The Journey Begins (Book #1)

God's plan for our lives is not static; He is continuously calling us to draw closer, to climb higher and to move further. In that process, He is moving us out of our comfort zone to His land of promise for our lives. That process includes time in the wilderness. Many times it is easier to see the truth that God is teaching us through the lives of others than it is through our own lives.

"***The Journey Begins***" is the first book in the "***Lessons Learned In The Wilderness***" series. It chronicles those stories, those examples and those truths as revealed through the lives and experiences of the Israelites, as recorded in the Book of Exodus in sixty-one bite-sized chapters.

As you read one chapter per day for sixty-one days, we will look at the circumstances, the surroundings and the people in such a way that highlights the similarities to our lives, as we then apply those same truths to our own life journey as the Lord God Jehovah leads us through our own wilderness journey.

The Wandering Years (Book #2)

Why did a journey that God ordained to take slightly longer than one year, end up taking forty years? Why, instead of enjoying the fruits of the land of milk and honey, did the Israelites end up wandering in the desert wilderness for forty years? Why did one generation follow God out of Egypt only to die there, leaving the next generation to follow Him into the Promised Land?

In the journeys through the wildernesses of my life, i can look back and see where God has turned me back from that land of promise to wander a while longer in the wilderness. God has given us the wilderness to prepare us for His land of promise, but if when we reach the border we are not ready, He will turn us back to wander.

If God is allowing you to continue to wander in the wilderness, it is because He has more to teach you about Himself – His Person, His purpose and His power. "**The Wandering Years**" chronicles through sixty-one "bite-sized" chapters those lessons He would teach us through the Israelites' time in the wilderness as recorded in the books of Numbers and Deuteronomy.

The book has been formatted for one chapter to be read each day for sixty-one days. Explore this second book in the "**Lessons Learned In The Wilderness**" series and allow God to use it to apply those same lessons to your daily journey with Him.

Possessing the Promise (Book #3)

The day had finally arrived for the Israelites to possess the land that God had promised. But just like He had taught them lessons throughout their journey in the wilderness, He had more to teach them, as they possessed the promise.

And so it is for us. Possessing the promise doesn't mean the faith adventure has come to a conclusion; rather, in many ways, it has only just begun. Possessing the promise will involve in some respects an even greater dependence upon God and the promise He has given you.

"**Possessing the Promise**" chronicles the stories, experiences and lessons we see recorded in the books of Joshua and Judges in sixty-one "bite-sized" chapters. The book has been formatted for one chapter to be read each day for sixty-one days.

Explore this third book in the "**Lessons Learned In The Wilderness**" series and allow God to use it to teach you how to possess the promise as He leads you in the journey with Him each day.

Walking With The Master (Book #4)

Our daily walk with the Master is never static – it entails moving and growing. Jesus was constantly on the move, carrying out the Father's work and His will. He was continuously surrendered and submitted to the will of the Father. And if we would walk with Him, we too must walk surrendered and submitted to the Father in our day-to-day lives.

Jesus extended His invitation to us to deny ourselves, take up our cross and follow Him. "**Walking With The Master**" chronicles, through "sixty-one" bite-sized chapters, those lessons the Master would teach us as we walk with Him each day, just as He taught the men and women who walked with Him throughout Galilee, Samaria and Judea as recorded in the Gospel accounts.

The book has been formatted for one chapter to be read each day for sixty-one days. Explore this fourth book in the "**Lessons Learned In The Wilderness**" series and allow the Master to use it to draw you closer to Himself as you walk with Him each day in the journey.

Until He Returns (Book #6)

Moments after Jesus ascended into heaven, two angels delivered this promise: "Someday He will return!" In this sixth and final book of the ***Lessons Learned In The Wilderness*** series, we will look at what that journey will look like ***Until He Returns***. No matter where we are in our journey with Him – in the wilderness, in the promised land, or somewhere in between – He has a purpose and a plan for us.

In this book, we will look through the lens of the Book of Acts at what that journey looked like for those first century followers of Christ. Like us, they weren't perfect. There were times they took their eyes off of Jesus. But despite their imperfections, He used them to turn the world upside down. And His desire is to do the same thing through us. Our journeys will all look different, but He will be with us every step of the way.

Like the first five books in this series, this book has been formatted in a way that you can read one chapter each day or read it straight through. Whichever way you choose, allow the Master to use it to encourage and challenge you in the journey that He has designed uniquely for you so that His purpose is fulfilled, and His glory is made known.

* * *

For more information about these books, including how you can purchase them, go to
wildernesslessons.com or kenwinter.org

ABOUT THE AUTHOR

Responding to God's call from the business world in 1992 to full-time vocational ministry, Ken Winter joined the staff of First Baptist Church of West Palm Beach, Florida, serving as the associate pastor of administration and global mission.

In 2004, God led Ken, his wife LaVonne, and their two teenagers on a Genesis 12 journey, that resulted in his serving with the International Mission Board (IMB) of the Southern Baptist Convention. From 2006 until 2015, Ken served as the vice president of church and partner services of IMB, assisting churches across the US in mobilizing their members to make disciples of all peoples.

From 2015 until 2018, Ken served as the senior associate pastor of Grove Avenue Baptist Church in Richmond, Virginia.

Today that Genesis 12 journey continues as Ken labors as a bond-servant of the Lord Jesus Christ in the proclamation of the gospel to the end that every person may be presented complete in Christ.

To read Ken's weekly blog posts go to kenwinter.blog

* * *

And we proclaim Him, admonishing every man and teaching every man with all wisdom, that we may present every man complete in Christ. And for this purpose also I labor, striving according to His power, which mightily works within me.
(Colossians 1:28-29 NASB)

* * *

PLEASE JOIN MY READERS' GROUP

Please join my Readers' Group in order to receive updates and information about future releases, etc.

Also, i will send you a free copy of ***The Journey Begins*** e-book — the first book in the ***Lessons Learned In The Wilderness*** series. It is yours to keep or share with a friend or family member that you think might benefit from it.

It's completely free to sign up. i value your privacy and will not spam you. Also, you can unsubscribe at any time.

Go to kenwinter.org to subscribe.

* * *

BRIARWOOD GIRLS

Mariel Gates

BRIARWOOD GIRLS

Vanguard Press

VANGUARD PAPERBACK

A CIP catalogue record for this title is available from the British Library.

ISBN 978 1 784659 81 3

Vanguard Press is an imprint of
Pegasus Elliot MacKenzie Publishers Ltd.
www.pegasuspublishers.com

First Published in 2021

Vanguard Press
Sheraton House Castle Park
Cambridge England

Printed & Bound in Great Britain

Dedication

To all the Aubreys

Never be a prisoner of your past. It was a lesson, not a life sentence.

Anonymous

Forward

The scariest thing in life (other than having kids) is staring down the barrel of your own demise, on the brink, and not knowing whether to let go or fight like hell. No one blames the cancer patient for being sick or succumbing to the disease, but everyone cringes at the addicted. I didn't want to be a drunk. I didn't ask to have my life's work thrown down the toilet in one year. But that's all it really took. One year, less actually, to lose my friends, family, respect, career, and athleticism. There were many moments in that year that I wanted to die. I didn't want to wake up from a blackout, I drank to escape myself, my failures, even my successes. I could never live up to the person I had created in my own mind. I wanted to be it all, an attorney, an international triathlete, thin, rich, smart. I wanted it all or I wanted none of it at all. Believe me, I got closer to the latter.

Rehab is a bad word. No one willingly volunteers to be stripped of their world as they know it and dumped into a place full of drug addicts, alcoholics, sex addicts, creeps and crazy people. Seriously, who would want that? No one.

I know all rehabs are different, different counselors, residents, atmospheres. But if an addict isn't ready to

change they aren't going to recover, ever, not even in rehab, where you can still surprisingly enough get drugs.

The scariest thing in life is walking through the doors of a rehab facility. It would be easier to die… it would be easier to step in front of the L-train. People who go to rehab because they honestly want to be free from the shackles of addiction — my hat's off to you. I humbly believe they are few and far between. Most people that enter rehab enter it unwillingly, either by law, by intervention, or by threat of family or friends. Most people that enter a rehab facility don't do it for themselves, they do it to make someone else feel like they are doing the right thing. "Oh, I helped Nancy get into rehab…" Yeah? Good for you, I hope it made you feel better. Poor Nancy went through all nine rings of hell so that you would still pay her rent when she got out. Nancy was one of the ninety percent of addicts that couldn't get clean, didn't really want to deep down, and died under a bridge. This story isn't about Nancy.

Chapter One
Briarwood House

I walked up the cracked concrete stairs of Briarwood House, a big yellowish Victorian that sat oddly close to the Columbia River. The steps smelled like mildew. My duffle bag suddenly weighed a hundred pounds. Every fiber in my body was screaming at me to turn around and run, just leave, drop the bag and find a cheap hotel to hang out in until this all blew over. But it wouldn't blow over, would it? I knew if I ran off to a hotel room, I'd end up dead in less than a week.

I looked at the brass placard to the right of the door. I thought it would say this was a historical building. All it said was Briarwood House. Even though it was only forty degrees outside, I started to sweat. I grabbed the brass door knob and pushed open the heavy oak door. My heart pounded so loudly that I was sure the three or four women in the sitting room could hear it. I walked up to the front desk, a solid oak panel. *Like a bar,* I thought. I dropped my duffel bag full of clothes on the floor and waited for someone to come 'check me in'.

A thin woman with a fake tan approached the desk and looked directly at me. As soon as we made eye contact, I looked down, pretending to assess the things

I had brought.

"Hi, you must be Aubrey, I'm Janet, we've been expecting you." A woman said with an overly eager-to-meet-you voice.

"Yeah." I managed just above a whisper. I had never been a quiet person. But this new atmosphere that screamed my failures sucked the loud right out of me. I wanted to disappear.

"I'll need your bag. We have to go through everyone's personal effects, you will get it right back, I promise you." She was smiling at me as she peeked over the edge of the wooden slab to see how much I had brought. I grabbed the nylon straps and heaved it up onto the desktop. I suddenly thought of the make-up bag, iPod, and running shoes inside. I prayed silently that the iPod would not be confiscated.

A wave of anxious nausea rolled over me like a small tsunami. I thought I might get sick.

"If you are carrying a cell phone or anything, we need that also. There are no phones allowed, and no iPads or smart watches."

Handing her my cell phone from my jeans pocket, I took one last longing look — no new texts, no missed calls. I powered it off and took a deep breath before handing her my iPhone.

"We don't allow pictures to be taken in here." She said as if that explanation would make me feel better after being stripped of my only connection to the outside world. There was no way out now. No way to text

someone and plead for help — not that I had anyone left to willingly help me — no way to Google an Uber ride out of here. I was officially checking in to the Briarwood. I had no idea how long I was going to be here, tears caught in the corner of my eyes, my stomach twisted. I was about to cry with big heavy heaves, it was coming. I was legitimately scared and alone. I balled up my fists in the ends of my heather gray Boston College Track and Field sweatshirt, my nails dug into my palms. I couldn't remember how I managed to end up with a track and field sweatshirt from Boston, I'd only run there twice in college. I desperately wanted to rewind time about a year or back to the moment I got the sweatshirt. I could start from there. I'd make a lot of changes to the way I behaved, I wouldn't make so many mistakes.

I looked back at the door, my cab driver was long gone. I was stuck, frozen in place. I wanted this to not be happening, I wanted my mom. I was sure the ladies in the sitting room were gawking at me and trying to figure out what I was in for. Janet traded me my phone for a few papers to sign a waiver, HIPPA forms, release of information forms. I didn't really read them. I just signed where her perfectly manicured red fingernail pointed for signatures.

"Jamie here is going to take you up to your room and show you around. We have an evening meeting at five o'clock and dinner at six. You are expected to be at both," Janet said curtly. Her soft smile had disappeared

into a hard line. She turned around with my bag in her right hand, my cellphone in her left, and headed away from me down a hallway that was for 'staff only'.

Out of nowhere a thin, very pretty woman in her forties appeared at my side. "Hi." Her voice was soft and welcoming but a little too eager to greet me. I wasn't checking in to the Quinta. She pointed to the staircase by the sitting room. "Follow me, I'll take you to your room and once Janet is done, she will bring your bag up and you can put your stuff away."

The women who had originally been sitting in a tight little circle chatting were now watching my every move, silent, sizing me up. I looked away and back to where Jamie had indicated we were going. I quickly caught up to her on the stairs and followed her into the first small bedroom on the right-hand side of the hall. It had two twin beds, each with its own night stand, and a small dresser on the opposite wall. It reminded me of a child's dresser, small and plain.

"The longer you've been here and the more faith the staff have in you the better the accommodations. Maybe someday you'll be in the eyrie. The girls here call it the eagle's nest."

"What?" I stammered.

"It's a triple on the third floor. Three women get the whole floor to themselves, it's really nice."

Yeah great, exactly what my goal is... to end up with two other roommates in this crazy house for even longer than I planned. I could feel the cynicism taking

over. By the way, I had only planned on being here thirty days. The shortest amount of time possible according to the website. Traditionally girls were at the Briarwood ninety days. Their testimonials on the place had been all over the website, stating how grateful they were to have stayed. But ninety days sounded like forever to me and I was determined to prove to these people, and to myself, that I was 'better' in thirty days.

"Cool," I managed. My mouth had gone impossibly dry.

Suddenly I realized that there was someone in one of the beds, a light quilted cover pulled up over her head.

"That's Mary, your roommate." Jamie said in practically a whisper.

I nodded.

"Beside each bed in the house is also a nurses' call button. It's hanging on a string by the headboard." I looked at my new bed and sure enough, hanging neatly beside the bed was a long white string, and at the end of the sting was a red plastic rectangle.

"Here." Jamie rounded the corner of the twin bed and waved me over. The quilt on the bed looked like it belonged in a farmhouse, white with light blue accents and small square quilting patterns. It was either very old or someone paid extra for them to look this way.

Jamie grabbed the string and held up the little red plastic piece. "If you or your roommate are ever in distress you press this together and the nurses' alarm will sound, kind of like a fire alarm. So please don't use

it unless it's absolutely necessary. It's not a call button for a glass of water."

I let out a short laugh. Jamie shot me a look, a 'this is absolutely not a joke' look. I glanced down at my feet, my toes wiggled inside my pair of gray Uggs. Jamie got up from the bed and I followed her quietly down the hall where she showed me a bathroom and hall closet with extra toiletries. There were laminated signs to the nurses' station pinned to the wall, complete with arrows.

We passed a couple of larger bedrooms with two full sized beds in them and what looked like their own bathrooms. Jamie then showed me the stairwell leading up to the eyrie before taking me back downstairs to what I could only assume was the living room of the old house, off of the ancient kitchen.

"Any questions?"

I could smell something like spaghetti… It was *not* my mother's spaghetti. It smelled sweet like the kind you buy in bulk glass jars. My mother's was spaghetti spicy, sauteed onions, tomatoes, peppers, garlic, olive oil. I took a deep breath and tried to feel the solid ground under my feet.

"How many girls live here?" I asked looking up at Jamie. She stood a good three, maybe four inches taller than me. Her thin frame made her look even taller.

"We try to keep it to twelve at a time. We have room for fifteen but I've never seen Amy, she's the director, let more than thirteen girls be in the house at one time."

I looked around the room we were standing in. There were five chairs arranged in a semicircle at the back of the room, each chair had a spiral notebook placed neatly underneath it. Jamie explained that this is where we did small group meetings once a day and, in the evening, a larger AA or NA meeting was held here at five. I looked at the clock on the wall above a white board. It was almost five. Instead of asking me to sit in a chair, though she motioned to a wooden, built-in bookshelf on the wall. It was stained the color of all the trim in the house, a honey oak color. But instead of books there were pillows neatly arranged in each square cubby.

“Grab a pillow and a spot on the floor.” She gave me a half-hearted smile. “It’s five o’clock so everyone should be in here for a large group meeting in just a second. Jamie walked out of the room and I turned to grab a pillow off the shelf. It was an ugly throw pillow my mom would never have on her couch, let alone in our house. Dark gray, corduroy, no frills, it was oddly heavy in my hands and I wasn’t sure if these were for sitting, laying down or what. As I clumsily held the pillow there was a buzz of voices in the hallway. My stomach instantly twisted. A gaggle of girls and women walked in, and were all coming towards me, all of them taking long looks at me, the new girl. A few of them didn’t break from their current conversations, and grabbed pillows from the shelf to my left and tossed them onto the floor next to each other. *I guess we sit on*

them.

"So what's your preference?" A young girl's voice interrupted my thoughts and I looked up to see a girl with a tattoo on her neck, her nose and left eyebrow were both pierced and the nose ring moved when she spoke. I couldn't quite understand the question. "What are you in here for? What's your drug of choice?" I opened my mouth to speak but no words came out.

A short fat woman with a commanding presence and husky voice boomed, "Everyone take a seat… We have a new resident, her name is Aubrey. Please be respectful. I know you can all remember what your first day was like. Show her around and be kind." She gave a pointed look at the tattooed girl in front of me. "Oh, and after dinner tonight we get to watch *When Harry Met Sally*." There was a bunch of "Ahhhs" and grumbling noises from the room… I was frozen with my pillow still in my hands. I'd never seen the movie. But I knew Meg Ryan was in it so that had to be a plus. Before I could even think of the other actor, the short stocky woman turned to me. "Welcome, Aubrey." She motioned for me to take a spot on the floor between two women and I obeyed, sitting awkwardly on the throw pillow.

"Okay let's open tonight's meeting with a prayer."

The meeting opened with the serenity prayer, it was a blur. I was so nervous I could hardly stand it. I just kept praying that no one would call my name. I wanted to dissolve into the carpet. I didn't belong here with

these people. Their mantras and mindless platitudes. But I was frozen. Unable to get up and run out of the building.

After the meeting was over, Jamie came and found me and told me my things were in my room. I was grateful for the excuse to take a minute to myself. I didn't feel much like joining people at dinner. When I got to my room, Mary was gone. My duffel bag was on my bed and a 'Welcome to Briarwood' packet that looked like a travel brochure with house rules and regulations lay next to it. I flipped through it and put it in the nightstand drawer. Under it had been an intake form with a post-it note with my name on it. I put it on my pillow, *a little light reading for tonight.*

I moved slowly, taking my clothes out of my bag and refolding each piece to fit in the drawers of the small dresser. I was grateful for the scent of cedar when I opened the dresser, the smell reminded me of my grandparents' home when I was little.

As I gently placed and reorganized my clothes, I thought of my grandfather and my grandmother, what would they think of me now? I had been such a rising star in the family. Our family had always been so focused on getting an education, starting a career, doing things the right way and being successful. I had loved my grandfather with all my heart. My earliest childhood memories are of holding his hand and walking down to feed the horses on his ranch. He was a doctor, but a rancher at heart. He and I had spent countless hours

together, saddling horses and riding them around his property, even taking them out on the gravel roads surrounding his house. We talked about what I wanted to do when I grew up. The answer was always the same. I wanted to be a judge. I wanted to wear the black robe and wield the gavel. I had imagined myself presiding over civil cases saying, "Order in my courtroom". Banging the gavel for emphasis. My grandfather would laugh and tell me I'd be good at it, but that I needed to study hard, and stay straight. I did the former. I studied hard in high school and then in college. I had no problem getting into law school, but something happened about that time and everything changed. I shook my head and tried to focus on putting my clothes away.

I was going to skip the social meal and try to adapt to my new surroundings. After putting all of my clothes away I was surprised to see that my iPod had survived the strip search, whether on purpose or by accident. I was grateful. I placed the white earbuds in my ears, turned it on, and lay down on top of the bed that was mine for the moment. I looked at the intake form, name, birthdate, age (as if they can't add) sexual orientation, *that was a new one.*

'Who did you grow up with? Until when?
Have you ever been sexually assaulted or abused?
Have you ever been physically abused?
What is your drug of choice?
When did you first start using?'

My god did I really have to do this?

I pulled the silver Briarwood pen off the spiral notebook I'd been given in the pile of paper.

Clicking it open and closed I hated myself for this. Every cell in my body wanted to revolt, throw the questionnaire away and just pretend I never got one. They'd probably just give me another and have me fill it out in front of someone.

I turned my music up and started with the simplest questions.

Name: Aubrey

Chapter Two
Mary

I must have drifted off to sleep, and no one had come to get me, because the next thing I knew, I was waking up to a girl screaming. It was dark, and I was disoriented. The clock on my nightstand, beamed 1:08 in red. Mary in the bed next to me was screaming, "Get off me!" at the top of her lungs.

I flipped over and reached the nurses' cord. I heard my papers fall to the floor as I fumbled to find the red button and squeezed. A loud beeping noise, like a dump truck backing up, filled the air.

Mary kept screaming, "Get off me, Get off me!"

I jumped out of bed and threw the overhead light on. There was no one with Mary. Mary stopped screaming and looked directly at me. Her brown hair was a crazy tangle around her head. Her dark brown eyes looked terrified and confused. She looked down at her button up pajamas, there was nothing on her that I could see.

The night nurse, whose name I didn't know, came jogging into the room. She pressed on the nurses call button again and the insanely loud beeping stopped.

She sat next to Mary, stethoscope in hand, and

started to assess her. As she did so, she turned to me. "Could you please wait outside?"

I nodded, grabbed my iPod off the bed, shoved it in my pants pocket and exited the room. I slumped to the floor in the hallway. The dark green carpet was soft beneath my hands, I rested my head on the wall and stared at the ceiling. I could feel eyes on me. Girls were peeking their heads out of their bedroom doors, but no one ventured out of their rooms.

I sat there, tired, scared, wishing I could just go home, and knowing that this was going to be my new normal for a while.

Mary was certifiably insane, and I was her roommate.

Another nurse, came walking quickly down the hall, she had a little square black shoulder bag with her.

She acknowledged me at the door

"Get her some Ativan," the first night nurse was telling the second.

Again, I had an overwhelming desire to cry and call my mother. *What the fuck am I doing here?*

Both nurses eventually came out of my room. The first one left and went back to the nurses' station, the second, a heavy, blonde woman, crouched down next to me rubbing her hands together. She smelled like hand sanitizer.

"Mary has panic attacks. She isn't dangerous. We gave her some medicine to help her sleep and you should go back to bed." She paused and looked down

the hall and back at me.

"Pretty exciting first night, huh?"

I looked at her in her big blue eyes.

"Listen, Mary is sick but she really wouldn't hurt a fly. This is her second time here. She doesn't have any family around and I think she just gets scared and overwhelmed. She has nightmares. If you feel like you need to change rooms you can always talk to Amy in the morning. Are you going to be okay?" she asked.

"Yeah, I think so."

The nurse got up and held out a hand to help me up. I took it.

"Try to get some rest."

I nodded and went back into the bedroom.

Mary was sedated, asleep on her side facing away from me.

I laid in bed looking at the ceiling for hours, crying, cursing myself for my failures, wishing I had the resolve to just be a normal person.

In the morning, Mary sat with her feet on the edge of the bed, her chin on her knees, hugging her legs.

"I'm sorry about last night," she said. She had the sweet voice of a child.

"It's okay." I felt guilty for judging her last night.

Her brown hair was still a wild mess. She immediately pulled a hand up to her head to smooth it down. The attempt was futile. There was something cute about the way she was suddenly self-conscious. I noticed the tiny diamond stud earrings in her lobes. She

came from money. Her silk pajamas confirmed that. I looked down, embarrassed that I had fallen asleep in my jeans and hadn't bothered to change them when everyone woke up in the middle of the night.

"I have nightmares sometimes," Mary said in a very matter of fact way. "Well, a lot." Her tone changed. "So I'm sorry I woke you up." "It's okay." I tried to sound reassuring. "I have them too." And that was the truth. I used to have nightmares about my cousin all the time. I used to use my anger towards him and the rest of the world as fuel to run fast. I'd run and run until my legs and lungs burned and I tasted blood. That anger got me a track and field scholarship. I was afraid to give it up. When I couldn't run any more and the nightmares plagued me I started drinking. I'd drink to pass out so that I wouldn't dream. Maybe that's what Mary did too.

"I'm Aubrey." I held out a hand. It seemed like a silly gesture but Mary took it.

"Mary," she said. Her eyes smiled just a little. I felt better about having her as a roommate and for a second I almost forgot that I hated where I was and why I was here.

"We'd better get breakfast before all the fruit is gone." Mary said looking at the hallway. "The skinny girls always steal all the fruit." She smiled as she made the last statement. Of course, Mary was one of the 'skinny' girls.

Over the course of the next few days, I learned where to be at certain times, which chores were for the

newbies — all the worst ones — and what people to avoid. Mary, my roommate, was unfortunately one of them at certain times. She could be so sweet one-on-one in our room. But in a group she often sounded angry, occasionally being reprimanded for her foul language.

The third morning I was there she was asked to talk about her nightmares during small group session. The meeting was led by Jamie that morning and the conversation had been about your feelings you kept in an invisible box or safe or something of that nature. I remember someone had drawn on the dry erase board a big outline of an old chest and the words 'secrets keep you sick' above it.

Mary acted as if everyone was out to get her. "Well, like everyone knows I'm schizophrenic, I was diagnosed when I was seven…" She was angry.

She looked around as if she expected people to be shocked. I might have looked it a little.

Mary talked about self-medicating with heroin, when her nightmares were really bad.

"Can you tell us about your nightmares Mary?" Jamie asked.

"I don't remember them." Mary's tone indicating she was done talking.

Jamie pointed at the white board. "We all have demons, Mary. This is a safe space. We are here to talk about some of the things that caused us to start using." You could tell Jamie was trying to be gentle but Mary was getting worked up.

"You want to hear the sick stories of how my dad's best friend, Jerry, used to love to have me sit on his lap? Or stick his fingers in me? Or get drunk late at night and come lay on me?"

"Mary, please." Jamie was only trying to get Mary to calm down.

"It's true, but I was just a crazy girl, right?" Mary sat, arms crossed, brow furrowed, glaring at Jamie. I was surprised by her bluntness.

"We believe you, Mary. We don't doubt that someone hurt you very badly and took something from you. You didn't feel safe and that's wrong, Mary. What happened to you was wrong."

Mary sat there fuming. She didn't talk for the rest of the session. I ached for her. I wanted someone to give her a hug.

The session ended and I went back to our room but Mary was asked to stay and talk with Jamie.

Later that evening Mary had calmed down. When it was just me and Mary in our room talking, it felt like we were just two normal roommates, often making light of an event that happened during the day. She was fifteen, and told me about growing up in Vermont, a single kid. She told me about how she had tried to get the voices in her head to stop talking by using. She had gotten her first fix from her dad's friend, Jerry. And while you could see it pained her to say his name, she openly admitted to him giving her drugs. She used the drugs Jerry had given her until she just couldn't stop and

she needed more. Her thoughts got out of control and that's when she'd run away from home and find a 'hookup'. I want sure if that meant she had sex for drugs or if she just knew someone who could get them. I was too embarrassed to ask, so I'd act like I knew exactly what she meant. She told me how she'd come home high and her parents were often too busy to notice.

Being from a well to do family, she talked about her father, a successful businessman who was often gone and made a lot of international trips. Mary's mother ran a charitable foundation. It sounded like all that meant was that she went shopping and out to lunch a lot. Mary came and went from her house as she pleased. She started using needles when she was thirteen and no one had been the wiser. It wasn't until money and jewelry went missing, that people got suspicious. At first, they had blamed a maid, Mary, too wrapped up by addiction to take the blame herself, had let the maid get fired. But the missing money continued, and soon, so did Mary. She'd spend a few nights away getting high, but she always managed to return. Then one night her parents found her outside, high, slumped against the front door and the brick wall of their house. She was so high she didn't know where she was. They took her to the hospital and then to detox. During these talks all I could think was that the poor kid was lonely.

In those first few days I also learned that 'nose ring girl', Roz, was blunt and tactless but she was really rather harmless. There was an older woman who was a

Seventh Day Adventist — so she couldn't do the prayers at meetings — and whose husband visited every weekend. And then there was Heather, a woman in her forties with three kids at home and what I could only imagine had been an incredibly abusive husband. Heather was a waif of a woman, frail, almost sickly. And finally, there was Ellise, who was skinny, tall, confident, but mainly kept to herself. There were a handful of other girls living in the house and every evening before bed, everyone had to line up in the hallway and get their 'prescriptions' from the nurse who worked out of a makeshift closet with a half door. One particular evening we had just come from an NA group where Mary had somehow managed to get her hands on some strings from one of the craft boxes. During the meeting she had made me a red and orange friendship bracelet. It had been too large for my wrist, so I had tied it around my ankle and given it an extra knot and tug to show Mary my solidarity. We smiled. Our silent secret. No one seemed to really care. And for a second my roommate and I were just two happy girls in the back of a meeting room.

That night as we stood in the nurses' line, I watched as each opiate addict took their Suboxone, various sedatives, vitamins, and other prescriptions. I remember thinking it was a wonder that we were in a rehab facility. All I received when I got to the nurses' station was a women's multivitamin because I hadn't met with the Briarwood nurse practitioner yet. All of a sudden, Mary

started yelling and cursing at Ellise in line behind me. I had no idea what had happened because I wasn't paying attention. But then Mary started yelling about taking her medication. Ellise backed away. Mary approached the nurses' station door and continued to yell and at the nurse about how Ellise was taking Suboxone which was just a drug substitute. The nurse picked up the phone and immediately started asking for Tim to come down to the nurses' station.

Tim —who I later found to be one of the therapists and a sex addict himself — came and told Mary she was going to have to go 'next door' if she couldn't calm down. It was the first time anyone had indicated that there was another building related to Briarwood. It was the detox and men's wing. I had never seen it, but I asked a few of the other girls about it. The pill poppers had all been there, detoxing off of opioids. It was the worst place they said. Like a hospital, four people to a room, sweating and moaning in pain, unable to even watch movies to get through the day. It sounded agonizing. And why they would take Mary to detox was a mystery to me. She was living in the rehabilitation house where she had been for months. But this threat stopped her in her tracks. She stood still for a moment and then stormed up to our room. *Oh great, another sleep filled night*, I thought. I wanted to go and talk to her and make sure she was okay, something nagged at me. But the evening went on, and I was called in to see the in-house nurse practitioner. She had me do some

memory tests and recite words and numbers back to her. She asked me about my history with depression and anxiety and then filled out a form for an antidepressant and anti-anxiolytic I was now supposed to take every evening.

That night, getting ready for bed, was the first time I realized that Mary wasn't in our room. I hadn't seen her leave with Tim. After her outburst I hadn't seen her at all. A strange panic started to rise in my stomach. Maybe she was with the nurse? They wouldn't have taken her next door… I pondered telling someone that Mary wasn't in our room. But then I remembered that she would occasionally sneak up to the eagle's nest and smoke stolen cigarettes out of the windows. She told me in confidence, but coming from a schizophrenic just off of heroin I wasn't one hundred percent sure this was the truth. I walked lightly down the hall and peeked into a few of the rooms. Roommates were quietly talking getting ready for bed. No one and nothing seemed out of place. I checked the bathroom and the shower. I was about to sneak up to the eagle's nest when Jamie appeared at the end of the hallway. She looked at me inquisitively, skeptically…

"Have you seen Mary?" I asked

"She's not in bed?"

"No, and I haven't seen her since the evening lineup at the nurses' station."

"Okay, well I'll check with Tim and make sure she's accounted for. Please go to your room," Jamie said

with an air of slight frustration.

I went back to our room, disturbed that I couldn't just look for Mary myself. I knew it was really none of my business but she was my roommate, and I had grown fond of her. I went to bed that night, alone in my room, worried about Mary. She was just a kid.

The next morning, we woke up for morning meeting and Mary was still not accounted for. The group leader, Jill, also a sex addict — married to Tim — had us all sit down for an announcement. Mary had run away.

She had slipped out in the evening after her outburst. Tim and Jill had notified the authorities and her parents had been called. There was nothing we could do. They assured us that Mary would be found and that we were to go about our days as normal. The whole thing was strange. Girls were whispering. Ellise chimed in that Mary was a loose cannon and she was probably dead under a bridge by now. A couple of the younger girls cried out dramatically when Ellise spoke. Yelling ensued. The meeting was over. Girls were separated and some sent to their rooms for journal entries. Ellise was sent to talk to Tim, and I just sat there. Still unable to wrap my head around the fact that I was actually there, with these people. Mary was gone.

Ellise came back into the room a few moments later and we started to talk. She apologized for saying what she did about Mary. Her stomach had been bothering her for a few days and she was angry about the pain and

the fact that Mary was always doing things to get attention.

I sat there and nodded but not in agreement, just to acknowledge I'd heard her. I wished I had something to do with my hands. I picked up a spiral notebook from under the chair and started reading the mantras, most of which were directly from the AA playbook. Some of them were from the therapists at Briarwood. Encouraging but mindless platitudes. *This is how you get out of here. You memorize this shit.*

Later that night we were scheduled to do a meditation where everyone could grab a pillow and lay down in the living room. The lights were dimmed and a meditation and relaxation expert was going to come in with some music and talk us through a meditation. I was told that people often fell asleep. Meditation had never been for me. I just prayed I wouldn't burst into nervous laughter and get reprimanded in some way. But before we could begin, Tim and Jill came into the darkened room, hand in hand. One of them turned the lights back on and gave us all a second to adjust our eyes.

"We found Mary," Jill said. "She's next door in detox and getting tested for things she might have been exposed to while getting high. Paramedics found her. We wanted to let you know that she's been found but we are all very worried about her. Relapse is very common and we are allowing Mary to return after detox but this is her last chance." Jill looked like she had more to say about Mary, but didn't. "We are going to cancel

tonight's meditation and allow for free journaling time instead."

"Is Mary okay?" asked Ellise, feigning concern.

"She's been roughed up, but she will be okay and she can get through this if she works her program," Tim responded. Jill still looked like she had something to say.

When Mary returned a week later she was hollow. There was darkness under her eyes, a look that she had aged overnight. She spoke quietly, she was scared she might have contracted AIDS from sharing needles. She looked like she had lost the biggest fight of her life, and somewhere inside I thought, *no, Mary, don't give up.* But Mary had already asked that her parents come and take her home. They were flying back to get her. Treatment wasn't working. I felt badly for Mary. She was just a sick hurting girl, lost, a stage four cancer patient. The only difference being, she didn't want to fight the cancer. And everyone could see that. That day she sat in the back hallway by the nurses' station drawing circles on a journal page. Every once in a while, she'd stop and bang her forehead with her palm as if she couldn't get a thought to stop replaying in her head. I tried to say hello to her, I remember sitting down in the hall next to her.

This Mary, the one that had returned from relapsing, scared me.

I sat there and tried to formulate something to say, something insightful or helpful. I opened my mouth and

then shut it. I had nothing and Mary wasn't really there anyway. Even if I had all the answers in the world, she wouldn't have heard me. That night was the last night she was my roommate. Her tiny body was posed in the fetal position all night, but I could hear her whispering something to herself. Just after lights out, I asked her if she was okay, but all she did was turn into her pillow. In the morning Jamie and a nurse came in to help Mary collect her things. Her parents had arrived and she was going to be taken back home. That morning as the smell of breakfast clung to the air, I remember watching Mary's father hover over the front desk. He was a good-looking man in a long black pea-coat. Beside him was her mother, who came in wearing sunglasses and did not remove them. They signed some papers, collected Mary's bags and walked swiftly out of the house with Mary between them. They got into a black Lincoln town car and drove away. No one had spoken a word, except for the receptionist who doled out the exit paperwork. And even she seemed quiet that morning. It was the last we saw of Mary.

I looked at my right ankle, still wearing her red and orange friendship bracelet. I said a little prayer to myself. *God, keep that kid safe.* Maybe if I wasn't so wrapped up in my own disdain for the place and for myself I would have been able to help her in some way. Mary, I was later told, overdosed in her parents' home three weeks after returning with her family to Vermont.

Chapter Three
Ellise

Ellise was furious about Mary's leaving. Everyone knew that Mary was still a very sick young girl and that she would have to get more help back home. Ellise was irritable and short-fused with everyone.

"Ellise, I know that it's frustrating to see people leave here, but we need to focus on ourselves," Jill had said in a house meeting. Ellise was visibly frustrated. She wanted to go home. But her agitation reached beyond Mary leaving… there was something deeper.

Ellise came from Portland, Oregon. I didn't know much about her for the first several weeks in Briarwood because she lived in the eyrie. She had fewer daily meetings — because she's been there longer — and she had outside meeting privileges, meaning she could go to NA meetings with a house staff member. All house employees, I found out, were recovered addicts or alcoholics. All the counselors, nurses, cooks and administrative staff.

Ellise reminded me of a taller Megan Fox. She had these amazingly light blue eyes with dark straight hair that made you take pause when she looked directly at you. She had a slight glare to her, even when she was

smiling. It wasn't off-putting, I could see how men would be attracted to her. She walked and talked in a way that exuded sexuality and confidence. I was intimidated by her presence. She dwarfed my five-foot-three-inch frame and her self-assuredness caught me off guard. For me, it was odd to have such a strong personality in a rehab facility. She wasn't rude by any means. She just spoke her mind and didn't hang her head in shame as she walked the halls, as I guessed I probably did.

The first time I heard Ellise's story was also the day I found out our sex addict counselors, Tim and Jill, were married. After Mary's departure girls had been shuffled around in groups. I was now in a group with Ellise, and a few other girls I didn't know yet, and Jill was our counselor. Jill reintroduced herself to our group. As we sat in folding chairs in a semicircle, she stood at the front of the room, arms wide, welcoming. There was a box of tissues in the center of the circle. On the flat white walls, hung mantras, 'Believe in the process,' 'Secrets make you sick,' and posters of the seven steps in AA, 'friends of Bill' it said. *Oh. My. God. We have landed.* I didn't want to look at the steps, to me they were kind of stupid. And extremely obvious. *Accept you are an alcoholic, check, feel bad about it, check, apologize to everyone for the rest of your life, find a higher power to pull your head out of your ass, no check.*

Jill rattled off her credentials and talked about

knowing the pain of addiction because she too had been there. The problem I had was that she had been a sex addict. I wasn't sure what that meant exactly, but I was shocked that she'd have the guts to talk about it openly. I was unnerved that she thought sex addiction and opiate or alcohol addiction were the same. To me, they were very different. But what the hell did I know, she was a counselor and I was her patient. Jill explained that she and Tim had met in a meeting years ago. My mind was immediately and unwillingly flooded with images of Jill and Tim getting it on in a bathroom outside a sex addicts' anonymous meeting.

It was hard for me to concentrate that day on anything anyone in the group said after hearing about Jill and Tim. In my mind I kept imagining Jill as a stripper, which was completely ridiculous, but I had the fantasy just the same. I realized I had completely missed what a young girl was talking about. She had obviously given her story a testimony of her addiction and the people she hurt, because she was sitting in a folding chair sobbing, and playing with a string on the cuff of her gray sweatshirt. She wiped her eyes with the same cuff. Her face was splotchy. Ellise stood up, grabbed the box of tissues and silently handed them to the young teen. When Ellise returned to her chair she spoke, "I'll go… thank you, Brit, for your honesty."

"Yes, Brittany," chimed Jill. "This is a safe space and telling our stories is the first step in healing." It was these kinds of statements that drove me absolutely crazy

about this place. The terms ‘safe place’ and ‘healing’, grated at my core like my mom’s metal cheese grater I used to cut my knuckles on every spaghetti night when grating parmesan.

Ellise introduced herself. She was twenty-five, she had grown up in an unhappy home. Her mother frequently took abuse from her father, yet refused to leave him because she was scared of losing her kids and her home. Ellise acted like she didn’t understand why her mother stayed.

But then, when Ellise was in high school she had found ‘love’ with a man who, like her father, ruled with a sharp tongue and heavy fist. Ellise had gotten pregnant when she was nineteen. Brian, her son’s father, owned a construction company and took care of her throughout the pregnancy and then afterward when little Brian Junior — BriBri — was born. Ellise, like all of us, didn’t ask to be an addict. Brian Senior had put her in the hospital with a broken wrist when BriBri was only six months old. Painkillers became her way of coping with his abuse. She took them to ‘zone out’ as she called it. Things didn’t hurt as bad. Ellise had suffered several fractured ribs after the broken wrist but had refused to press charges against Brian. When finally, she ended up in the same ER a third time, a social worker came to talk to her and convinced her to leave Brian for the sake of BriBri. The problem now was, she was hooked on painkillers. She used them to numb the pain Brian had caused but she couldn’t stop.

Once she started the separation procedure from Brian, things had turned ugly. Brian's mom had come over when Brian was out working on a housing development and found BriBri screaming in his crib, Ellise was unconscious in the bathtub. Brian's mom, April, had CPS called and Ellise was sent to the hospital. As if that weren't enough, shortly after that episode she had 'fallen asleep' behind the wheel of the family Honda Pilot and wrapped it around a cement barrier in the parking lot of a mall. Thankfully her son was not with her. But Brian currently had custody of little BriBri since news of Ellise's DUI and opioid addiction landed on a judge's desk during a custody hearing.

All she wanted was to get her son back. She was court mandated to be in rehab. You could see she was willing to say all the right things to get done with her program and out of the damn Briarwood House. Whether or not it was sincere was another matter. Ellise had been in the house long enough to know when to use the key words on the walls when she spoke. She talked about her 'triggers' and 'making amends' to the people she hurt, little Brian being of the utmost importance.

I felt badly for her. Her love for her son and her fear of her ex were very real, but so was her addiction. Ellise's story was raw and honest, while she spoke the rest of us listened and picked at invisible lint in our pants and sweatshirt cuffs. I knew I was never going to be so open. There was no way I could speak freely about my drinking, who I'd hurt, the way I'd failed everyone

including myself. I had done such similar things it was eerie. I had passed out in the bathtub, and for some reason, not drowned. I crashed my brand-new Mazda Six into various poles and ditches and managed to finagle my way out. I had completely destroyed the little gray car all on my own. I didn't share her love for pills so my stomach turned when she shared the details of her detoxes.

The worst was when Ellise shared the details of detoxing next door. Shaking, sweating, vomiting. She shared how she was rushed to the ER by nurses because her gut was so severely compacted, nurses thought it might be twisted. I cringed. I did not want to be one of these people. But I was. I would never say it out loud but I was one of them. I had woken up from blackouts in strange places with bruises all over and not a clue where they came from. Once I woke up in my own dog's bed reeking of urine. Once on the hard tile living room floor with blood on my lip. I knew I was getting closer to that moment when I wouldn't wake up at all. I started to get frightened of myself and my blackouts and eventually I was too scared to sleep alone. I didn't want my body to be found weeks after I died. For some reason, dying alone was much scarier than the thought that what I was doing was killing myself. I accepted that there would be a time I drank myself to death. But alone? Alone I couldn't do.

I started to date a childhood friend. I had never wanted to date him, I didn't even find him attractive, but

I needed someone with me at night in case I didn't wake up. I would wake up hungover and naked. I wanted to die of embarrassment. There was no way in hell I'd tell these stories to this group. To any group. They were secrets I'd take to the grave. *Secrets make you sick. Damnit.*

I was engulfed in Ellise's story, in her honesty. It was oddly comforting to know that I wasn't the only one who had done such stupid, foolish things.

She talked openly about things she'd do to get more pills, embarrassing things, illegal things, things she'd never do if she wasn't an addict. She talked about stealing medications from anyone she visited. She even hired a real estate agent and pretended to be looking at three-bedroom houses just to sneak into bathrooms and rummage through medicine cabinets. The real estate agent had suspected something was up and had told her not to contact her any more.

When Ellise ran out of pills there was a junkie that lived by her mother-in-law that she'd score from. The junkie had first approached her shaking his pants pockets and Ellise thought he was trying to come on to her. At first, she was appalled. But she soon realized that the junkie shaking his pockets meant he had something for her, and when she couldn't pay him money any more, she started giving him whatever valuables she had. Her grandmother's gold earrings, a pearl ring, a golden locket Brian had given her after an especially bad fight. She stopped just short of giving him sex.

Jill applauded Ellise's honesty. Obviously Ellise was making progress. Progress, I thought, the kind I would never make.

It wasn't long before Jill started talking about how Ellise would soon be released to go home. Ellise's time was almost up and she had completed everything they had asked of her in therapy. The only problem was Brian. Brian had come by to visit Ellise three times since she was admitted. He never brought their son, but he did bring pictures. He wanted Ellise to come home. He missed her. Their son needed a mother and a father, he told her. Ellise would walk around conflicted for days after Brian came by. She was moody and mean after his visits. I think everyone understood why. There were still girls like Roz that would give Ellise a hard time about being a bitch. But honestly, we were all there with her, wondering what she would do. Knowing she'd probably go back to Brian even though it was the wrong answer.

Jill and Ellise talked endlessly in small group meetings about how Brian, was a major trigger and he was bad for her on many levels. Everyone, including Ellise knew that. She and Jill would go back and forth talking about how to get Brain out of her life, how he was a terrible influence on BriBri. Jill and Ellise would talk about how she could gain custody back by showing that it was in the best interest of the child to be with her. She needed to document every time Brian had gotten out of hand with her. She needed to get a restraining

order and make sure there was a visit from Child Protective Services. Ellise would nod in agreement and weep into a box of tissues someone had handed her from the center of the circle. I think deep down Ellise knew she had to get away from Brian, but there was a history there. He was her son's father. He provided for them very well financially.

"You cannot leave Briarwood without an exit plan Ellise. Going home to Brian is not good for your recovery, or for you, and I think you know that," Jill said in one of our last sessions with Ellise."We can find a halfway house or an Oxford house for you, you'll be safe there, it's clean living, I'll get you the information after session," she said hopefully.

"Okay, thanks," was all Ellise said. I never heard more on the topic of her going home. But a few days later, with her requisite paperwork and travel bags in hand, Ellise stood in the foyer of the great Victorian house, ready to return to her son… and yes, Brian.

No one could stop her from getting into his truck. We all silently thought the same thing. *Nothing will change. She will relapse or he will beat her to death.* We all watched from the bay window as Ellise hugged Brian Junior. She swept him off the sidewalk and held him so closely you could almost feel the relief from inside the house. She stood there swaying with him for a long time. His tiny shoes, swinging from side to side, as he clutched his mother's neck. Suddenly I was overwhelmed with my own desire to be that little boy.

To be hugged so fiercely and feel the comfort in my mother's warm neck. To twist my fingers through her blonde hair and cry on her shoulder. I wanted my mom.

Chapter Four
Heather

Heather must have noticed me getting teary eyed at the sight of Ellise leaving. She had a worried look on her face. I knew it was for Ellise and not for me, but I leaned into her just the same. She put her long thin arm around my shoulder and I was surprised by her frailty. She and I had spoken a few times at dinner or around the fireplace after all of our daily meetings and I had never noticed how thin she was. She was always wearing bulky sweaters and whenever she could she was crocheting something. She seemed motherly and I wondered how on earth she had ended up at Briarwood. I had missed Heather's story. She had been in a different group than Ellise and me. I knew only the basics. She had moved to the area from from Kalispell, Montana, she was religious, her husband seemed to adore her, her children were grown, and her preference was alcohol. She gave me a gentle pat on the arm, and turned to the sitting room where her crochet bag sat neatly by the fireplace.

"I wish I knew how to do that." The words tumbled out of my mouth before I even had time to think about what I was saying.

"Oh, it's easy. I could teach you if you wanted."

"Oh, I don't know about that," I said. "My mother has made several valiant attempts to teach me how to knit, and I'm such an anxious knitter my needles always ended up locked in to the yarn so tightly you couldn't move them." I found myself smiling at the memory and Heather let out a small laugh.

"Come, sit." She pointed with her elbow to the spot next to her on the brick hearth. I obeyed, feeling ever so slightly like I was doing wrong by my mother to be learning a craft from someone else. The other women who were mingling about the doorway started to dissipate. There was an obvious lack of Ellise's presence. It was chore time and everyone was procrastinating including myself. The warmth of the gas fire was almost too hot on my back and I took off my gray monogrammed sweatshirt. Heather took a metallic crochet hook from her bag and wound some white yarn around it until there was about four inches of neatly spaced loops. She showed me how to wind the yarn around my fingers on one hand and use the hook with the other to create more hoops below the row she had already made.

Our quiet concentration was suddenly disrupted by a very loud, "Well, this sucks." The voice of Roz, the tattoo and nose ring girl, pierced the air. I jumped. Her name was really Rosylnn but she went by Roz. I looked up at her, she was staring at the crochet hook in my right hand. "Come on, Roz, I'm not that bad," I said with a

smile.

“No, not you, it’s like we need some energy in this house.”

She was holding out her arms like she was waiting for a bolt of electricity or a sign from God. Her tattoos peeked out from her sweatshirt sleeves. I had no idea what they were but they covered her arms. A giant lily wrapped around one side of her neck, like it was going to strangle her with its stem, the petals reaching up toward her left earlobe.

Heather put her work down and started to gather it neatly into her fabric bag.

“We should probably get ready for groups” she said, not looking at Roz but obviously irritated by the interruption.

“Ugh,” grumbled Roz

I handed Heather the crochet hook and skein of yarn she had lent me, but she held up her hand in refusal. “Keep it, we’ll work on it more later,” she said with a slight smile. There it was again, something motherly about her that drew me to her. I wanted to follow Heather up to her room and ask her why she, of all people, could be at a place like Briarwood.

“Okay, guys, to your groups.” Jamie strolled in picking up random cups that had been left out on the coffee table. I didn’t even notice they were there. She walked through the room making sure things were tidy. We all moved slowly towards the hallway and got ready to disburse into groups. I noticed that the anxiety I

originally had for going to 'group' had somehow dissolved without me noticing. As I walked to my room and as I rounded the corner, I saw Tim. He was standing outside my door talking to Heather who had apparently made it down the hall before me. She nodded and looked at me.

"Aubrey, can you collect your things? We are going to move you into a double with Heather." Heather looked at me approvingly. I had totally forgotten that Heather, Ellise, and Roz all shared the eagles' nest. With Ellise gone, Heather had asked to be moved to a double. I was next on the list to move up in rooms.

"Oh yeah, of course. Are you sure Heather? Don't you like the view from the eyrie?"

"It's great, but I think I'd like the quiet of a double." She gave me a knowing look. With Ellise gone, Roz would be a handful upstairs. I couldn't blame her for wanting to leave. After I gathered my clothes and took the sheets off of my bed, I walked down the hall to where Heather was moving into a large bedroom. It was a lot like a hotel room. Two full sized beds and its own little bathroom, it boasted to be the best room in the house. I could care less about the view from the eyrie. I was looking forward to having Heather as a roommate.

We shuffled our things around in silence and then headed down to our respective meeting groups. They were already in session. I could hear Roz talking and the sound of meditation music coming from the living room. I sat down on a folding chair next to a girl who

looked remarkably like Jamie. I had forgotten her name. "I heard you got Heather as a roommate," she leaned over and whispered.

"Yeah. I've been roommate-less since Mary left and I heard they are moving a group of new girls over soon," I whispered, trying not to catch Jill's attention.

Jill shot us a look from the front of the room to remind us to stop talking. I had no idea what the subject matter was about and I really didn't care that much. I leaned over and grabbed the spiral notebook from under my chair.

"Well, I heard she killed someone," the woman said.

"Janet! Please! We are trying to concentrate on our list of triggers, people are trying to work here. I'm going to ask you this once to stop talking, please," Jill threatened.

My eyes must have been as big as saucers. *What the hell? Was this Janet girl freaking nuts or what?* I wanted to move away from her. I looked down at my notebook and pretended to focus on the words in front of me. But I could feel Janet's eye on me. She was looking for a reaction and I wasn't going to give her the satisfaction.

Heather killed someone? No. Whatever, this lady was bonkers. But I was curious if the rumor had any weight.

No matter how hard I tried, I couldn't stop thinking of what she said. Jill looked at me and I snapped my

eyes back to my notebook. The rest of the meeting ticked by excruciatingly slowly.

“Triggers are what cause you to use… those people, places, things, events, that started your using and perpetuated it. Triggers are what we need to remove from our lives or, if we can’t remove them, learn to cope without using drugs.

“What you write today you will be going over with me in our one-on-one sessions so I want honesty, girls. I want you to be honest with yourselves.” *My god, this lady was driving me crazy.* I didn’t feel like getting honest with anyone. I liked to shove things down into that pit in your gut where you hide stuff and then try to ignore it. Then again that’s probably why I was in this fucking place. I had been shoving things into that hole since I was about six years old. At some point that hole fills up and overflows. I suddenly felt guilty for my thoughts. There was a part of me that wanted to get on board and get with the program but a bigger part of me just wanted to prove I was better than everyone else in the room. *I wasn’t as sick.*

“Okay, ladies, that’s it for today, have a good afternoon and I’ll see you all tonight.” Jill’s voice startled me.

I had written only two words in my journal, ‘failure’ and ‘success’.

That evening after dinner I found Heather in our room crocheting again. She sat cross legged on the bed her quilt covering her tiny legs.

"Hi… how was group?" I asked.

"Oh, you know, Roz took control over most of the subject matter…" She laughed lightly.

"I bet…" I said, imagining Roz.

I really wanted to ask Heather about her past but it was an unspoken rule that you don't ask people personal things like that outside of group. I went into the bathroom and changed into my pajamas, grabbed my journal and sat down at the head of my bed. I stared at the two words I had written. I was screwed.

"You know that thing won't write itself" Heather's voice snapped me out of my daze. I'd been staring at the two words, pen in hand, motionless. I turned and looked at her blankly.

"You've only been here a short time, the shift will happen if you want it to. With time and when you find a greater purpose than yourself."

Oh, gee, great, I thought, Heather was absorbing and regurgitating the very platitudes I'd come to mock in my head. My face must have given me away because she continued.

"I'm serious. That's why programs like AA work for people who want it to work, they find a greater purpose than themselves, a higher power."

"I don't know if I'll ever believe in a higher power, Heather." I wanted to say something smart to get her to change the direction of the conversation but I had nothing.

"You don't have to believe in God. You just have

to start being less about Aubrey and more about other people or other things. You're so wrapped up in what you can and can't control that you don't even want help. You want control. My girl, there is very little in life you will ever be able to control and the sooner you learn that the better."

I felt like she had just punched me in the gut. My face felt hot. How dare she tell me what I can and can't do or control. After all, wasn't she here because of a lack of control too?

"This coming from someone who knows so much about self-control." It didn't mean to come out, it was a private thought that somehow bypassed the filter. Heather's face dropped. She quietly put away her crochet.

"Heather, I'm sorry, I shouldn't have said that." I tried to backpedal.

She looked at me thoughtfully, chewing on the inside of her cheek. She looked skeletal.

"I know. You are angry and you don't want to be here Aubrey. Most of us don't. I'd rather be home with my family. You are angry at yourself and I think that's probably normal. I know I am."

There was a long awkward silence as I looked down and closed my journal. I ran my fingers down the bumpy spine. I used to have notebooks like this in college. College where I got As and Bs where I graduated with honors.

Heather spoke as if she read my mind again. "You

can't outsmart this disease. Believe me I've tried. I'm saying this not to aggravate you, but because I don't want you to end up like me, honey."

I cocked my head to the side, absent minded, like a puppy when you say a command they don't understand.

Heather lay her hands on the quilt and smoothed it out. She looked at them as if her veiny hands had the answers. "It was an accident," she said almost inaudibly. She turned her hands and examined the palms. The nightstand lamp cast a warm glow on them. She looked even smaller than before. "I was in a blackout and I don't even remember driving…"

"Heather, I didn't…" She cut me off.

"I will never forgive myself."

There was a long awkward silence. My questions hung in the air like static electricity. Anguish was written all over her body, it had a grip on her and it would never let her go. She had made a terrible, terrible, mistake. For some reason all I could think was, *cancer doesn't kill other people.*

Heather told me the story as it was told to her by police. She had no recollection of the event. She woke up in the hospital on a ventilator the day following the accident. She didn't know why or how she even got there, no idea what she had done. She was told that her car had drifted into the opposite lane of traffic and hit a man walking home from work at a welding shop off US highway 2. She didn't even know why she was driving out there or where she was going. She was arrested and

later charged with manslaughter. Heather had yet to face trial on the charges but her attorney had gotten her into Briarwood as a show of good faith that she was getting help. She had never gotten so much as a speeding ticket before. Her two children could hardly look at her, she said. Her husband was terrified she'd end up in prison. That's why he was here so often. He wasn't a controlling or abusive husband, he was just afraid.

Looking at Heather's folded body on the bed across the room, I felt like I should do something, say something that would be meaningful. But no words came.

"The rest of my life will be making amends sweetheart. And if I can help anyone not make the same mistake…" Her eyes had darkened.

"I drank to fill a void, Aubrey. I had everything, good kids in high school, a loving husband. I was at home baking a cake for no other reason than to do something when I got the urge to drink the vanilla."

"Vanilla?"

"Yes. Pure vanilla. I drank to get away from myself and ended up taking someone else's life." The words caught in her throat and came out thick. "My life might have been about keeping my family happy but I was still just doing it for me. The appearance of a perfect life. It wasn't until the accident and hitting this rock bottom that I came to see how selfish I was." Her hands moved as if she were spreading ashes on the floor.

"This is the shot we are given, and living only for

yourself or what you want other people to see is not living and it will kill you or someone else."

Her honesty shook me and I felt a little nauseated.

I wanted to get there. To a place where I could be at peace with myself, but in all my years I don't think I ever had been. From my earliest memories I was trying to get A grades in something, even childhood.

I moved to Heather's bed and sat beside her. I had the overwhelming urge to cry but the tears never came. Just a solid lump in my throat that burned like a hot coal. She petted my hair and draped an arm around me in a half hug. We went to bed that night emotionally spent.

Chapter Five
Roz

The next morning at breakfast three new girls were brought over from the detox unit next door. All three of them huddled together in flannel pajama bottoms and plain gray sweatshirts. We had all been given the gray sweatshirts on our first day. They had the monogram of a capital B on them, the cursive letter reminded me more of a winery logo you'd see in Sonoma California than a rehab. I noticed the pink and gray plaid bottoms also had the monogram on the left butt pocket. The wet chill in the air could permeate the drafty house on windy days and the sweatshirt had been a welcome gift in the evenings. The flannel pants were new to me. Maybe a detox thing. No one wants to detox with the shakes and the sweats in a tight pair of skinny jeans.

The girls looked cold, even though the house was probably seventy-two degrees, even warmer in the dining room off the kitchen. The girls were wide eyed and gaunt, they looked terrified.

"Oh well, look who it is," sassed Roz, "I guess ninety days in here wasn't long enough?" Roz had obviously recognized one of the girls from a previous stint at Briarwood. Roz was about the same age, I

guessed eighteen, but she clearly had more life experience. Or maybe it was the tattoos that made her seem that way.

"Sara. Don't listen to her, honey, you girls come get some breakfast," Jamie chimed. All three girls moved together to a table and exchanged glances. They picked at the chunks of melon and grapes on their breakfast plates that Jamie had gently placed on one of the solid round oak tables in the dining area. All three girls avoided the pancakes. They looked like they might puke.

"Not quite done with detox I bet. It must be getting crowded next door," Roz said just a little too loudly. She was standing right behind me in line for coffee. I grabbed the pot and started to pour the sour black liquid into a cup that read 'You've Got This,' when Jill and Tim came into the eating area. I always felt a little uncomfortable when they were in the same room together. I didn't know much about them or about what sex addicts do, but it made me squirm just slightly.

"Good morning ladies," said Jill. "We have a couple new faces today and so there will be some shuffling around with our groups and bedroom situations. Once you've eaten, please come into the group room to get your schedules. Also, the nurse practitioner will be in today so if you need to see her for anything please make an appointment at the nurses' station."

Tim and Jill left for the meeting room while the rest

of us milled about taking sidelong glances at the three new girls. It was obvious which one was Sara, she was the only one talking. She seemed to be pointing things out to the other two girls. She had a slight air of superiority about her, like she knew the way things worked and she was going to take these other two pill poppers under her wing. As they talked quietly it was hard not to notice how close they seemed to be, like sisters, bonded by detox. Breaking the awkward silence again Roz walked up to Sara, "So what the hell happened?"

"Oh you know, I just couldn't stay away from Marcus."

"Damn, girl."

"Yeah..."

"Well, I hope you feel better... I'm up in the eagle's nest if you want to talk, catch up, like old times." Roz smiled and scrunched her nose, making her nose ring move upward.

Sara was obviously embarrassed by Roz's invitation.

"Thanks Roz..." Sara turned to the other two girls and introduced them to Roz. I managed to miss their names as I walked by their table and into the meeting room still clutching my hot, acidic brew.

Heather was already in there talking to Tim and Jill, she never came down for breakfast, so I wasn't surprised she was already getting her schedule. She glanced up at me and nodded with a half-smile. I held

up my cup as if to say cheers and then felt absolutely ridiculous about the motion. Heather made her way back to the hall with her paper schedule in hand. My eyes followed her out of the room.

I was abruptly met by Tim's overly cheery face. He wasn't very tall, maybe five foot nine, and his head was really round for being a fit looking guy. He had a well-groomed beard and hipster type glasses. I could see why someone might be attracted to him, I could not see why Jill would be. She was probably an inch shy of him, dark, almost black long straight hair. Her movements were fluid like she was a dancer in a former life. The tops she wore were just this side of provocative. Today she had donned a leather skirt, tall riding boots, and a gray V-neck sweater that made her look like she had fake boobs.

"Here ya go, Aubrey." Tim handed me a piece of paper and I realized I had been staring at Jill's cleavage. My face felt hot.

"Thanks," I mumbled and turned to go, but Tim interrupted my exit with a sideways step. It felt like one of those awkward moments in a high school hallway when a guy would walk up to you wanting to talk and you really just wanted to get to class.

"How are you doing? We haven't talked much since Mary left and I want to make sure you are getting along okay."

Well, it's not the goddamn Ritz and I am pretty sure this wasn't my ideal vacation destination. I thought.

"I'm good, I mean, it's good. Thanks."

"Everyone treating you okay?"

"Yeah… thanks…" *What the hell was this guy's angle?*

"Ok well, just so you know our group starts in about ten minutes, so I look forward to getting to know you better."

What!

I immediately scanned my schedule. Sure enough, my morning meeting had been moved to nine a.m. with Tim, not Jill.

Freaking A. Roz was in my group.

I paused for a moment. Tim felt my immediate sense of insecurity and jumped on it like one of those snow foxes after a rabbit.

"We will get you talking won't we. It's important that we shuffle people around in groups so that the discussions don't get stale. Sometimes someone will feel comfortable sharing in my group but not Jill's and vice versa."

I looked at him. The coffee I had been relishing was now burning a hole in my stomach. I was starting to feel a little more comfortable in Jill's group and I really didn't want to have to share with Tim. On top of that, I really didn't want to have to share with Roz.

I looked down at my unfinished mug.

Tim patted me on the shoulder and walked toward the dining room.

I took my half-finished coffee with me to my room

and changed out of my sweat pants and into a pair of jeans. As I returned to the meeting room for group with Tim and Roz that familiar nervous and anxious feeling returned.

Maybe if Roz is in my group she will talk so I much I won't have to do any talking. The thought brought some relief.

I entered the meeting room. Roz had changed into her traditional torn black jeggings and wore her Briarwood sweatshirt like the rest of us in the meeting room. She had her legs crossed, one foot lazily flapping up and down in a rhythmic motion. Her battered black and white Converse shoe bounced up and down as she looked at the spiral notebook in her lap. She was chewing on her thumbnail with an anxious expression, like she was about to deliver her graduate dissertation.

Roz had definitely not gone to college. I could imagine her in another life, a blossoming arts student. Her short black hair swept to one side almost like a boy's. The tattoo around her neck was barely visible when her head was down. For a second she could almost be a normal college age kid, waiting for class to begin.

Tim was suddenly standing at the front of the meeting room drawing something on the dry erase board. He looked small. His Levi's were just a little too short making him look even shorter than he was. He had the sleeves of his button up shirt rolled up exposing his lean forearms. As he wrote, I wished for a moment that I could be back in a college classroom.

Roz snorted. "Really, Tim? We're doing this *again*?" She was looking at the board where he had written 'A Letter to Myself', on the board.

"Some of these ladies have not had the opportunity to do this exercise yet, Rosalynn. I know you have and so I want you to think about anything that might have changed for you. For the rest of you, we are going to write a letter to ourselves. This is to your future self in five years. I want you to write what you hope to see yourself doing at that time. When thirty minutes are up you will come get an envelope, address it to yourself, seal it, and give it back to me. Go ahead and start whenever you are ready, you have extra paper in your spiral notebooks."

Fantastic. What do I see myself doing in five years? Hell I don't know. In five years, if I'm still alive, I'll be thirty. Maybe I'll fall in love with a hot doctor and... come on Aubrey... I didn't exactly plan on getting myself into this mess, I didn't plan on losing everything... all I ever wanted was to... what? What did I want to do?

I thought about Heather. "It's not going to write itself," she had said.

Suddenly Roz stood up, and her folding chair fell over. She stormed out of the room totally pissed off.

"Rosalynn, get back here and sit down" Tom's voice was commanding but Roz didn't turn around and she didn't return to her seat. Her toppled chair lay pathetically on the floor. The other girls in the circle

were looking at the doorway through which Roz had left. They gaped. You could hear the second hand on the clock tick. No one moved. After a few minutes you could hear girls settling back in their chairs, some of them were writing. Sara seemed to be writing vigorously.

Tim got up off of his chair and set his notepad down. He left the room silently with his hands in his pockets his head lowered as if he had been hit with bad news.

I looked down at my notebook and I was surprised that I had written, 'I hope you can find someone to love and start a family.' I didn't remember writing the words down… but there they were clear as day. Something deep inside me shifted. Like plate tectonics. It was slow and small and very deep, but it caused a tidal wave of emotions. It felt like a spring that had been wound so excruciatingly tight had finally started to release in my very being. I had the urge to laugh and cry at the same time, but I did neither. I squirmed in my seat, I felt crazy.

There was movement in the doorway and I was grateful for the interruption from my own thoughts.

Roz came back in with Tim and returned to her seat with her arms crossed against her chest. I stared at her wondering what had made her so mad.

"Rosalynn will you please explain what just happened? Let's talk about what you are feeling and why." Tim sounded like a therapist you'd hear on TV.

Dr Phil or Oprah.

Roz sat frozen for a second looking down at her shoes.

"I was diagnosed with hepatitis. The nurse told me yesterday. Because of my drug use, my liver is all messed up and so I'm pissed because I don't see myself anywhere in five years. It makes me mad. I feel mad. You're a prick Tim, you knew I just found out about this and you want me to rewrite where I see myself in five years! This assignment was for me wasn't it to re-evaluate where I'd be or whatever."

Roz looked like she wanted to take a knife to Tim.

"Rosalynn this exercise is one we do with all our residents. The diagnosis you were given is not necessarily a life sentence. I'm sorry you are doing this again but maybe it's a good time to re-evaluate. It was not intended to be directed at you." Tim took a deep breath. "I want you to write the letter again."

Now Roz was pissed. Her face had gone a shade of red and her lips were pursed. She grabbed her notebook with force and yanked it open almost tearing the pages.

"Fine."

"Thank you," said Tim.

All of us had been staring at Roz and Tim, and we returned to our notebooks almost in unison.

The next fifteen minutes were the slowest fifteen minutes ever. Everyone was uncomfortable. There was a tension in the air that was palpable. You could hear pens on paper and the sounds of girls breathing.

"Okay. Time's up."

We all put our papers down and filed to the front of the room for our envelopes.

Everyone returned to their chairs and Tim sat in the front of the room holding a stack of worksheets. Worksheets were good that meant no talking. I let out a breath I didn't know I was holding.

"Can I ask a question?" asked a new girl in flannel pants.

"Of course Hannah. What's up?" Tim responded.

"What's hepatitis? I mean is it like AIDS or something?"

Tim opened his mouth to respond but Roz was faster.

"It's a liver disease. It's not HIV moron."

"Roz! Watch it and your language. Please." Snapped Tim.

"Sorry," she mumbled.

Hannah looked down at her hands, her expression was sheepish.

"I'll always have it… I have to go in for more liver tests. It's shit though… I fucked it up from using." Roz was fighting back tears. "You get it from sharing needles," she added.

There was something that Roz wanted to say,

Tim's fingers were twisted together and he was looking at Roz as if he didn't know whether to reprimand her for cursing or encourage her to talk more about her diagnosis.

"When we give in to our addictions there are consequences, everyone in this room has had to face them. We all do so in different ways. Once you decide that what you get from using isn't worth the consequences any more is when the real work begins and we can recover," Tim said.

"But that's what I did! That's why I'm here! I've been here for months and *now* I'm sick! How is that fair? You can go on fucking Jill in the utility closet and you are all better? But I'm trying I'm doing the work and now I'm sick."

Now Tim was the one that was five shades of red. Tim looked sternly at Roz. "Life isn't fair, Rosalynn… it can take months for certain communicable diseases to appear in blood work. I can tell you have something to say so why don't you share your story with the new girls."

Roz rolled her eyes and mumbled something inaudible about Tim and Jill.

"Why don't you speak so everyone can hear."

Tim stood up and passed around worksheets for everyone but said nothing else.

Roz snatched one angrily. "You want me to talk about me, or you?"

Tim stomped his foot in anger. "Rosalynn!"

"Fine, fine." She looked at her hands as if she was deciding what story she wanted to tell, then took a deep breath.

"I started using when I was fourteen after my

parents split up. Kids at school, my friends, they were all into it for fun, but I couldn't seem to stop. I dropped out of school in the tenth grade and ran away from home. For a while I was living with a kid named Cruz in his car. We'd score and drive to the coast and chill for a few days at a time. One time we got into this huge argument because he'd met some chick he wanted to start dating, or doing, I dunno, but he decided we were done. He took me back to my mom's house but she wouldn't take me in.

"I didn't really have anywhere to go so I actually lived under our house for a little while until my mom put a piece of wood over the hole I was using to get in and out of and she hammered it shut. I ended up homeless. I wandered around Tacoma sharing drugs whenever I could with whoever I could. My mom and dad ended up finding me strung out and sick downtown working a corner for dope. I was really sick. Anyway, they promised to get me help and get me clean and let me come home with either one of them if I finished a program...I just got so messed up along the way... I couldn't turn back and at some point I just gave up... When I saw my parents together I knew I had to try, try to come home again. I wanted to be home again. But now I'm like really sick and I don't know what that's going to look like. I guess I'm mad, because I really do want to go home to my mom..." Her voice trailed off.

"We are glad you're here, Rosalynn." Tim sat at the front of the room.

It was quiet again. My stomach fluttered with nerves.

“Okay, I’ve given you all some homework for our next meeting. I want it all filled out and we will talk about the responses tomorrow.”

The meeting had ended.

Poor kid, I thought looking at Roz. Drugs had always scared me, needles especially. I didn’t know how anyone could try using needles to get high. I knew that it happened but I’d never seen it or met anyone else who’d tried it.

I stood and collected my things and was about to exit when I heard Roz ask Tim if she could play. Curious, I paused at the door to see what she was talking about. An old piano sat against the far wall below some foggy windows. It probably hadn’t been used in quite some time.

“Yes, that’s fine if you aren’t meeting Jill right now, just please try not to be disruptive and when the next group comes in, in thirty minutes, you’ll have to close it up.”

Roz nodded and made her way back to the piano. There were storage boxes and large tubs of crafting materials she maneuvered around. I was eager to hear what she’d play.

Tim gave me a look as he exited the room and I knew I had to return to my room soon before getting in trouble.

Roz sat down at the piano bench and pulled back

the cover from the keys. She touched the keys directly in front of her softly as if they were flower petals. Her delicacy with the keys surprised me. Slowly she began to play. It was soft and classical, a piece I'd surely heard before, *Moonlight Sonata*.

As she played, she moved with her hands ever so slightly rocking. Her music was beautiful. I was taken aback. Punky, loud, heroin addicted, crass Roz could have been a concert pianist. I walked to my room quickly to tell Heather. Something like this had to be shared. But when I got there Heather wasn't alone.

Chapter Six
Angela

Heather's closest friend in the house was a woman named Angela. I didn't see her often because we somehow managed to always have different counselors and groups. Since becoming Heather's roommate I saw her more, she'd stop in to talk to Heather when I was coming or going from a group or a meal. She often sat on the edge of my bed and it seemed to me she talked *at* Heather, not really *with* her. Heather would acknowledge her with nods and 'hmms' but she rarely looked up from her crocheting and met Angela in the eye. I would have found this strange if I didn't know Heather better.

The only time Angela's presence really had bothered me though, was when I wanted Heather, or my bed, to myself. I would get annoyed that she would beat me to my own room after dinner and sit on *my* bed to talk to *my* roommate. In an effort to show her I was irritated, but not be rude, I would feign a hello, grab my journal and head down to the foyer. I often found the foyer of the house was empty of housemates. It was a little darker than other rooms, the fireplace was rarely going, but it felt like I was just in someone's house in

that room, not in a 'facility'. I'd often pick the formal chair by the draped window and fold myself into it. I'd open my journal and try to think of what to write for my next one on one. It was my little space when I couldn't be in my room or didn't have a group or meeting.

I had been at Briarwood for several weeks now and things started to feel more comfortable. I didn't get nervous walking into rooms before group discussions. I knew where things were and what to expect each day. Breakfast at eight a.m., group at nine, journal time, an early lunch at eleven, free time and one-on-one meetings with a therapist, — Jill or Tim, I luckily met with Jill. I don't think I could have faced a man counselor — afternoon meeting at two, crafts or meditation, AA/NA meeting at five, dinner at six. There were occasionally movie nights but for the most part that was it. It was a schedule, I found comfort in the routine even if I wasn't always comfortable talking to people.

While groups still felt clichéd, the one-on-one counseling sessions did get easier, more of a fluid conversation rather than me answering questions with one-word responses and picking at my cuticles until they bled. Jill would ask me about my day, and once we'd exchanged niceties she would review my journal work and ask me about what I had written. In the beginning I was caught off guard by her intrusiveness. I hadn't realized our journals were going to be read in front of us by a counselor, sneaking sidelong glances at

us from time to time as she read through the previous day's dronings. At first, I hadn't written much. I wrote about what I saw, what I ate, how trite it all seemed, I wrote about what the group meetings were about and who spoke. But as the days passed, I started doing what Jill had encouraged me to do, I started writing about how I was feeling during the day, how nervous I had been at times, how crazy I felt, how angry I was at myself, how disappointed I was and how disappointed my family must be. We hadn't gotten into what my 'triggers' were, but you could tell that Jill was letting me steer the boat at first, in hopes that I'd be comfortable enough with her to really open up.

I learned to recite the mantas. When you used key words like 'amends' or 'rock bottom' you would get an automatic head nod of approval from Jill. As she started probing a little deeper into things I had written some details of my past came out. In a journal assignment titled 'My Anger' I had to write about the various roots of my anger. Not the day-to-day I stubbed my toe or dropped a contact lens down the drain kind of anger, but the anger that lives in you. The anger that you carry and don't let go of. It's there even when you're happy, even when you are on top of the world, it's there, it's just masked well by good stuff.

Anyway, in this assignment I wrote about being a six-year-old girl, I wrote about how I allowed myself to become the object of my cousin's affection. We saw each other often during the summer and during

holidays. And every visit, I'd wake up with my pajamas on inside out, or not on at all. I'd wake up with a soreness between my legs that I was ashamed of. I didn't know the words for what was happening to me when I was six, but I knew enough to be ashamed. I could recall sitting on my grandmother's kitchen counter crying to someone, an aunt maybe? But I was unable to articulate what was going on and eventually the family member got frustrated with me and my lack of communication skills and put me down on the floor and told me to go play outside. It was a story I hadn't told anyone. Ever. And again, I felt it. That small tectonic plate seated deep inside my bowels shifted. I couldn't talk. All I could do was sit silently and shiver. I wanted so desperately to cry but I couldn't force the tears to come, I never could. I could only pull my body up and into itself, my arms hugging my knees. A futile attempt to warm what wasn't cold.

Jill did not press me to give her any details, she did not push me to tell her more about any of the assaults. She let me absorb the gravity of it all. Jill's resolve during our session gave me a newfound confidence in being able to talk to her on a daily basis.

During group meetings I still never volunteered to talk, but I started to enjoy listening. I'd watch Heather's hands as she crocheted some rather amorphous blanket or scarf. Her hand movements were hypnotic. She usually sat next to Angela on these evenings. I didn't mind, because I was starting to hear the other girls'

stories, not just as druggies but as women who felt deeply about others, hurt deeply themselves, and were just never given the right set of tools to cope. I occasionally felt like I could outsmart the system somehow, but that idea was slowly becoming less important as I found similarities in all of our stories. Heather's words never left me. I had to be less about Aubrey and more about something or someone else. I looked at Heather, Angela sitting awkwardly on a cushion next to her. Maybe she was right about everything. I needed to *want* to change and I needed the silly mantras on the wall to not annoy me, but to motivate me somehow.

Looking at Angela and Heather, they were polar opposites. While Heather looked like a frail and ageing ballerina, Angela looked more like a gal on her way to a shot-put event. She was heavy but solid looking. Her short brown hair framed her face in a very pretty way. Add her wire rimmed glasses and she looked professional, even in a gray Briarwood sweatshirt. I guessed she was probably thirty five. Apparently she had been an aspiring attorney at a sizable law firm in Washington. Her problem, as I found out from listening to her talk to Heather in our bedroom, was that she was too nervous to enter a courtroom. One of the associates at her firm was celebrating something once, and they all went out for a martini lunch. Angela, not wanting to be a prude, had a drink too. She had a short motion hearing in front of a local judge soon after, and found out that

alcohol was a perfect relaxant and confidence booster. She spoke clearly and confidently at the hearing, and had found a cure for her nerves. It wasn't long before she started taking a swig of vodka out of a flask in her desk before she'd go to court or meet with opposing counsel.

The flask in her desk quickly became a crutch, a habit that over the course of many months, she could not break. She'd start drinking in the morning to even herself out, and she learned how much she could tolerate throughout the day. She was what she called a 'functional alcoholic'.

One particular evening I was reading over a worksheet assignment from Tim. I had been sitting at the head of my bed with my knees up and Angela came in. She let out a sigh and I looked up at her. She was holding her own pillow as if she intended spending the night. She obviously wanted to talk to Heather, but I wasn't about to leave my own bed for her to do so.

"May I?" she asked, pointing to the foot of the bed.

"Sure thing." I said and pretended to scrunch up a little bit more. Heather was sitting up in her bed, legs stretched down and covered by her blanket, with her crochet bag and accoutrements splayed out in front of her. I suddenly wondered if this was some sort of defense tactic against having Angela sit on her bed.

"So I have to write this assignment on 'Regrettable Incidents' and I don't even know where to start." I wasn't sure if Angela was talking to me or to Heather. I

assumed Heather, so I kept my head down facing my journal.

"What's wrong?" Heather asked.

"Well, I feel like the whole thing is regrettable. I mean. I screwed up my life and I'm embarrassed about it all."

"Just pick one and go with it. I'm sure your counselor will have you explain more in session or one on one. Who is your counselor?"

"Tim."

"Okay, so just write about one thing. Write about something that you did while drunk that you regret and I'm sure in your meeting with him it will turn into a larger conversation." Heather was very matter of fact. Maybe we had bothered her enough with our own problems.

She put down her crochet and looked at Angela.

"What's really the problem? We all have regrettable incidents. Just pick one."

"This assignment just brings up so many memories I'm ashamed of and embarrassed about. I just don't want to even think about how horrible they are. I mean, I just want to erase them all and go back to the person I was before all this shit."

Don't we all, I thought.

"Honey, there is no point in playing that game in your head. We can do that until kingdom come and nothing will change the past and what we've done. It's just an exercise to get you to open up and realize what

addiction actually does to you."

Angela looked at me and back at Heather.

It really was a simple exercise and I wasn't exactly sure why Angela was in our room complaining about it.

"Heather, I just… I blew up my life."

We all did, dumbass, that's why we are here. I was getting annoyed. I clicked my pen top a few times and pretended to check if the ink was working by making little circles on the top of my page.

"Why don't you just tell us what you've written about and see if that helps." Heather was trying to diffuse the situation before I asked Angela to get the hell off my bed. I shot Heather a look. She shrugged, an 'I dunno. I'm not a counselor' look on her face.

Angela took a deep breath and I could feel my bed move with her.

"My regrettable incident was unfortunately the last time I set foot in a courtroom." She started to read from her journal. "I had been drinking during the day to calm my nerves before court and I must have overdone it pretty good because all I remember was that I was in the King County Courthouse and I got confused as to which courtroom I was supposed to be in."

Okay, I was listening now.

She moved uncomfortably. "I walked into the wrong courtroom and it was already in session but I was too drunk to really notice. I remember rolling an ankle on the way up to the defense table. And so I took off my shoes. The whole incident is fuzzy and I am pretty sure

I was in a blackout because later my boss told me that I put down my shoes and my briefcase and approached the bench to ask what matter was being tried. Which, by the way, is completely against the rules of court. But before I got to the bench to ask, I stopped and I vomited all over the floor. Right there in front of the judge, the other attorneys, their client. Oh my god, it was horrible. I had to be carried out by security and triaged by paramedics in the hallway of the courthouse."

I gaped. I'd never heard such a crazy story about someone in court.

"Well that oughta do it, I'd think," said Heather. She was staring at Angela. I laughed to myself. Angela was still looking at her journal.

After a second she looked up and continued her story, but she was no longer reading. She was telling Heather her story now, and she was bitterly ashamed.

She told us that the courtroom had to be shut down, and her client, a poor sucker fighting his second DUI, was left in courtroom four without counsel. Angela had gotten sick in the wrong courtroom and left her her client hanging. She embarrassed herself, her firm, the judge, and a whole host of other people. She was later met at the hospital by one of the partners at her firm. He had been told by physicians that she had suffered alcohol poisoning. He had been hoping that it was just a stomach virus, but rumors had already started that she had been drunk.

Apparently he told Angela that she should have

asked for help before her problem got so bad. They would have gotten her help. But because she had failed to come to them for help and had instead embarrassed the whole firm, she was given a pink slip and the rest of the month's pay to not come back. Not that she wanted to. She was far too embarrassed. She tried to get help through the bar association, they offered her people to talk to, but soon she was drowning her embarrassment and shame with more alcohol, until she ended up unconscious on a city bus and was again transported to the hospital.

The bar association had sent her multiple requests to address some errors in paperwork she had filed, but she had failed to respond to them. Shortly thereafter, she was relieved of her legal privileges by the Washington bar association.

That was her story.

We all had embarrassing stories. Stories I thought I'd never share. Maybe if I didn't share them it would be as if they didn't happen.

I had always tried to wait until the evening to drink and I did so to disappear. This lady had actually been a functional day drunk so that she had more confidence.

Well, until she didn't.

"Wow, honey," Heather said. She had stopped crocheting and was facing Angela intently. "I don't think you had any problem with the assignment." The three of us let out a little giggle, even Angela who had been so anxious about sharing her story.

“The things we do…” Heather’s voice trailed off.

The three of us sat for a few seconds in silence. I thought of Heather’s predicament. The seriousness of it all. I had found Angela’s story entertaining but it too was quite serious. She had blown up her life. We all had and I had no idea how any of us were expected to rebuild. For a fleeting moment I thought, *it would be easier to die.*

Angela looked like she would cry. She pressed her fingers into her eyes from under her glasses. She was too embarrassed to go back home.

“You know, this isn’t my first rehab,” she said somberly.

“I tried another form of ‘rehabilitation’ at her home.” She used air quotes. “All they did was prescribe antabuse and do some sort of brainwave biofeedback. I’d sit in this reclined chair with sensors on in this dark room and this guy would play soft music and dim the lights. It was relaxing but hardly rehabilitative.” She laughed at her own memory.

She said she tried the alternative therapy for two weeks before leaving. Angela drank the night she left the facility.

“I’m going to tell you what I told Aubrey.” Heather said softly.

“No treatment or rehab is going to work until you want it to. But you have to want it to work one hundred times more than you wanted to drink.”

Angela slumped, as if she’d been reprimanded by

her mom for eating too many cookies. "I know. I've heard that before."

Jamie walked by and popped her head in our doorway. "To your room, please. It's almost lights out."

Angela slowly stood to leave and my bed released under her weight.

"Thanks for listening."

"Thanks for sharing," Heather responded.

Maybe Heather should be our counselor.

After she had gone I put my journal down on the nightstand and rolled onto my side looking at Heather. She was collecting her yarn and placing it neatly in its bag under her own nightstand.

"You are so good to her. Patient, I mean."

Heather looked at me thoughtfully. "We are all works in progress."

Ain't that the truth.

"Just because someone's baggage isn't the same size and color as yours doesn't mean it doesn't weigh the same." Heather almost sounded southern.

I smiled and rolled into my back.

"Goodnight," I said to her,

"Goodnight."

For a moment I almost liked being at Briarwood. Though I'd never admit it.

Chapter Seven
Family Day

There's a day at Briarwood dedicated to the family members of residents. Anyone close to the addict is encouraged to come and join in Al Anon meetings and counseling in the men's unit/detox unit. My parents both came on that day but I didn't see them, they still weren't ready to see me. Honestly, I don't know that I was ready to see them either. I imagined Mary's mom, entering Briarwood in her sunglasses. My mother would likely have been the same way. Embarrassed. Raccoon eyed. Maybe if she didn't make direct eye contact with people they wouldn't see her. With her Raybans on no one would recognize her inside or outside of the facility. I was surprised to hear that both my parents had attended that day. They were still married but my addiction had been a spike in their relationship. A wedge. They had dramatically different views on what 'to do with me'. My father, whose fear had made him angry, was torn apart by my near death experiences. He had found me on several occasions, pale, clammy, barely breathing. He had picked me up in his own arms, and rushed me to the hospital in his own truck. Nurses would later recount how, on my latest visit, he had

stormed through the ER doors yelling for someone to help me. He didn't have time for the paperwork for my admission, he wanted me on a gurney and in being treated before he signed any damn paperwork. And people listened. My father was larger than life, is larger than life. He may only stand about five foot eleven but his wide shoulders, narrow waist and strong legs give him the appearance of a man with authority. He was typically soft spoken, but on these occasions where his daughter's life was on the line, he was a lion.

My mother, though scared, was also embarrassed. She could tell her friends and family that I was sick but admitting with what had proven nearly impossible. "Cancer would have been easier to deal with," she had said. Not just because it was a diagnosis her friends could swallow and empathize with, but because there was a clear treatment and plan for dealing with cancer. You could cut cancer out, radiate it, fill it with chemotherapy and immunotherapies. Cancer didn't lie, cheat, steal, rob you of your loved one in a way that addiction did. You couldn't get fired over a cancer diagnosis. Cancer patients didn't go missing under bridges. I had wished a million times I had cancer.

Although I wasn't there at the family therapy session, I was given a piece of artwork my parents had created that evening. They had been asked to make a sculpture out of clay that represented where I stood in the family dynamic. What they made surprised me. They had designed what looked like a tree, with me in

the middle, holding my mother and father as limbs. I held them together. I was the trunk of the tree. When Jamie knocked on my door and brought in with her the oddly constructed piece of clay, I didn't know what to think. For the longest time I didn't know what to make of it. It was ugly. Jamie could tell I was confused by the piece, and then she explained what she saw. I was what held my parents together. I was what tore them apart. I was their center. That thought hollowed me out. It felt like someone had attached my insides to a vacuum cleaner and sucked every vital organ out. I folded onto my bed. The sculpture on my nightstand. I couldn't cry. I wanted to but I couldn't. I just stared at the brownish red 'tree' that my parents had created. Neither of them being particularly artistic, this would have been hard for them to do. I could see them balking at the idea of making a clay sculpture. Exchanging funny looks as if it were a bad joke. I tried to imagine them clumsily putting the two narrow limbs on the trunk, quietly arguing over how to smooth down the seams. One branch looked kind of like a child's hand off to the side, the other curved up with three trident like smaller branches. A bent, three pronged fork. I fingered the dark clay trunk. It was hard now, from being baked in the men's unit oven. I would have loved to have seen them make the sculpture together, been a fly on the wall for that exercise.

Heather entered the room quietly, "Are you all right, honey?" She asked. It was past lights out but

because it had been a day disrupted by family members our routine had been off and no one had disciplined us for it.

"Not really," I responded, the side of my face pressed into my pillow.

"I heard your folks came."

"Yeah, but they didn't want to see me."

"Give them some time, they are scared and they are angry because they love you so much."

I sat up and leaned against the headboard and faced Heather as she slowly lowered herself onto her bed.

"Something hurting?" I asked

"Always." She gave a half-hearted laugh.

"How was your meeting with your husband?"

"Jerry? Oh, he's doing all right. Working a lot these days to keep his mind off things."

"Remind me what he does?"

"We own a steel fabrication company, so he outfits dairies and manufacturing plants with the parts they need to run their enterprises. It's like custom steel work for big machines."

I nodded. It sounded interesting. But there was something odd about this tiny woman talking about steel fabrication.

"He's been dealing with my lawyer so I can focus on being here." She looked around the room. The off-white walls and generic farming paintings made it look like a hotel room. A modest one with no extra seating area, no kitchenette and no TV.

"I wish I wanted that."

"What?"

"To be here. I find the group meetings trite and the counseling kind of ridiculous. I don't buy the mantras on the walls. When I look at them they piss me off and I want to tear them down, rip them up, and tell Tim and Jill they are full of crap."

It was the first time I had admitted out loud what I had been thinking all along. I was stunned and felt my face flush. For a split second I was worried about what Heather's response would be.

There was a thoughtful pause before she spoke. She slowly got up and for a second I was afraid she'd leave the room. Instead, she sat down next to me on my bed. She put her hand gently on my thigh.

"I know I made you upset before when we talked, honey, you have to want this. You have to want to change so bad you'd be willing to walk through fire to never drink again… If you don't want this you aren't ready and you won't get better. Sometimes people really do have to hit rock bottom to want to change, but that want, it has to feel like an almost primal need…"

The only 'primal need' I had ever felt was to drink. There was a time not so long ago that my primal need was to run and run hard burning up whatever anger and hurt and misplaced emotions I had. But that desire to run had been cut short with a series of injuries. I used to be afraid of alcohol and drugs. There was a time in my life I refused to drink because I didn't know how it

would affect me. I was afraid of losing control. I think my fear of it was really my conscience saying *you won't know how to stop.* I had such disdain for people who drank and especially people who drank and then drove putting everyone else in danger. Funny how I became what I despised. It was grotesque. I was grotesque. The disease, if you could call it that, was grotesque.

There had been times I'd tried to stop drinking over the past few months. I would tell myself *not today* and then after five o'clock I'd get jittery and anxious. I'd start pacing around looking for something to entertain me or take my mind off of the itch. But the itch would grow and grow and grow until I had to scratch it. I just had to. It was like I was being held underwater and I had to take a drink to come up for air. I'd wake up the next morning unaware of how much I had consumed the night before. I would have one glass of wine and watch *Greys Anatomy*, but by the time the show was over, so was the bottle, and I'd reach for another.

As I sat thinking about this disgusting routine I cringed. It was gross. It was beyond gross. It was... addiction. I couldn't stop until it killed me. Thankfully my father had found me before it really did kill me. When I woke up the last time in the hospital, I had seen the fear and desperation in his eyes and I had promised to get help. To come here and get better. But now Heather was telling me that it wasn't necessarily about where you go, it wasn't about 'getting better' it was about feeling the need to get better. My need to get

better was not as strong as my need to drink. And that was the linchpin.

“How? How do I get to that place of need?” I asked her.

“That’s the biggest question. If I had the answer, I’d be a millionaire helping people get sober all over the country. But honey it doesn’t work that way. It’s not a formula I can give you. This isn’t a logical disease. People argue over it being even *being* a disease for this very reason. If you could find a neuroscientist who could flip the switch, addiction wouldn’t have a place here. Unlike other diseases, the only cure is yourself. I was trying to help you see this before. For a lot of people this is why AA or NA works, they find this ‘higher power’ that they believe in and need instead of the drug.”

“So God is the drug?”

“To some people. To them believing that you can give yourself and your problems over to God, is better than drugs.”

“Phhhffff,” I didn’t even know how to respond to that statement. My family had never been particularly religious and I knew very little about organized religion. Heather could see the disbelief and frustration clouding my thoughts.

“What do you want out of this life?” she asked bluntly.

“What do I want? Well, to not be an alcoholic, is one, maybe have a family someday, do something that

matters, run again. Make my parents proud."

Jamie suddenly appeared in the doorway. "Lights out, ladies."

"Yes, ma'am," we said in unison. Heather lifted herself slowly from my bed and went to the bathroom to get ready for bed. A few minutes later she returned, slowly climbed into bed and pulled her white patchwork quilt up to her ribs. She smoothed it out with her hands. There was a lot she wanted to say.

"I want to want it," I said in a low voice.

"That's a start." she responded turning her end table lamp off.

That night I sat there staring at the ceiling again. *I do, right? I do want this?*

The next morning I was called into a one on one counseling session with our head shrink. I had never been in Amy's office before, nor had I talked with her. We had acknowledged each other in the hallway a few times, but all I knew was that she supervised the other counselors and rarely did any scheduled time with residents.

I was nervous.

My guts were making loud gurgling sounds and I was starting to sweat just enough to be noticeable. Amy walked me to her office. Her heavy frame was wrapped in purple — purple skirt, purple shawl, purple scrunchie holding up a silver messy bun.

She opened the door and allowed me to enter first, and directed me to sit on a couch opposite her computer

desk and chair. She pulled a folding chair out and placed it in front of me. We sat almost toe to toe in her little office. I could smell her perfume, it was nice, not florally, not sugary or overwhelmingly sweet, but clean and crisp.

"It's nice to finally get some one-on-one time with you, Aubrey."

I smiled. I was going to try to be open and honest and find out how you cultivate the feeling of *need...*

"How are you feeling today?"

"I'm okay, I guess."

"Yesterday was family day. You didn't see yours, I see."

"No. I didn't. I guess we just aren't ready." I wanted my words to be solid coming out of my mouth, but instead they were followed by a stone in the back of my throat, a feeling I was about to cry.

"I see. You know, that happens a lot here. Maybe next month they will be ready."

Next month! I looked around her small office. There was a large window behind her desk, but the blinds were down and you couldn't see what was outside. I felt like I needed fresh air. I was starting to suffocate. I felt trapped.

"I wanted to go over what is in your file currently. The amount of time you spend here has a lot to do with how you progress through our program." It was like she had read my mind. "I have some notes here from Tim and Jill that indicate you do not speak in groups or class,

you never share in meetings, you are 'withdrawn' and 'sullen'. Does that sound like you?"

I opened my mouth to argue, and then snapped it shut. My initial reaction was to defend myself, but it had been true. I hated telling people about myself or my addiction. The thought of what I had done, who I had become, made me feel dirty. A kind of dirty you could never wash off. I was afraid that it was the kind of dirty everyone would still be able to see and smell on me after I left Briarwood. If I ever got 'well' I would still have this neon sign above my head screaming, 'FAILURE!'

"I don't think I'd agree with 'withdrawn and sullen'... I don't like speaking in groups and I don't want to share my 'story' with the other girls here... I guess I'd prefer the one-on-one instead of telling the whole world my business."

"Hm," she said. "I see." She went on. "I think that is hard for everyone. Opening up about their most shameful moments is really difficult, uncomfortable, even painful."

She rearranged the papers on her lap and looked back up at me. Her hazel eyes were starting to get that milky look to them, like my grandmother's had when she was still alive.

"I know it's scary to tell people about what we've been through. But it really is important. You see, once you open up you can start to look at yourself again, and move past it. We need to address this thing head on. When you are ready, I really encourage you to tell your

story in group. I think you will find it cathartic."

Cathartic, huh?

"I guess I'm embarrassed."

"Honey, everyone feels the same way about their story, we don't take pride in our failings. We need to move past the shame and start getting our hands dirty with some honest work. Do you want to get better?"

There it was again, do I want to get better? I think so. Yes I want to but it just seems so damn hard. I don't want to face it. I just want someone to give me an injection and tell me I'm cured, I'm no longer an alcoholic.

"I do." My voice was horse with emotion. I was mad at myself for my lack of control. I pulled my legs up and sat cross legged. I pulled my hands inside my sweatshirt sleeves. I wanted to disappear. I wished there was a way I could just figure this out on my own.

"Okay." Amy straightened up in her chair. She looked through a few pieces of paper in her hands before pulling out a worksheet and handing it to me. "We are going to meet again in a couple of days. I want you to have this completed by then. And, I want your goal between now and then to be to share, even if it's just a little, at group meetings."

"Okay." I looked down at the paper she had given me. Who I Do This For. Why Is Getting Sober Important to Me? Who Would Be Affected If I Die. *Grim.*

"Great," she said. She stood up. My indication that

the meeting was over and it was time to leave.

On my way back to my room I passed Roz in the main hall that ran behind the dining room and main meeting room. She was holding a chocolate chip granola bar.

“Holy shit, did you have to talk to Amy? What did you do? Are they kicking you out?”

“What? No Roz. It was just a meeting.”

“Well, I hate to be the messenger or whatever, but the only people who see Amy are people getting kicked out or other counselors.”

“I’m not getting kicked out, Roz.” She was pissing me off. There was something so irritating about her. It was like she actually enjoyed being at Briarwood and her seniority made her that much more intolerable.

I was spared having to talk with her any more by a loud beeping noise. We looked at each other wide-eyed. That was a medical alert from someone’s room. Jamie and a nurse with her stethoscope swinging around her neck, went jogging by us toward the stairs to the residents’ rooms. Our eyes followed them up the stairs, we exchanged anxious glances and immediately followed.

Heather.

I don’t know how I knew, but I did. Roz and I reached the landing and sure enough Jamie was standing in the entrance to my bedroom, cell phone in hand. She put it to her ear,

“Hi. Yes, I need an ambulance to 1921 Columbia. I

think we have a patient suffering a heart attack.” Her words were quick and clipped.

Roz grabbed my hand with hers. It felt cold and slightly damp. I looked down, her other hand still clutched the granola bar.

“Ladies, I need you to go downstairs.” Jamie’s words were direct, punctuated by the gravity of the situation. Her cell phone was still in her ear. She looked into my room

“We have a nurse assessing her now.”

She looked back at Roz and I, frozen in place. “Now, ladies!”

Roz dropped my hand and we turned and jogged back down the stairs and into the front foyer.

I was not the praying type. I didn’t really know how to pray, or to whom. But as I stood there in the foyer I prayed for the first time, a true, desperate plea, for someone to save Heather. My hands were clasped in front of me, fingers gripping each other. And though my eyes were frozen on the stairs that lead up to our room, I was sending every deity a petition for her safety.

Girls started to filter into the foyer around us. Whispering. By now everyone knew something had happened to my roommate. I felt oddly uncomfortable, their looks had not been accusatory, rather they gave me worried exchanges.

It had seemed like too long, but finally a fire truck and an ambulance pulled up out front at the same time. We all watched through the bay window as two

paramedics in blue jumpsuits hurried up the concrete walkway with a yellow stretcher and medical bags.

They came right in through the heavy front door and the receptionist hurried around the front desk and pointed them up the stairs.

Moments later the paramedics had Heather, barely conscious, oxygen mask on, laying on a stretcher, hustled out the front door. I didn't get a clear look at her face. I wanted some indication that she was still with us. But everything was very quick, people spoke in clipped tones and orders. We were informed that Heather would be taken to Saint Alphonsus, as it was the closest hospital.

All of the residents watched from the big bay window as the paramedics loaded her small frame into the back of the ambulance and drove off, lights flashing. We were all quiet.

There wasn't a single girl at the house that didn't like Heather. There was nothing *not* to like about her. She was sweet, motherly, not the type of person I'd ever have expected to meet in a rehab facility. But just the kind of person I felt like I needed to be around. *Mom.*

For the next hour or so the whole house was a-buzz. A rumor started somewhere that Heather had attempted suicide, others said she had a heart attack, there was even a question if Heather had somehow managed to get her hands on some alcohol product and swallowed it. None of those rumors were founded. But all night, there was gossip. That evening's meeting centered around

Heather. It got to the point that Tim had to stop everyone and call a house meeting. Around eight o'clock that evening we all sat around in a semicircle on the meeting room floor and listened to Tim recount the events of the day and the doctor's diagnosis that Heather had suffered what looked like a heart attack but wasn't. "She suffered from what they call 'broken heart syndrome'," he said. He sat down on the folding chair that represented the head of the group or meeting leader's position. "It's a rare condition that occurs after someone has suffered a particularly great loss or severe emotional stress. In this case, Heather is facing both. She has a long road ahead of her and I expect everyone to be very supportive of her when she returns."

"Heather is coming back?" Angela was shocked. We all were.

"Yes. The doctors at Saint Alphonsus wanted to observe her for at least the night, maybe tomorrow, but she will likely be returning here."

I let out a breath I didn't know I was holding. Tim looked at me.

"Is there anything you'd like to add, Aubrey?" His tone was sincere. He knew that I had developed a fondness for Heather.

"No… I'm just glad she's going to be all right." My eyes drifted around the room to all the girls sitting on the floor, most of them were cross legged, A few of them wore their Briarwood sweatshirts. They murmured in agreement.

That night as we lined up for our nightly medicines, people were abnormally quiet. Even Roz. We leaned against the old stucco walls, and stared into space. For some reason I didn't want to go to bed in my room alone. I was very suddenly and sharply reminded that I was still afraid of being by myself. I knew that when I was alone my thoughts would wander to far, dark agitated places. I knew that when I was alone, especially in the evening, I'd get anxious and jittery, and that was the time I wanted to be rid of myself. Heather had a way of keeping me distracted with small talk and crochet.

When I was alone I wanted to disappear. I wanted to take something to make me disappear. I didn't want to die necessarily, I just wanted to be a spirit floating about the rooms, observing life and no longer living it. I had already fucked mine up, so it wasn't really worth living any more, but I would like to be an observer.

I knew this was probably one of those times a patient should see a counselor about what they were feeling and thinking. I didn't have the nerve to go seeking anyone, especially not Tim. I wanted Jill to appear and recognize my internal conflict going on. I wanted someone to pull me aside. But no one did.

That night, and for several nights afterward, I fantasized about sneaking out of the house. The window in my room didn't open far enough for me to squeeze out, and I wasn't going to just walk out the front door. There was no way to go through the kitchen to get out without being seen. I replayed different scenarios over

and over in my head. *If I could just get out without being caught I could quickly find my way to a grocery store or even a convenience store, I'd run back and get in bed and no one would be the wiser.* I just needed to calm the jitters and anxiety and go to sleep.

I was not getting better. This much was obvious. I had been in Briarwood for almost a month and I hadn't had any of these feelings before. My old alcoholic self, had returned in the absence of Heather. I couldn't be alone. Finally, I walked down to the dining room. It was past lights out, but I really didn't care. I think somewhere inside I wanted to get caught. I wanted someone to know how I was feeling. I was certain that Jamie was on shift tonight and was probably hanging around in the foyer or up at the front desk, but she wasn't.

I was surprised to see a thin woman, with dark hair swept up in a messy knot, sitting in the dining room, her back to me. It looked like she was bent over a cup of tea. She had a gray sweatshirt on, so I assumed it was a new resident. But when she turned, I saw it was Jill. She looked surprised to see me.

"You should be in bed," she said, wiping the mascara from the corner of her right eye.

"I know, I couldn't sleep."

"Heather?"

"Yes? No…not really…" My voice trailed off. I really wanted to talk to her but I just couldn't find the words. My eyes searched the walls desperately.

"Here, come sit." She pulled out a chair.

It was against the rules for me to be down here and most likely against the rules for her to be inviting me to join her for tea, but I was grateful for the invitation. Even if it meant that I'd be admonished by Tim later. Suddenly the thought of Tim made me nervous, where was he?

"Don't worry. It's just us. Tim's at home and the nurses are in the back." She read my mind again.

"Are you okay?" I asked. It was always easier to ask other people about their problems than it was to try to explain and untangle my own. Besides, I actually was interested in what was going on with Jill.

"Marital differences." Jill turned to me and half smiled. "It will be okay."

"I'm sorry," I said, not meeting her in the eye.

I wasn't really sure how to respond, I was the wrong person to talk about relationships with. I'd only had two relationships that really meant anything. One back in college, and I had no idea what happened to it. It just kind of dissolved as we spent time apart one summer. The other, well, died.

The other men who I'd dated casually were just 'gap fillers'. I was realizing my fear of being alone went beyond just my alcoholism.

Suddenly there was a cup of hot tea in front of me. I had been in my own head so deep that I hadn't seen Jill get up and fill a cup for me.

"Thank you." I grabbed the string of the tea bag and

began bouncing the little packet up and down in the hot water.

"Are you thinking about Heather?" she asked.

"Actually no. I mean, I really hope she's okay and she comes back soon. I miss her. But no, I just can't sleep."

"Can't sleep, or hate being alone?" Jill's words were soft but her directness was unexpected.

I looked her in the eyes. You could tell she'd been crying. The whites were bloodshot and her mascara had been cleaned off. She was pretty even with no eye makeup, even after crying.

I sighed. "It's being alone, I guess. I get uncomfortable in my own skin. Like I want to peel it off and walk away from myself a completely different person."

Jill smiled. "Oh, I think we all know that feeling quite well."

I smiled into my tea. "Yeah but, for some reason… I just can't get through it." I doubted I was making any sense but I didn't have the words for how I was feeling, or rather, I didn't have the guts to explain.

"Get through what?"

"Get through the night."

Jill looked at me thoughtfully and put both hands around her cup, her thumbs rubbed the top edge.

"Anxiety and depression are really common at night. Especially for people who are prone to it like us. You know, I was the same way for a very long time. I

used to need someone to be with me at night, addict that I am. It wasn't until I started getting help in meetings that some of that anxiety went away. Then eventually, I met Tim and we would email each other every night until we'd fall asleep. I guess that's how we fell in love." She looked as if she might cry, again. But she took a sip of tea instead. "Tell me about it. What's going on in Aubrey that you can't get away from?"

"That's one way to put it." I gave her a half smile and settled into my chair a little more. "I guess I get anxious, jittery even, I need to get out of myself. I think about my failures, I think about being alone, and I just want to unzip myself and disappear. I want to disappear but not like die... Just sleep for a while or something..." I couldn't quite get the words the way I wanted them.

Jill looked from me back to her tea and bounced her tea bag up and down. Thinking.

"I know you have a hard time with the statements on the walls here. Especially the ones about finding your 'higher power' but that's where it comes in. What we are trying to help you see is that, when you feel anxious and jittery, you need to be able to turn to something bigger than yourself to take over. Some people hand it over to God, other people imagine something else — it's a way to put your demons somewhere else. It takes repetition and time, but it works."

These were not the words I wanted to hear. I took a large gulp of hot tea to swallow my frustration and the lump that was forming.

Jill could see right through me.

"You can always borrow mine."

"Your what?"

"Well, until you find your 'higher power' you can borrow mine."

I looked at her skeptically.

"I'm serious, just picture Sam Elliot on a horse with a western background..."

I laughed. "Sam Elliot is your God?"

"No, he's just what I picture my higher power to be..." She smiled sheepishly.

"I don't think that's going to work..." I smiled and looked down at my tea, the steam had stopped rising off of it.

"Might as well try. When your jitters get bad."

"Okay." I smiled lightly. "On that note, I'm going to head back to my room."

"Hey, since you don't have a roommate, why don't you try reading."

"Reading?"

"You need a distraction. Grab a book out of the foyer and just give it a try, maybe you can out-read the jitters tonight and we can address the rest tomorrow."

"Thanks, Jill."

I stood to go and was reminded she too had an issue that evening. "Are you sure you're okay?"

"Oh yeah. Someday you'll get married and you'll see, it's not all it's cracked up to be sometimes. Sometimes being an adult really sucks."

"Yeah." Didn't I know it?

As I walked to the foyer I smiled at the thought of getting married. Jill saw a future in me. Maybe I could get better. Maybe I would have a second chance at life.

The foyer was dark but a reading lamp was left on over my favorite chair. And behind it was a small bookshelf with a random assortment of novels people had left over time. I looked over the titles. Many of them were romantic bodice-ripper type books, but one title stuck out *The Power of One*, by Bryce Courtenay. It was the title, not the synopsis on the back that made me pick the book. It actually didn't sound like a book I'd traditionally pick off of a shelf. But that night, as I read about the young Peekay and his lofty dream to be the welterweight champion of the world, another one of those plates deep inside seemed to shift. The book made me feel like running again. I wasn't one for meditation, but little Peekay had a place he went in his head that I could imagine. Why I imagined it in black and white I don't know, but I could go there with him. Jumping from stone to stone across a wide shallow creek. Getting to the other side and sitting under the limbs of an old tree. In my mind the tree resembled a mangrove with wide exposed roots I could sit on. Courtenay's book gave power to a very powerless creature in my mind. Maybe I could fight for my sobriety as his character fought for the welterweight title. Maybe, just maybe, my flame would not go out.

Chapter Eight
The Second Month

I went everywhere with my book. I gripped it like a child would her teddy bear. It sat under my chair during small group meetings and next to me as I sat cross-legged at the others. I used it to avoid talking to people at breakfast. I read splayed out on my bed to avoid Angela. I would open it and stare at it during lunch, and on the second or third day of this new ritual Jill asked me in small group if I was enjoying my book. She pointed under my chair.

"Yes, very much." I leaned over and grabbed it from beneath me, placing it squarely on my lap I smoothed down the bumpy front cover.

Suddenly it was as if nothing could hold the words back. "It's about a boy in South Africa during World War Two, who decides he wants to be the welterweight boxing champion of the world. He is horribly abused at boarding school and gets the nickname Peekay. On a train ride to visit his grandfather he meets a famous boxer who shows him his gloves and teaches him that boxing, or rather difficulties in life, are about leading with your head and letting your heart follow.

"For the longest time I've heard that 'fake it until

you make it' line and I never really got it until reading the book. Peekay is learning to navigate the world, alone, but everytime he meets someone he is able to learn something from them, walk away with the tools he needs to get through another trial. His medicine man taught him how to meditate, and I've never been one for meditation, but I can really see where he goes in his mind, I can see the stone steps in the creek, the waterfall, all of it.

"Right now I'm at a place in the book where Peekay is working in a mine, getting physically stronger and earning money for school. He's really a smart guy, and he's had to outsmart a lot of dangerous people along the way. He's also internalized a lot of really wonderful ideas, ones that I think I can use in my own life..." I felt the eyes of everyone in the room room on me. I had been talking about a book, *a book*, most likely not read by anyone else in the room. I had never spoken so much in group.

"What kind of ideas?" Jill asked.

"Well..." I wanted to say that *God was a shithead,* because that's what Peekay had told his mother. But I didn't really think that was true any more, and I don't think Peekay really felt that either.

"I guess I like the idea that if you put your mind to something, even if you can't start out wholeheartedly, your heart will get there if you keep telling yourself you can."

Roz laughed. "You sound like the Little Engine

That Could."

"Roz, I think that's exactly what she's saying, just in a more sophisticated way," said Jill.

Roz looked like she'd been slapped.

My eyes were locked on the book cover. My face felt hot. The familiar desire to disappear returned and I put my left leg under my butt as if I could shrink that way.

"Okay, why don't we all try something different today?" Jill looked around the room but I refused to make eye contact.

"Your assignment tonight is to write your own epigram or saying. Like your own personal motto. What would it be?"

"I can be sober!" Roz said sarcastically.

Jill ignored her and went on. "This is like a statement you will tell yourself to get through tough times. I don't want you to use any that are on the walls in here, I want you to write your own."

There was grumbling from most of the girls in the room.

Group was over. I leaned down to pick up the rest of my things when Jill approached me. "Thank you for sharing today."

I smiled half-heartedly. I felt like I had cheated because I had discussed a book in group and I had yet to share my story.

By the time my thirty days at Briarwood rolled around, I was given a few more 'privileges'. I was

finally allowed to go outside. Outside really only meant that I could sit on the front porch or back patio, but I jumped on the opportunity on day thirty-one. That morning I stood on the porch of the old Briarwood house and I took a deep breath. The wet air was so refreshing, all I wanted to do was sit on the old wooden porch swing and breathe the air outside. The swing had white paint flakes peeling off, but I didn't care, I sat on it anyways, clutching my book. You couldn't see the sidewalk from the swing so no one could see me either. There was a big hedge in front of the porch that gave the east side of the window, and the swing, privacy from the outside world. The house didn't look any different than any other old Victorian on the block. Its yellow paint was peeling slightly but there was no big sign or billboard announcing that this house was an inpatient rehabilitation facility. There was only a small placard to the right of the massive oak door that said 'Briarwood' and that was all.

I sat on the swing and folded my legs up beside me. There was a slight breeze and the heavy smell of juniper made me think of my grandparents. They always had a huge juniper branch over their fireplace during the holidays and it made their whole house smell like cedar and gin. I had fond memories of my childhood visiting them. We saw them quite often when I was a child and I had spent a lot of time with them during college, helping them around their ranch in the summer. Moving sprinklers, feeding horses, driving the tractor around the

corral moving manure. My grandparents were the very symbol of a family matriarch and patriarch. They were my father's parents, together since the sixth grade. My grandfather worked and my grandmother stayed home with the four kids. They had weathered it all, wars, recessions, the loss of a child, and they had remained together for nearly seventy years. When they passed, they passed almost together. My grandfather first, my grandmother a month later. They were always together. Her heart couldn't take being apart from his.

I leaned my head back on the swing back and stared up at the ceiling. The paint was almost gone on the eaves.

That's what I wanted. I remembered being with them at a doctor's appointment once, and watching my grandfather, well into his eighties, help my grandmother into her coat. It was a simple gesture, a tender one, one that stuck with me. *I wanted that someday.* They spoke volumes to each other with an expression. They knew each other's life stories because they were in it. I know it wasn't always a perfect marriage, I'm not that naive. I'd seen my grandmother, upset over something my grandfather had said, 'accidently' dropped broccoli in his wine glass at dinner. My grandfather abhorred broccoli, his wine was ruined. But the argument had been won, and he ceded. There were many other arguments I'm sure I missed, wars that were waged behind closed doors. They were a traditional nineteen fifties family and they were not about to let the rest of

the world, or even family, see their faults. The only fault they may have had was their enjoyment of the drink. I was probably six years old the first time I made my grandparents a gin and tonic. They started drinking at five o'clock on the spot and didn't quit until bedtime. Gin before dinner, wine with dinner, scotch after dessert. *Ugh.*

The thought of gin made my stomach turn. Even in my most desperate of times I couldn't swallow gin, it made me gag. I had tried to sneak a shot of it once in my grandparents' pantry but all I had managed to do was upset the entire contents of my stomach into the hall bathroom toilet. Oddly enough, I loved the smell of juniper.

"Aubrey. Time for group." Jamie stuck her head out the front door and reminded me that I needed to come in and get ready for the morning's meeting.

I got up from the swing, dusted off my bottom, and headed inside. The smell inside left much to be desired. It was stale, like too many bodies in one place. It wasn't dirty, just warm and the air was thicker than outside. I wandered into the meeting room and took my seat. Tim was leading the group today and he looked like he might get sick. He had run his hands through his hair too many times and it was all messed up on one side.

"Good morning, ladies."

"Good morning, Tim." We sounded like school girls welcoming the principal.

Roz let out a puff of air and everyone looked in her

direction.

“Before we get side tracked today…” Tim started. “I have some news…” He took a long pause and rubbed his hands together anxiously. “Several of you knew Mary, she was with us for a while and left about three weeks ago after a relapse.” My heart sank, I felt like lead had been injected into my legs, I couldn’t move.

Tim cleared his throat uncomfortably. His weight switched to his left leg and he brought his right hand up to smooth down the hair on the back of his head.

“Mary is gone. She passed away yesterday morning. Her parents called to tell us and thank everyone here for trying to support her.”

I looked down at my right ankle, the strings from the knot of my friendship bracelet peeked out from underneath the hem of my jeans.

Tim was looking at the ground shaking his head. “This is serious business, ladies. Almost two hundred people in this country die every day from a drug overdose. I read somewhere that alcoholism is the third leading cause of preventable death. Only about ten percent of alcoholics and addicts get help and recover.” Tim was visibly frustrated and shaken by news of Mary. He shifted his weight again, then walked over to the corner of the room and grabbed a chair. He propped it down in front of us, sat, and put his face in his hands. His palms pressed into his eyes like he had a terrible headache. “You have to see what is happening here… You have to want to be here and want to get better or

you need to leave."

I felt like he was speaking directly to me but his head was looking down.

Jill, who had been leaning against the hall entrance, walked into the room and placed a loving hand on Tim's back. He didn't look up.

"Ladies, I am going to take over the group today." She patted Tim, he stood, gave her a quick hug and a kiss on the top of her head and left the room without saying anything else.

"We care about you guys. We spend months with you, trying to get to the root of the problem, trying to help you see your disease as it is, a disease." She sighed. "Tim's right, we can't save anyone, no matter how hard we try or want to. We can't save you. You have to do that. Coming here was a step, we try to give you the tools you need, but this has to be a commitment to a new way of thinking about things. A new way of coping. A new way of life."

The girls around me squirmed slightly, settling back into their seats. Sara was twisting a piece of her silky brown hair anxiously. Roz was even looking a little uncomfortable. Her Converse feet were planted firmly on the ground, her elbows on her knees.

"Addiction is an unbiased enemy, it can hijack the life of a brilliant CEO or a hard-working fireman. It doesn't care if you are brown, yellow or purple, it doesn't care what side of the tracks you grew up on. Anyone can be an addict, once that switch is flipped in

the nucleus accumbens it is incredibly hard work to ignore it."

"Nucleus accumbens?" Sara asked

"Yes. Sorry, it's what people call the pleasure center of the brain. We will actually be talking tomorrow about how drugs affect the brain, but for now let's focus on what Tim was getting at. *Need.* You need to *want* to change." Her words were punctuated.

Jill led the meeting like any other, except there was a seriousness about her and the rest of us that wasn't there before. Mary's death had affected everyone. Even Roz was unusually quiet.

After the group meeting I found Heather had returned and was in our room resting. I didn't want to bother her so I went back down to the dining room and rummaged around for a snack. With a nutrigrain bar in hand, I went to the foyer to read in peace. When I got there, Jamie was sitting in 'my' chair. She had been crying. I could only assume it was because of Mary. She looked up at me.

"I'm sorry. I didn't mean to bother you." For a second I wasn't sure where to go. My body felt out of place in the house.

"No, no, it's fine, come sit." She wiped her face and her nose with a small towel I recognized from the kitchen.

"Were you and Mary close?" I asked.

Jamie let out a little laugh. "No actually, I found her to be one of our most difficult residents. Oh, don't get

me wrong I feel terrible about what happened and I feel awful for her parents, but I think we all knew that Mary didn't want help."

She picked up her towel with her right hand and tried to smooth out the mascara under her eyes. "I'm actually a mess right now because I was dumped." She looked at me with a broken smile. "I really liked him." Tears were coming back strong now and I was caught off guard. "We were together for three years, and I actually could see us having a future together." The words started to catch in her throat and she stopped, playing with the towel in her hands. She looked up at the ceiling like she might talk out loud to God, but she didn't. She twisted the towel and looked back down at it as if she could ring out her tears. "Ugh I just feel like I should have seen this coming. Like all good things eventually come to an end, ya know? I just wasn't ready for this."

"I'm sorry, Jamie… It was totally out of the blue?"

She looked at me as if she had forgotten who she was talking to. She shook her head. "We had been arguing over my job, it's demanding, it's a lot of hours, but I love it, it's what I'm good at and I want to be here. He thought it was sucking the life out of me and I didn't have enough time and energy for him. That was kind of true. But apparently he'd had enough." She put her palm up to her temple and leaned against it and into the chair wiping her nose with the towel in the other hand.

"I'm sorry," I said again. Wishing I had a way to

heal what was hurting. “I know what it feels like to lose someone you saw your whole life with…” There was that awkward pause again and Jamie looked at me with expectant eyes. Whether she wanted to hear my story or just needed the distraction, I’ll never know. But I lowered myself to the fireplace with my book on my lap. I traced the words with my fingers and thought back to another time. Another time and place and a different Aubrey.

“Back before all this,” I waved my hand around to indicate Briarwood, “I was with someone on and off for almost seven years. He was the first one I was ever with. He was athletic, handsome, we loved a lot of the same things. You’ll never believe this, but our first date was actually in Ireland.” I looked up to see Jamie’s expression. She wasn’t crying any more and she looked honestly interested. I looked back at my lap, remembering the time as if it were yesterday.

“I had been living in California with an aunt of mine and he was working as a manager of a restaurant in Florida, and we met at this running and training camp. I had flown out there expecting to only be there a week or so, but after meeting him I decided to stay longer. By the end of our time at the camp he asked me if I’d be his date to a wedding in a few weeks. I said ‘sure’ and before I knew it, we were meeting at JFK to go to his best friend’s wedding in Shannon, Ireland.” I laughed at my once carefree self. “He was fun and romantic. From day one it was like we’d known each other forever. The

only problem I ever really had was his lack of ambition. I wanted everything — I wanted to be a professional athlete, a lawyer, someday a wife and mom, and he was okay just sitting at home watching ESPN on a loop. Once he had a friend over for dinner and actually told this guy that I was going to be his 'sugar mama'. We were all hanging out in our little rental house and I remember being kinda stunned that he expected me to take care of him, but I guess that's the direction things were going. I always wanted more, I could never just be happy with where I was at the moment. Like I had something to prove to someone, ya know?"

Jamie was leaning in listening to me.

"I decided to go back to school to become a lawyer and he wanted to come with me, but I just couldn't imagine coming home from school every day with mountains of homework and him just sitting on the couch with ESPN on. So I said no, but we didn't really break up. I went to school and would fly back to Florida to visit and he'd fly out to see me. I could see us getting married after graduation and having kids… But then one day, right before graduation, I got a call from his mom. He had been in a terrible car accident. He was flown by helicopter to Saint Mary's in Miami. They put him on life support and all we could do was pray. I was headed out to see him, I was literally on the freeway to the airport, when his mom called and asked me not to come. She didn't want my last memories of him to be of him in this rotating bed on life support, swollen and well, a

vegetable.

"I was never the same after that. That's actually when I started drinking at night. I couldn't talk to Seth at night any more to get to sleep, so I would drink and pass out. Every night it became my thing. I had an injury so I couldn't run at the time. I tried riding my bike instead but then I got hurt even worse. Everything just started to fall apart. I started drinking even more. Then it started to get scary because I would have to drink to sleep. I started getting jittery in the evening and anxious. I couldn't *not* drink. I drank to disappear, to not think about things. I didn't see my future any more, not one I wanted anyway. I couldn't run, couldn't ride my bike, didn't want to be a lawyer any more, I had lost Seth… So I drank myself right off a cliff, just decided to put the car in drive and go for it. I drove over a two hundred foot ravine in a failed attempt to kill myself, I guess." I shifted awkwardly. The brick hearth underneath me was digging into my thigh uncomfortably. I had never talked about my attempted suicide with anyone. "The paramedics found me without a scratch and claimed it was a miracle. But I couldn't stop, not even after that."

I pressed my hands into the book and fought back the rock that was forming in my throat. "I drank so I didn't have to face my losses. I lost Seth, and soon after I lost my job, family members and friends slowly exited stage left when they saw me going down in flames. I wanted to die but I was afraid to actually do it. I went so far as to wrap my closet in blue tarps so that when I shot

myself my parents would have less to clean up. But I couldn't do it, I couldn't pull the trigger…"

Suddenly I realized where I was in my story and I felt completely embarrassed. "Oh my God, I'm sorry." I looked at Jamie, her lips were parted and she was looking at me intently. "Jamie, I'm sorry, this was about you and your breakup and I totally turned it into a thing about me and my baggage."

Jamie smiled, her blotchy red face was still pretty even after crying. She smiled at me "You did it."

"I did what?"

"You just told your story."

I let out a sigh. "Yeah well, for the most part."

"I'm sorry about Seth," she said.

"I'm sorry about… what's his name?"

"Devon."

"I'm sorry about Devon." There was a pause. "It's really his loss."

Jamie climbed down off the chair and came and sat with me on the brick hearth. She wrapped an arm around me in a hug.

Just two broken girls hanging out.

The soft sound of a classical piano separated us. "Who is that?" Jamie asked, but not directly to me.

"I bet you it's Roz," I said, "You haven't heard her play? She's amazing."

Jamie looked at me quizzically, shook her head and stood up.

"Come on," she nodded toward the hallway and

stuffed a corner of her well-used towel in the back of her jeans as if she would use it later to clean.

I stood up, realizing I had smashed a nutrigrain bar, still in its package. I tossed it in the garbage as we left the foyer and started down the hallway to the group room.

In the group room a couple of girls sat on pillows on the floor, a few of them had their journals with them. Tim and Jill sat in chairs against the wall behind everyone. They looked like satisfied parents at a kids' recital. Everyone was quietly facing the front of the room where Roz sat at the old piano. She was playing *Moonlight Sonata* again but slower this time.

I slowly walked up to the semi-circle of girls. There was a small space between Heather and Sara, so I squeezed in and sat cross legged on the floor. Heather's boney shoulder bumped me in a hello and she turned and smiled at me. I smiled back, sincerely happy to see her back with us again.

Sara leaned towards me without facing me and whispered, "Roz wanted to do something for Mary. Tim said we could get together for a little while here if we wanted."

I nodded. I didn't need the explanation but I could tell Sara was trying to be friendly. I found that I appreciated it, where I once might have found her rather obvious remark annoying.

Roz finished the piece and sat for a second looking at the keys before carefully shutting the wooden bifold

cover over them.

The girls on the floor clapped lightly.

"Thank you, Roz," Jill said as she approached the front of the room. She clasped her hands in front of her chest. "That was very nice. Now we should all return to bed. Tomorrow, if you are with Tim you will actually be meeting in the foyer."

"Aubrey," I jumped as she addressed me.

"You need to meet with Amy first thing. She will be expecting you in her office."

Oh shit! My homework! I had completely forgotten to write anything. I accidentally made eye contact with Roz who was coming down off the makeshift stage. Her eyes got big and eyebrows raised, all of her facial jewelry raised with them.

I was surely going to be reprimanded.

My stomach turned and I could feel my heart rate rise with anxiety. I had never in my life forgotten to turn in a homework assignment.

That night I stayed up scribbling, and crossing words out. The next morning, Heather woke me. I had fallen asleep writing. I got dressed quickly and washed my face. Heather asked me if I was okay. . I shook my head. I'd have to talk with her after I met with Amy. She gave my shoulder a squeeze and let me go. I hurried out of our room with my journal and started down the hall to Amy's office. I stopped ten feet from her door, put my things on the ground and put my long brown hair into a high ponytail with the hair band that sat

permanently around my wrist. I needed to pull it together. As if putting my hair up would help. I was just going to have to fake confidence and tell her it had been a busy week. I bent down to grab my book and journal and once again saw my friendship bracelet peeking out from under the ratty hem of my pants. I tucked it up under the cuff of my jeans, stood and almost collided with Jamie who was coming out of Amy's office.

"Whoa," she said, smiling at me. "You okay there?"

"Yeah, sorry. I didn't mean to almost take you out."

Jamie smiled. "No worries. Are you sure you're okay?"

"Yeah."

"All right I'll see you later." She smiled and headed down toward the hall to the group meeting room. She had recovered from last night, the redness on her face was gone.

I tried to compose myself and took a deep breath, but I could feel the solid mass forming in my throat. I entered Amy's office.

Amy was sitting behind her desk typing something into her computer. She looked over the top of her glasses at the screen and pecked at the keys. The way she typed made the keyboard look awkward, as if the letters were always moving away from her.

"Just a second, honey." She didn't look at me. Her messy bun was losing tendrils around her face and it made her look flustered. I sat down on the couch with

my journal and my book on my lap and waited nervously. When she finally stopped typing she took her glasses off and set them on the desk pinching the space between her eyes. She stood up slowly, rounded the corner of her desk and leaned against it facing me. Again she was dressed in purple again, from head to Danskin toe.

"I just spoke with Jamie about you."

My stomach grumbled loudly and I looked up at her a little embarrassed.

"It sounds like you and she had quite the talk." Her hands braced herself against the desk behind her. I didn't know what to say in response so I just looked at her blankly. Preparing myself for her to ask me about my unfinished homework assignment.

"You know, it's an awfully good sign when a resident can use their own experiences to help someone else in an emotional time."

She turned and grabbed a folder off her desk behind her, and a pad of paper. She flipped through them until she found the one she wanted. She scanned it with her eyes for a moment and then looked at me.

"You aren't finding the system here as offensive as you did in the beginning are you?"

I was surprised by the question. "I, I guess not. I haven't really thought about it that much. I mean, I still struggle with some things but I do see the purpose in a lot of the exercises we do here. If that's what you mean."

"It is. Good. Now, I know Mary was your

roommate and her passing has really affected the house. I'm wondering how you are doing with the news."

I thought about my response, words I wanted to say rolled around in my mouth like marbles. There wasn't a 'correct' response here but I was anxious to tell her how I really felt. "I'm angry at her." Was all that came out. I looked up at Amy and her look was probing. So I continued, "I knew she wasn't getting better, we all did, I'm sad and I'm angry and I'm frustrated. I guess when she left with her parents I was hoping things would be different for her. But deep down I knew they wouldn't be."

"I think we all agree with that." Amy looked down at her mary janes and rolled her ankles outward and then back in. She looked up at me. "The last time we talked, we talked about wanting to disappear, you drank because it helped you disappear and fall asleep. I want to talk about that feeling. Can you remember the first time you felt like you wanted to disappear? Maybe not necessarily drink, but that first time you felt you wanted to be invisible. It's a feeling we've all had."

"Gosh, I bet I was in the first grade the first time I wondered if I was 'different'. I was the responsible kid and I had to sit by our first-grade teacher during reading time and pinch her foot if she fell asleep while reading *Black Beauty*.

"I think I feel too deeply. I felt different from other kids even then. Like I wanted to take on their pain so that they didn't have it, ya know? I met my best friend

in the second grade because she was crying and alone behind one of those modular buildings. I remember asking her to be friends, hoping that that would make her stop crying and be happy. I remember being the only kid in the third and fourth grade to have to deal with a parent that had cancer and feeling like I was in the way at home all the time. But I just wanted to help. I wanted to be the one that was sick so my dad wouldn't be. I wanted to see everything that was going on with my dad, but at the same time I was afraid to. He had to spend so much time away getting treatments and he'd come back looking differently. Thinner, with horrible burns on his neck.

"I remember putting aloe from a real aloe vera plant on her skin. I can still smell it, even today the smell of aloe makes me sick to my stomach.

"I wanted to disappear every time I ever made my parents mad. I wanted to be the perfect kid growing up and I had to get straight As. I hated going away to college because I was scared. More times than I can count or even think of, I wanted to disappear then. In college, I mean. I loved it but I think I hated it more. I always felt awkward, out of place, in the wrong place, never in college did I feel comfortable in my own skin." I stopped talking, thinking that I had probably gone completely off base with my answer to her questions.

"Is that when you started drinking? In college?"

"Yes and no. I was really afraid of drinking, but when I did, I did it to pass out. I only did it a few times

and then I came back around. Tried to focus on running and being a scholar athlete."

"So you were a binge drinker?"

"I don't know that I would say that. There were just a few times in college I drank too much. I don't really know why.

"I was never the person I wanted to be in college. I guess I wasn't as fast as I wanted to be, I wasn't getting the attention the other girls on the team got from the coach or even from the guys on our team. I always felt out of place and like I never had the right thing to say. In class I was fine, I actually really got along well with my professors one-on-one but I was terrible in our sections. Sections were these small groups that met outside of lectures. I hated getting called on. I knew the material but there was this feeling that if I spoke everyone would laugh at me. They never did but that's the fear I had."

Amy looked at me and down at her pad of paper. "In your intake paperwork you described a childhood sexual assault. I know you spoke to Jill briefly about it. But I think maybe it's something we should explore together."

My throat closed.

"It was a family member, a cousin?"

"Yes." My voice was small.

"How old were you?"

"It started when I was about six, it continued until I was about ten or eleven."

"And no one found out."

I shook my head 'no'. This was a subject I'd already discussed and I didn't want to go back there.

"You know, sexual assault is very prominent in addicts and alcoholics, I know it's not a subject you'd like to discuss but is is something you will have to process when you are ready."

I moved uncomfortably on the old couch. I wanted to sink into the space between the cushions and never come back. *Who the hell 'processes' molestation? What does that even mean?*

Amy fidgeted with her fingernails, cleaning some nonexistent gunk out from under her nail. She pressed herself up from the desk and stood before me.

"Jamie told me that you lost someone really close to you, and that might have been what triggered your drinking."

"I did. But I don't think that was the only cause. In a matter of months I had lost Seth, and got really hurt on my bike..." My voice trailed off, remembering a completely different time in my life. A time when exercise had been the drug. I ran or rode every day. I had been super fit and it suited me. I was a decent cyclist, a better runner, a great triathlete.

"What happened?"

"I was on my road bike, racing a collegiate race in Kansas, and went through the back of a van window. I don't remember the actual accident but I remember just before and then after, in the hospital. I broke all my

fingers on my right hand, severed my ulnar nerve, I had a lot of road rash. I was airlifted to the nearest hospital and stitched up and given an MRI where they found swelling at the base of my brainstem. I was all alone there, no family, no friends. My team was still racing and they didn't come pick me up from the hospital until much, much, later. I basically had baseball mitts for hands, they were so swollen. I couldn't dress myself or cut my own food. My parents didn't come out to help me, I don't think they knew how bad my condition was. I didn't have many friends I felt comfortable enough around to help me with things, like getting dressed. It was a really dark time. I wanted to disappear. Not die necessarily. Just disappear. It was obvious to me that I was alone. That loneliness grew and grew and grew until I started drinking and then pushing the few people I did have in my life completely away."

There was a pause as we both imagined the trauma.

"And that's when you attempted suicide."

I was surprised Jamie had told Amy everything.

"Yes." I didn't need to fill her in on any of the details. It was becoming clear that Jamie had laid out my story for Amy. Why, I don't know.

"Did you ever go talk to someone about these things? A counselor? A teacher?"

"No. I mean, my parents forced me to much later. I think they were afraid to lose me and made me go talk to this guy at a clinic. He stank and I didn't respect him at all… it was a waste of time. Sitting in his office made

me angry."

"I see. You weren't ready. That's a lot of loss to deal with. You lost Seth, it sounds like a big part of your identity was lost after your accident... In some ways parts of your childhood were lost too. You had to grow up fast to help with your dad."

I knew Amy was trying to make eye contact but I couldn't look at her, not without crying. I bent over and scratched at an itch on my shin that wasn't there. Sat up and reorganized my things. There was more. There was a lot more but I couldn't openly bring it up. Amy sighed. I finally looked up.

"Have you ever been on an antidepressant?"

"No." I shook my head and played with the edges of my journal.

"I guessed as much, not if you've never talked with anyone about needing help." Amy raised an eyebrow.

"There was always a part of me that knew I needed help."

"Are you ready now? For that help?"

Three weeks ago I would have given an automatic response, I would have said 'yes' but there wouldn't have been any weight behind the word. I thought about Heather, Mary, my parents and then I thought of myself, as a young Aubrey before all this mess. I opened my mouth to talk but it was dry. All the moisture was behind my eyeballs and then it happened, in big heaves and waves, that tsunami I felt on the first day broke through the many barriers of anger and denial and self-loathing

and I cried. It was messy and seemed to come from a place too deep to touch. I cried for myself, for my family, for Mary. My throat seized on every breath. Amy sat next to me on the couch holding a box of tissues. Her warm hand came to rest on my back between my shoulder blades. I hunched over my legs, snot and tears mixed. I grabbed some tissues and wiped at my face folding it again and again after each motion. One box was not going to be enough.

A knock on the door reminded me I was on a schedule. Amy stood up and went to the door, using her body to block the view of whoever was outside from seeing me.

“Can I come get you in a few minutes? Thanks.”

Amy closed the door and returned to her spot in front of me leaning back against her desk with her hips. Her arms folded across her chest.

“We are going to get you started on something right away. We are going to get you feeling better.”

I nodded still looking at the disgusting tissues in my lap.

She returned to her chair behind her desk and shook her mouse awake. She began pecking notes into the computer. I finished blowing my nose. I wasn’t crying any more but my breath was ragged. I was exhausted.

“Okay, then, I’m going to have you go down and see the nurse practitioner today, I’ll email her the order and you can get that done. I want us to give this a try for a couple weeks and see how things go.”

"Thank you." My voice was weak.

"Let's get together in a couple days, I want to see how you are doing, okay?"

Amy pushed herself up from her chair, my indication that it was time to leave, so I gathered up my journal and my book and headed for the door.

"I'm glad you like the book," she said over the top of her computer.

"I do. Thank you." I turned and left her office, I felt like I had run a marathon. All I wanted to do was go lay down in my bed.

When I got to my room, it was empty. I had expected to see Heather, but she wasn't there. I turned off both of our tableside lamps. Put my journal and book down, and lay on top of my bed.

I was making progress. I was doing the work. My heart just needed to follow.

Heather woke me up hours later.

"Honey, you missed lunch, are you okay?"

"It's that late!" I looked at my alarm clock.

"Jamie told us to let you rest. She saved a plate for you in case you are hungry."

I rubbed my eyes, still puffy from my waterworks earlier.

"No one is going to notice." Heather smiled, looking at my puffy eyelids.

"Um, you just did."

"Yeah, but I'm your roommate. Everyone is too busy gossiping about Roz leaving."

"What? Roz is leaving?" I asked in surprise. I sat up in bed, eager for Heather to fill me in.

"Her insurance didn't cover her stay here, and apparently her funds are gone. She's been here ninety-days and can't pay for another month. It's kind of sad actually. She seems scared to go. They are giving her a free week here to sort out her exit plan."

"Oh my gosh. Is she okay? Did she go ballistic when they told her?"

"I don't know, I wasn't there. Apparently someone came over from the other house to fill in Amy about the financial issue. Roz met with them. I have no idea how that conversation went. Anyway, how are *you*?"

"Oh, I'm okay, I was just really tired after meeting with Amy. It's been a long couple of days and I think emotionally I'm exhausted.

Wow, Roz is leaving. Does she know where she's going?"

Heather laughed lightly, amused by my ease of distraction with petty house talk. "I haven't heard."

I felt a twinge of jealousy for Roz, getting to go, but I also knew neither she nor I were ready. Roz was still working out some kinks. Her anger got the best of her. I just hoped she'd learned what she needed from this place to make it on the outside.

Chapter Nine
Sara

Sara had been to Briarwood before. This was her second attempt at getting sober. She was a coke head, but like most of the girls here, she would readily use alcohol or other drugs when her drug of choice wasn't available. The first time I saw Sara, she had come over from the detox unit with a couple of other girls and she seemed young, shy, a little embarrassed that she was back at Briarwood again. She struck me as the type of girl that really just wanted to please people. She was like a puppy that way, tell her what shape you want her in and that's the way she'd bend. She was friendly but younger than me so we didn't really socialize. Not that rehab was really a place for socializing. I'd guessed that she hadn't been through more than the eleventh grade. She was naturally very pretty and had a Jennifer Garner look about her, just petite. When she smiled she had the cutest dimples that made her seem so innocent. Which I guess she really was, barring the drug use.

On a particularly warm day in March the air conditioning in the old house wasn't on or wasn't working, and when we all came down for morning groups we had T-shirts and tank tops on for the first time

since I'd been there. Some girls even had boxer shorts on. I wore an old Nike T-shirt and some capri sweatpants. When I entered the room the only chair available was the one closest to the hall, farthest from the cracked windows. It was muggy and the air felt stagnant. Sara sat next to me, her skinny arms poking out from a pink tank top that said PINK on it in white. She also wore sweats. As I put my notebook down on the floor I noticed there were circular scars on her right upper arm. They were circular and seemed to fan out almost like little suns. I wanted to ask her about them, but Jill walked in and drew a deep breath.

"Sorry it's so hot everyone, we are working on it. If you want to try to crack the windows any more over there Roz that would be great."

Roz stood up and tried to crank the windows open but the old hinges didn't want to move any more.

"What about that fan?" Jill pointed to the ceiling and Roz flipped a couple of switches on the wall until she found the one that turned the large overhead fan on. She was about to return to her seat when Jill said "Roz you can turn the main lights off."

I was hoping this wasn't going to be another meditation class. Roz shut off the overhead light and slumped back into her chair. Jill took off her cardigan and wore a V-neck sleeveless blouse that once again boasted her fullness.

"I know we are all uncomfortable so we are just going to have to make do with what we have. I had

Jamie run out for some more bottled water. Hopefully we can get some air circulating here. That being said, I still expect that we will get through some pretty tough material today."

Jill went to the wall closet where movies and the portable TV were usually stored and brought out an old slide projector I didn't even know we had. She wheeled it to the center of the room and aimed it at the recently cleaned dry erase board.

"If you want to take notes you may, but if you just want to listen that's fine too. Today we are going to look at what makes addiction a disease in my book. We are going to look at the physiological changes that take place in your brain when you 'use'."

Jill plugged in the machine and tried to line up its light as squarely as she could on the dry erase board. She then brought out a binder filled with slides and started arranging them in the circular carousel to be used by the projector. Most of the girls watched her quietly assemble the frames. They were probably as old as I was. I hadn't seen a slide projector in years.

"What is that?" asked Sara

"Oh honey it's a slide projector, haven't you ever seen one?"

"No, is it like the old movies?"

"No, honey, it shows you picture by picture what's on these small slides." Jill held up a small square and inside it was a small picture, too small to see from where we sat.

“The projector will pass a light through them and the images will appear on the white board a hundred times larger.” Jill smiled. “I know this thing is really old but the information on them is just as relevant today as it was when they were made.”

Jill turned on the projector and the familiar sound of a fan and clicking began. I was almost prepared to see pictures of my parents when they were teenagers. My grandparents had loved showing slides of their ‘kids’ when we’d visit. After a massive dinner my grandfather would set up the projector against a blank wall in the living room and he would click through slides of my dad at a lake, fishing, playing football. My grandfather would narrate the same stories again and again. My favorite parts were always of their horses. Dad riding a gelding as he raced across the pasture. Dad was young, bent forward in his saddle, reins in one hand, holding his hat on his head with the other. He looked like he could take on Napoleon.

For a second I thought, *I hope I didn’t break that man.* I hoped I hadn’t made his life such a hot mess that he was unable to fight if and when he needed to. He is stronger than me though, he was never an addict.

We all looked forward to the white board. There in front of us was a picture of the human brain sliced perfectly down the center. There were lines with the names of each piece of the brain — the cerebral cortex, the hippocampus, amygdala — and in bright red lettering the nucleus accumbens. The outlined area

looked like an ear on its side.

"We are going to talk today about the pleasure center of the brain. This is the area of the brain that has an increase in dopamine activity when we use drugs. It's the part of you that says 'ahhh' when you get a stimulus you like. Now this isn't always a bad thing. We want dopamine to be released and enjoy things, but this part of the brain, after continual use of our drug of choice, starts to change the way dopamine receiving neurons regulate proteins in our brain. These changes to the pleasure center of the brain lead to changes in this." The slide was switched for us all to see the frontal lobe structure of the brain. It was outlined in red and labeled clearly. "This is the frontal lobe of your brain, if you touch your forehead and the top of your brow line that is the part of the brain we are talking about. And what do you think it controls?" The room was silent.

I raised my hand as if in class. "Impulse control, judgment, social behaviors, it's what makes us think 'oh drugs are bad, I shouldn't do them' it controls risk taking behaviors. That kind of thing."

"Exactly, Aubrey, very good." Jill smiled and winked at me and clicked a button in her hand to the next slide. I was proud of myself for remembering some of my neuroscience days. I hadn't completely destroyed my brain cells. Yet.

"Addiction is very complex. We try these various drugs out and our brain shouts 'yeehaw' but before you know it, you are continually chasing that first 'high' and

soon it takes more and more to get that high that you were after. This need for more and more is the development of tolerance and dependence and soon a person finds, they have no control. They need some level of that drug in their system to feel 'normal' not even high... the more you have used the more you have changed the pathways in your brain, you have changed your physiology."

Sara's hand shot up. "Can it be changed back? Like can it heal?"

"That's an excellent question, Sara, and I'm not a neurologist but yes, it can. Studies have shown that after several years of absence a person's brain can heal. There are a few exceptions though. People who abuse alcohol for a long time can have permanent brain damage and people that use drugs that have been laced with other chemicals can have lasting damage. Meth-users, for example, are at high risk of severe and permanent brain damage because of the solvents used in creating meth. I have a few slides to show you what I mean." Jill fiddled around with a few of her slides. An image of a butterfly appeared on the board. It wasn't really a butterfly, it was just the butterfly shape.

"See this is what the frontal lobe is supposed to look like, this butterfly shape here is the lateral ventricles. This is what a brain looks like without prolonged drug use." She switched to the next picture. The dark butterfly shape had grown substantially, like a hole in the center of someone's brain. "This is after

prolonged use of ecstasy. Now, this doesn't occur with all addicts, but it is a sharp reminder of what structural changes do take place when drugs are used for any length of time.

"Like I mentioned earlier, long term alcohol use can also cause Korsakofff syndrome, what we lay people call 'wet brain.' It is brain damage that mimics dementia and even amnesia. A chronic alcoholic develops confusion and an inability to process certain emotions because of damage to the hippocampus and amygdala."

The next few pictures were of the bottom part of the brain just below the olfactory bulb, a little polyp type structure labeled the amygdala and hippocampus.

You could feel the nervous energy radiating from Sara.

Jill cut to the next slide, and then the next, they were all black and white pictures of junkies on the street. They were sick and high and looked disgusting.

"Drug addicts have changed the way they view risk. They do things that they never would have done before becoming dependent on a drug. Once they have affected their frontal lobe, all impulse control, typical behavior, judgment, is lost. Out the window. It's why we get to the lowest of lows." Jill flipped through a few more slides of drug addicts and then to some grafts.

"This can be changed with prolonged abstinence from the drug. But the pleasure center of the brain will need something to fill the void. For people in recovery,

exercise can be a great way to release endorphins and focus on healthy life choices, not deadly ones."

We looked at a chart that had followed addicts in recovery over a period of ten years. There was a huge drop off at years one and two, then it stabilized and even went up a little the longer the person was in recovery.

"As you can see, the highest mortality rates are for those in their first years of sobriety. A lot of times what happens is an addict will relapse after some time has gone by and the tolerance they have built up to their drug of choice has dropped. But they go out and they use as much as they did before getting sober and they end up overdosing. Sometimes it doesn't even take that much."

Jill clicked through more slides with statements from the FDA, maps of states with the highest uses of cocaine, heroin, alcohol, ecstasy, and LSD.

I bent over and grabbed my journal. I didn't particularly want to take notes but I needed my hands to be busy and I found myself moments later writing a letter to my dad. Jill's presentation ended twenty minutes later. She turned the lights in the room back on and walked solemnly to the front of the room.

"It's not a pretty picture, is it?"

She looked down at her ballet flats.

"I think that's enough for today, from me anyway. I'll be around for tonight's optional movie night, I'm not sure what Jamie has picked out for you guys, be here at seven if you want."

We all slowly got up and started to collect our things and leave. Sara lingered, waiting to talk to Jill alone.

After group I found myself absentmindedly picking through a basket of granola bars in the dining room. After I decided I really only wanted the chocolate chips in one I moved on to see if there was any candy out. Sara was suddenly in the room with me. She approached me and waited until I found what I'd wanted. I grabbed a couple of Hershey's kisses and started to unwrap one clumsily.

"How do you know all that brain stuff?"

I looked up at Sara, she met my gaze.

"I studied it a lot in college."

Her eyes got big. "Oh." Looking down, she said, "I didn't finish high school but I'm going to get my GED once I'm outta here."

"That's a good idea." I wasn't sure why we were having this conversation.

"Do you think you could help me with something?"

"Maybe, what is it?"

"I'm having trouble with some homework Tim gave me and I was wondering if you could explain some of it."

I was kind of surprised since: (a) I didn't know Sara very well, and (b) homework assignments were usually pretty simple 'tell us about yourself' kinds of things.

"I can try," I said, "I'm not exactly an expert in recovery." I smiled but Sara's face didn't change so I

dropped it. “Sure, when do you want to sit down together?”

“Maybe during the movie? It’s going to be *A Star Is Born* and I’ve already seen it. Have you?”

“No.”

“Oh, well, maybe you’ll want to watch it then.”

“No, no, I’m happy to help. Let’s get together tonight and if we finish early I’ll catch the end of the movie.”

“Thank you!” Sara almost squealed and I cringed as she bounced out of the room.

I was always saying ‘yes’ when people asked. It was a character flaw by this point. I was constantly getting stuck doing things I did not want to do and with people I did not particularly want to do things with.

‘Aubrey will you help set up for fall ball? Aubrey will you help with all the garbage left from the dance? Aubrey can you help me with my Spanish homework,’ which was code for do my homework for me. How did I get stuck doing other people’s homework in rehab? Seriously.

Later that evening, Sara stuck her head in my bedroom door. I was sitting cross-legged on my bed reading my book when she chimed, “Knock, knock.” Heather looked up at me from her crocheting with a quizzical look.

“Come on in, Sara, have a seat.” I moved so that my back was against the wall instead of the headboard and we could sit together without sitting on top of each

other.

Sara nodded at Heather, who went back to her busy work, and sat down next to me. She held her journal and a small book.

"What have you got?" I asked curiously.

"Okay, well Tim gave me this book to read, called *Living Sober* and I have to write about 'Letting go of old ideas'."

"Okay… I haven't read the book, but I follow you so far."

"Well, it's based on AA and you're an alki, right?"

It felt like I was slapped in the face. I hated labeling myself and here comes this young kid with addict slang? I didn't know if I wanted to laugh or punch her. "An 'alki' okay, well sure but I don't really do the AA thing."

"Oh." Sara slumped, as if I couldn't help her at all.

"Let me see." I pointed to the book, and she handed it to me. She had bookmarked the section on 'letting go of old ideas', but it was quite apparent she hadn't read much of the small book.

"I don't understand what he's talking about." For a second I didn't know if she meant Tim or the author of the book. She was looking at the pages in my hand.

"Okay, let's see." I started to read. It was obviously written in the nineteen seventies. The language was old, but not that old. I could see why she had trouble navigating the prose. As I got to the end of the chapter she was supposed to have read, something stood out to

me:

'It is now well established that willpower all by itself is about as effective a cure for alcohol addiction as it is for cancer. Our own experience has verified that repeatedly. Most of us tried going it alone, hoping either to control our drinking or to stop, and we had no lasting success in either endeavor. Even so, it wasn't easy to admit we needed help. That, too, looked like a sign of weakness. Yes, we were being taken in by another myth. But we finally asked ourselves: Wouldn't it be more intelligent to seek out and tap a strength greater than our own than to persist in our futile solo efforts, after they had time and again been proved ineffective? We still don't think it is very smart to keep trying to see in the dark if you can simply switch on a lamp and use its light. We didn't get sober entirely on our own. That isn't the way we learned to stay sober. And the full enjoyment of living sober isn't a one-person job.'

Sara had brought to me a short essay that basically stated that stigma be damned, change the way you think about certain things, look at your problems with a clear mind and find another way to solve them rather than your old pattern of trying to 'disappear' or drink. It also screamed to me that I couldn't muscle through this one. We needed each other.

We used drugs to avoid certain problems, issues and failures. That is until we couldn't any more and then we are in trouble. Face that shit straight on and get it over with, was what I read. The essay explained that

finding happiness required a new way to view a life without alcohol, not as an embarrassing way of life, but as a happier way of life in which you could see more truths, more solutions to problems.

I needed to get better. I used to cringe at the word sober because it made me feel dirty, but I needed to get sober, not just stop drinking but find a life where it wasn't useful to drink any more. I needed to find enjoyment again. Heather had been right many nights ago. I needed to find something more important than me to do this for, and I couldn't do it alone.

I sighed and turned to Sara. "I think what Tim wants you to do is write some things down that you used to use over, like triggers. He also wants you to write down thoughts and ideas that stop you from getting sober."

"Okay. Like, wanting Marcus to love me?" She looked at me, brow furrowed into little lines across her forehead. "You are really smart, huh?"

"Oh, I don't know about that. If I was so smart I probably wouldn't be here."

"But Aubrey, the book just said, the smartest people in the world can become addicts. It's not your fault. Maybe that's the thinking you need to let go of."

Damnit kid.

I smiled. "You know what, Sara, I think you are the smart one." I winked.

Sara scrunched up her petite little nose and smiled. "I wish I would have been able to go to school like

you," she said. "I think if my parents weren't such a mess, I'd never ended up with Marcus, never gotten into drugs. Who knows."

"Yeah?" I didn't know much about her story or where she came from. So I waited to see if she would elaborate.

"My dad bailed on my mom and me and my sisters when I was like eight. Mom didn't have a steady job, but she had lots of boyfriends who would come by and help out. If you know what I mean." I didn't but I sat there engrossed in the beginnings of her story.

"My older sister took off with one of them when she was sixteen. One of my mom's guys." Sara looked at me with big blue eyes. "My mom was pissed. She drank a lot and yelled at us a lot and so I tried to just keep Kinley out of it, she's my little sister. We'd walk to school together and I'd make sure she had everything she needed. We'd eat breakfast and lunch at the school and that was pretty much all we had all day unless one of mom's boyfriends brought by pizza or KFC. I was about twelve or thirteen when my mom let her boyfriends do stuff to me for money. The first time, I kicked and screamed and got the snot beat out of me. It was easier to just let it happen, then at least mom got money and food for us. Sometimes clothes. Some girl at school started a rumor that my mom was a hooker and I got in a fist fight with her and sent home with a week suspension. My mom almost kicked me out for that. Instead she used me to pay rent. She said I was sixteen

and if I wasn't going to school I was going to work for her. That's when I met Marcus. I was walking down to the Circle K near our apartment with some money my mom gave me and I almost ran right into him. He asked me why I wasn't at school and I told him I got in a fight. He laughed and bought me a cherry coke. We sat there outside the gas station and talked for a long time. He asked if he could see me again and I was so excited. I started sneaking out at night to be with him. At first, we smoked weed, but later he gave me lines of coke. It wasn't long before he'd hook me up before I had to go make rent for my mom. It made it easier. I didn't want to do it. But I could do it floating outside of my body. I was going ninety miles an hour ya know? Soon I was basically living in his car with him. Getting high all the time. Trying not to think of my little sister, stuck there with my mom. When my mom got arrested last year, Kinley came looking for me. CPS was going to take her. I had to get sober for her, so I could help take care of her. So I tried. I tried really hard but I just couldn't. So I eventually found this place. Tim pulled some strings and got me in on a scholarship but I screwed it up when I relapsed. Kinley's in foster care and it's my fault." Sara leaned her head back against the wall and closed her eyes. She bit her bottom lip as if to stop crying.

"I gotta do it you know? I gotta get straight and get my GED and a job. I gotta see Kins again."

She leaned into me and I wrapped an arm around her frame. I wished I had pearls of wisdom to impart to

her. I wished and prayed for something to say. But all I could muster was, “I’m so sorry Sara. That’s a lot of responsibility to put on yourself. But I know you can do this.” It was half-hearted. I didn’t know if she could, I didn’t know if I could. But I was going to follow Peekay’s example and do the work. My heart was coming around.

Chapter Ten
Oxford house

A few mornings later I was woken up by the sound of men's voices below us. I sat up in bed and looked at Heather. She was already awake trying to arrange her dark-graying hair into a messy bun on the top of her head. "Who is down there?" I asked as if she'd know. Heather pulled a bobby-pin out of her mouth and stuck it into the base of her bun.

"No idea"

I was anxious to get downstairs and see what was going on. I threw on a pair of sweatpants and tugged a bra up and under my shirt. I quickly walked down the hall in my socks, trying to pull my hair into a ponytail at the same time. There were a few girls in their pajamas standing on the landing, looking down the short stairway. From the landing you could see three big guys in jeans and matching Briarwood Sweatshirts trying to pull a treadmill down the hall awkwardly. I jogged down the stairs and through the dining room to the meeting room. The area where the piano once sat behind some storage bins had been emptied. The men pushing the treadmill now had it on its side and were trying to fit it through the hallway door. There was a noise behind

me as Tim and another guy from the men's unit brought in a stationary bike. A few minutes passed and a small audience of girls watched excitedly as the equipment was arranged in a makeshift gym. Enough machines for half a dozen girls to work out at the same time.

"Hey, Aubrey, come test this out for us." Tim was smiling. I looked down at my feet and back at Tim.

"That's okay, just jump in here and see if we got it working." I jogged up to the wooden stage area and hopped up to the treadmill. I tried to suppress my excitement about having a gym. I tapped the 'GO' button and the rubber mat immediately started to move. I pushed the 'speed up' button and sure enough the ground beneath me moved faster. I was jogging in my socks and suddenly realized nothing hurt. My shin where I had broken my tibia years ago didn't ache, there was no pain in my arm or my shoulder, my hands weren't numb. I was elated. The treadmill was going 4.5 miles per hour (a quick walk) but I was bouncing happily in my socks.

Jill walked into the room and joined Tim at his side. "Can you believe it?" she asked her husband. "I think Aubrey is smiling." I slowed the treadmill and flashed Jill a sincere but overly wide smile.

"See, there it is again," she mused.

I turned off the machine and stepped off. Jill gave me a side squeeze. And I came down into the meeting room, which was now full of residents.

"Well, it looks like everyone is here. So we might

as well announce now that you guys have a place to work out when you have free time and there aren't groups going on in here."

Tim followed up, "These were all donated by some very generous benefactors who also help maintain Oxford House, a sober living house here in town. Please, please, please, treat these machines with respect"

Everyone seemed quite pleased except for Roz, she stepped forward. "Where's the piano?"

"We put it in the foyer by the fireplace. It's still here." Roz seemed to relax.

"Exercise is wonderful for recovery and we didn't have the means to do this until now."

You could hear the girls around me murmur their gratitude.

"I hope you girls enjoy it and again, please treat the equipment with respect."

I felt an excitement rise in me. I hadn't run in months, maybe even a year, and I was anxious to try it out again. My legs twitched in agreement.

"Okay, after morning group if you want to, you can come up here and try these machines out, there are free weights under the window. Just please be respectful of each other too," piped Jill. On that note, girls disbursed to get dressed and ready for their morning groups.

"Thank you, Tim."

I smiled, and turned for the dining room. For the first time in a while I felt honestly happy. Whether it

was the prozac or the thought of getting some exercise, it felt like a weight had been removed, and I could breathe a little easier.

During my meeting that day with Amy she could see that my mood had changed.

"I'm so happy to see this new improved Aubrey," she teased lightly.

"I don't know about new and improved, but I definitely can tell that I feel different"

"You have less anxiety."

I thought about it. She was right, that nervous knot that I lived with in my stomach had seemed to release a little. I felt like laughing and crying at the same time.

"I still feel a little crazy," I smiled.

"But you seem happy. Let's keep you on the low dose we have you on and hopefully you can test out our new gym and see if that helps too. I don't think I have much for you today, I just wanted to see if you were doing well on the new medication."

I thought about my evening line-up with the other girls, taking medication from the nurse, and how simple it had been. Once it seemed odd that everyone was lining up for drugs.

"I have to let you know, too, that Jamie will be sitting in on some of our meetings and she will be shadowing me for a while. She decided to become a counselor and will be doing her two-thousand hours of, basically student teaching, here at the house."

"Oh wow," I said, "I had no idea Jamie was getting

certified to do that."

"Yes. She has been doing night and online courses for a while now. You know, we encourage our residents to think forward about what they might want to do when they get out of here."

"You mean like work here?"

"Well, to work here you have to have two years of sobriety, but what I am getting at is that you won't be here forever and you might want to start thinking about where you will go and what you will be doing then. What you would want to be doing."

I swallowed hard. The anxiety I was so proud of getting rid of was returning. Amy sensed as much.

"You don't need to know right now. I just want you to start thinking about it. You don't want it to be sprung on you like it was on Roz."

I thought about Roz. She was leaving soon and I hadn't heard where she was planning on going.

"She's lucky enough to have landed a spot at the Oxford House here. It's quite hard to get into and there's usually a waiting list. But Tim was able to get her a room."

"Oh man…" I wasn't really sure how to respond to this news. I knew Roz was leaving but I had no idea what an Oxford House was like and whether it would be a good fit for her or for me. I kind of doubted it would be good for either of us. I suddenly realized that the continuity of the Briarwood schedule was something I'd grown used to and felt I needed. What would I do

without a schedule?

"Are you okay?" Amy's voice shook me awake.

"Yes. I guess I just have no idea what I'm going to be doing and that scares me."

"Will you go home with your parents?"

"I don't think so. I don't think that where they live has anything to offer me. The town itself is small and I don't know what I would do there."

"I see. Are you interested in going to the Oxford House?"

"I don't really think so. I think the idea of going back to school sounds fun, but I honestly don't know."

"Well then, that will be your assignment for the next time we meet. I want you to come up with a list of exit strategy ideas and we will go over them together."

"Okay" I knew there was trepidation in my voice. The pit in my stomach had returned. I felt sick. *At first you didn't want to even come in here and now you are afraid to leave? That's ironic.*

As I left Amy's office, I realized the high I'd been riding from the morning had hit an all-time low. I peeked into the meeting room. No one was there, no one was using the exercise machines either. I don't know why I found that odd, but I did. *Go figure, a house full of junkies doesn't want to exercise.* But I wasn't a junkie. All of a sudden I heard Sara's homework assignment ringing in my head. New ways of thinking. I had to get this sarcastic voice out of my head. I went to my room and changed into some capri sweats and a

tank top. I laced up my old Asics running shoes, and I headed back to the exercise room. I was going to run this one out and see if I could come up with some exit strategies.

I stretched, haphazardly, and climbed onto the treadmill, first setting it at a swift walk then a jog. My jog turned into a run, sweat was forming on my chest and lower back, my legs felt fine even though I wasn't really going *that* fast. But my lungs burned as they stretched in a way they were unaccustomed to for so long. I stopped the machine and then set it back at a walk. I was breathing hard. Sweating, I had not come up with any answers but I felt better, like the physical exertion had forced out the anxiety. I did some sit-ups and then some planks. Dripping sweat on the old wood floor. I needed to tell Tim to get sweat towels.

Roz came into the room as I was finishing up with a butterfly stretch. "Wow, look at you," she sneered. She was in a particularly nasty mood. I guessed it was because she was scared. She was leaving and honestly, I'd be scared too. Roz dropped the big plastic trash bag she was carrying on the ground and tried to tie the top into a knot but it was too full of clothes.

"Here." I jumped up and gave her my extra hair elastic, the one I always had on my wrist. I pulled the corners of the bag together and used the elastic to make a mini-garbage bag ponytail. "It might not last long, but it will get you to the foyer." I smiled.

Roz looked at me, her dark eyes searched mine.

"Thank you."

"You know, I never got to tell you what a wonderful pianist you are."

"Thanks," she said again, this time with a little more Roz-like attitude.

"Where did you learn to play?"

"I took lessons as a kid, played through high school. It just kinda stuck. Whenever there's a piano around I always want to play."

"You could probably be a piano teacher if you wanted." I didn't know why I was trying to cheer her up, but I needed to say something.

"I doubt it." She looked at the plastic bag. "I'd better get this to Jamie." She turned and moved toward the dining room entrance.

I wiped my hair back from my brow and turned to leave. "Hey, good luck, Roz. I mean it," I said over my shoulder.

"Thanks." She didn't turn around.

That afternoon, two girls from the Oxford House came over and did a little presentation for us on what it was like to live at their house. The first girl was a tall, stout, blonde with lots of makeup on. She was apparently a hairdresser at a local salon. The other girl, was equally tall but thinner and introduced herself as a waitress at the Woodlands Café, a hot spot for breakfast. They took turns explaining that not everyone has their own room, but the longer you live there the better the view. There were currently nine girls in the house, Roz

would be number ten. They explained that everyone has chores. Everyone has to make it to a weekly evening meeting, and everyone is subject to random drug tests. But there was free cable TV and WiFi.

"Rent is only one-hundred dollars, but you are in charge of all your own food and necessities," the blonde one said, looking at the other girl. "Yup. Any questions?"

No one raised a hand, and so Jill approached the front of the room and thanked the ladies. "Bethany and Amber will be here for a while if any questions pop up." She smiled and turned to talk to the visitors.

I got up and headed for my room. I had a sudden urge to talk to Heather about my 'exit strategy' or whatever. For some reason, listening to the girls drone on about random drug tests and group living made me upset.

Before I got there I ran into Jamie in the hallway. "Oh hey, congratulations." She looked confused. "On doing the whole counseling degree, that's really cool."

"Oh." She grinned. "It's been a process but I'm finally seeing the light at the end of the tunnel."

"I had no idea you were doing evening classes."

"Most of it has been online, but yeah. The local community college has a pretty great program. I was lucky enough that Amy pulled some strings for me to stay here to do my clinical."

"That's awesome." I suddenly felt either jealous or sad, I couldn't figure out which.

"I think it was a big part of Devon's problem." She looked at me with a strained expression. "I was all about this place." She waved her hand around indicating the Briarwood. "His loss" I gave her a half-hearted smile, and turned to go back to my room.

Heather was laying on her bed, with her eyes closed. I wanted to shake her awake and ask her what I was going to do with my life but she looked peaceful. So I grabbed some fresh clothes and went to shower.

As the hot water streamed down my back and neck, I looked at myself. I had gotten soft over the past year. I used to have a six pack but now my belly just lay flat, no muscle tone. I wiggled my toes, remembering a time when I had only a few toenails due to all the stress on my feet from running. I actually had cute feet again. My legs ached and I stretched under the steaming water. It was almost more than I could bear, the pain of the heat. My skin was bright pink when I got out of the shower. I put on my clothes, brushed my hair and went back into our room.

Heather was still sleeping, so I grabbed my journal and tried to think of things I could do when I left. I wrote down, 'gym, job, apartment, find a roommate'. I looked at Heather and I wondered what her exit plan would eventually be. There was a very real chance she would end up sharing a jail cell. I shook the thought out of my head and looked back at my page. Roommate. It stood out to me like a flower in winter. I had never in my life wanted to have a roommate. I mean, I shared a house

with Seth, but that was totally different. The thought of having a female roommate was foriegn. But it sounded kind of nice. I could picture decorating a little space of my own with some plants and my books, my bike, maybe some framed art from a Hobby Lobby. I smiled at myself. Getting a job would be the interesting part, there wasn't a single shred of me that wanted to go out looking for paralegal work or clerical work in an attorney's office. I cringed. The atmosphere there would be more toxic than working at a liquor store.

Jamie had started classes at the community college. I wondered if maybe I could just be a student again for a while. I smiled. But that would cost money. I needed to get on the internet and browse local job listings on Craigslist. Maybe that would get my brain working.

Heather stirred in her sleep. I looked up at her. She stretched. "Oh jeeze," she smiled. Her hair was a mess, and her black shirt was all wrinkled from sleeping on her side. She tried to smooth it down and then moved her hands up to her head.

"Are you okay?" I asked. "Looked like a good nap."

Heather closed her eyes and smiled widely at me. "What are you working on?" she asked, as she picked up bobby-pins from her nightstand.

"Oh, I'm doing homework for Amy. I am supposed to come up with a plan for living on the outside."

Heather's eyes were wide. She gaped at me. "You're leaving?" She was shocked.

"No, no, we haven't even talked about an exit date. Just an exit strategy."

"Sounds to me like they are preparing you to leave!" Heather was almost shrill, you could see the worry in her eyes.

"No, really, we haven't talked about me leaving yet at all. It's just an exercise. It came up because Roz is leaving and she kinda got kicked out of here."

"Yeah, I know." Heather finished pinning her hair up and swung her skinny legs off the edge of the bed.

"You going down?" she asked

I looked at the clock. "Shit." It was time for our evening group already. I put the journal down and closed it, tucking the pen securely inside the spiral edge.

When we got downstairs the whole house was in the dining room instead of the meeting room. Everyone was standing around a table with cake on paper plates in their hands. No one was really eating, but I wondered if I'd missed a birthday.

"Roz, you are going to be just fine!" Sara chirped.

As we got closer to the table, it was obvious that the staff had decided to give Roz a little going away party.

Roz was sitting at the table in front of the blue and white cake, eating an edge piece and licking the frosting off of her fork. Her tongue had turned blue.

"Thanks, Sara, but you are just excited I'm leaving so you can have my bed in the eagle's nest up there." Roz nodded to the ceiling.

Sara laughed uncomfortably. "Yeah, you're

probably right."

I nudged Sara encouragingly. "We are going to miss all your sarcastic comments, Roz." She looked at me and stuck her blue tongue out. "Exactly."

"Maybe you'll play us one last song?" Jamie's voice came from behind me. I was glad to see she had joined us. She might be on her way to becoming a counselor, but she felt like 'one of us' to me. Jamie held up her plate to toast Roz from halfway across the room. "We are going to miss you," she said, taking a bite. Jamie turned and left the room.

Roz put down her plate, "All right, all right, let's do this." She stood up and wiped her hands on her black jeggings. We all followed her into the foyer. The piano had been placed where my chair was, and I was just now realizing that 'my chair' was gone. I looked around for it anxiously but it wasn't in the room.

Roz sat behind the keys and began to play.

I looked for Heather. She was crouched down on the fireplace hearth, eyes closed, letting the music wash over her. A perceptible calm, that I wished I could feel. Angela had claimed the spot next to her.

The following day, Roz was gone and there was an obvious void. I knew there were more girls coming over from next door, but no one would fill Roz's loud space. It seemed like people moved more slowly that morning. I wasn't feeling hungry so I decided to try the treadmill again. Much to my own dismay, my legs were so sore I could hardly bounce at a light jog. I forced myself

through twenty painful minutes and then decided that the bike was probably a better option. I needed to ease my way back into running. I sat down on the recumbent bike and started to spin my legs. A little green bar indicated how many watts I was putting out, which at the time was not very many. As I watched the light, Sara entered the room and got on the treadmill beside me. She had headphones in and started to walk briskly, moving her fists in a way that reminded me of an old-lady-speedwalker around my neighborhood growing up. All Sara needed was a headband and some 1990s' ankle weights.

"What?" She could feel me looking at her and she laughed.

"I didn't take you for the exercise type."

"I'm not. But after all that cake last night I think I'm going to have to walk like ten miles," she joked.

Something about the moment felt good. The exercise, the companionship. I looked around the room. It didn't bother me any more. I didn't really even see the posters on the walls. They were there, but at some point they had stopped screaming at me and I had stopped getting agitated.

Chapter Eleven
Exit Strategy

The next morning, I woke up and Heather was already awake. Her lamp was on and she was smiling to herself crocheting something new.

"You look too happy." I grumbled and pressed my face into my pillow. My body ached everywhere from exercise. It was a good ache, one I hadn't felt in a while, and it reminded me I still had muscles even if they were really weak right now.

"My husband is visiting today."

"Oh, yeah, I forgot. How are things going?" It was a very general question. I sat up not really sure if I should ask about her court case, their business, or even their relationship. It was none of my business, but Heather wasn't the type to tell me so.

"Well, I'll find out more today, I'm sure. I'm just looking forward to seeing him."

I wondered what it would be like to be married. Marriage, from what I'd seen was difficult enough. I wondered how they did it. They had more than most on their plate. "You must love him a lot."

She looked at me like I had four heads. "He must love me a whole lot to put up with my hot mess, but yes.

I believe I do."

Suddenly I thought about asking her how the shop was doing, without her there, and with her husband dealing with her legal matters, maybe they needed some help at the front desk or in the office, if they even had a traditional office.

I cleared my throat, nervous to even approach the subject. Heather looked at me. "What? What's wrong?"

"Nothing, nothing is wrong. I just, I've been wondering about what I might do when I get out of here and I was wondering if you guys might have any part-time or full-time office work I could help with." There was an extremely awkward pause. Or maybe it just felt that way to me. I was afraid to look up at her, afraid I'd crossed some invisible line. "I mean, I'm a quick learner and I'm happy to pretty much do anything. I have a lot of administrative experience."

Heather put her crochet down in her lap. I looked up at her. I couldn't read her expression.

"You know what, I'd be happy to ask Jerry today if we could work something out. I know he's always looking for good people. I've been out of the business for so long now that I couldn't say for sure, but let me run it by him and I'll let you know."

She smiled at me and I felt relief. I didn't know if what I had asked her was appropriate or not. There was a piece of me that felt guilty asking, but I had to start somewhere. Today I was going to do my assignment for Amy and I felt a rising enthusiasm. I wanted to laugh at

myself. I felt totally ridiculous getting excited about a homework assignment in rehab. But here I was. I hadn't felt like this since college, when I poured myself into a neuroscience research paper. I wasn't exactly getting ready to write a dissertation here, I tried to tell myself, but it was too late, I was excited. I was going to go ask Amy if I could borrow the house computer to look for a job or an apartment to rent, maybe if someone was seeking a roommate. I couldn't have an exit plan without researching what my options were.

A cold shiver ran through me giving me goosebumps on my arms.

I sat up. *I was looking forward.*

"Now you are the one looking too happy." Heather's voice was light.

"I think, maybe, I can see past yesterday a little bit." I grinned. "I'm going to go jog. See you soon?"

"Yes, honey. Have fun and run a lap for me."

I bounced out of bed and threw on a pair of sweats, a sports bra and my running shoes. Today was going to be a good day.

By the time I had clocked thirty minutes on the treadmill most of the excitement was gone but I had a goal, a plan to do research for myself, and that fueled me.

I showered and forced myself to sit through our morning meeting without squirming too much. I was so anxious to ask Amy about computer privileges, I hurried down the hall to her office as soon as group was over.

And that's when I realized it was Saturday. Amy wouldn't be in until Monday. All the elation I had felt that morning turned into frustration and anger. Anger at myself for being such a dope, getting excited about doing a stupid assignment. Anger at Amy for not being there. Anger at the world.

I went to the front desk hoping to plead with someone about calling Amy and getting permission to use the computer. But when I got there I saw Jerry holding Heather in the foyer. She had crumpled herself in half her face in his lap sobbing. Jerry stroked her hair and looked like he was going to cry too. For a moment we made eye contact, his eyes were desperate. I backed away from the scene. My heart sank. I was getting angry about something so trivial. Here was Heather, again, reminding me the world is not about Aubrey. It isn't about any of us really. It's about all of us together crashing into one another. Heather was right, we have so little control over our own lives, it might be best to just focus on what we can do for others. Narcissism had gotten me so far.

I walked back to my room and paced around. My single track mind had been so preoccupied by what I needed to do for me. Now I was obsessing over what I could do for Heather. There was no group downstairs. I couldn't do anything for Heather right now. But I could run again. So that's what I did. I laced up my Asics and went back to the makeshift gym. My legs weren't as sore as I anticipated them being. So I ran. I wanted to

run until I could come up with some answers, but all I got was a cramp in my right calf that you could literally see. My foot arched up in a terrifying position and I almost screamed. I limped off the stage and into the hallway toward the nurses station. When I got there I was surprised to see Jamie sitting behind the half door reading a textbook.

"What on earth did you do to yourself lady?"

"I was trying to exorcise some demons and I think they got the better of me." I winced in pain.

"Okay, Okay, let's see if we can relax that foot and stretch this out."

"Damnit!" I didn't really mean to yell, it just sort of, boiled over.

Jamie looked at me in surprise. "Does it hurt that much?"

"No, I just really want to scream right now."

Jamie laughed at me. She wasn't patronizing, she just shook her head. "Girl, I have been there."

She had taken my shoe off and was rotating my foot around in a clockwise motion, trying to get ankle and calf to relax. Her cold hands felt good on my skin.

"You wanna tell me what demons you were running from or should I know?"

"Have you ever started a day thinking 'this is going to be a great day', and then it turns to shit in like five minutes and everything just feels like the world is out to get you?"

Jamie laughed again. "Like every other day."

I smirked at her, “Yeah, right.”

“Seriously. We all have days like that occasionally. What turned your cider sour?”

I had never heard that expression, was that even an expression? I had to smile at that. “I woke up this morning thinking I’d make headway on my exit strategy homework for Amy and I forgot she’s not here so I can’t use the computer. So I was really mad and I walked into the foyer and saw Heather sobbing with her husband, so that only makes me think the worst is about to happen.”

“Really? Your bad day was about a computer?”

“Well, when you put it like that. I was really looking forward to looking forward, you know?”

Jamie looked at me thoughtfully. “What were you going to do with the computer?”

“Look up options for myself once I leave here. I’m not going home to my parents. I don’t have a job any more, I need to find a new place to live, a new job, probably change my name and reinvent myself.”

“Change your name, huh? You running from the feds or something?”

“No. Just embarrassed. Did you know, Sara called me an alki the other day?”

“Well, aren’t you?”

I looked at Jamie and she looked back at me totally amused. We both burst into laughter. *I’m such an idiot.*

“Okay, how’s this, you hang out here and don’t look at porn or anything, and you can use my laptop.”

My eyes must have been wide as saucers. I didn’t

know what to say, so my mouth just kind of hung open for a second. "Can you do that?"

"Of course I can. I'm a counselor here, too. If you are using the computer for an assignment or for rehabilitation purposes, why not? But if I catch you on a dating website I'll have you thrown out." She smiled at me. "Kidding. Well half kidding. No dating websites, okay."

This whole interaction had me back to feeling empowered. I thanked Jamie and she let me use a folding chair in the hallway outside the nurses' station to sit and work. The first thing I did was pull up Craigslist ads for reception and administrative work. I stayed away from anything law related. There were tons of ads for cleaning services and marketing positions that looked like scams. But it didn't seem like there was much out there. I found one opening at the public library for a part-time job and several school administrative positions that required prior work experience in education. I was starting to lose hope in the endeavor. I tried to remind myself I still had time and I switched gears and looked for 'roommates wanted'. Now that was a plentiful area on Craigslist. There were people seeking just about anyone to rent a room from them. There was even loft space over a garage available. I kept scanning down to the older and older posts and one specific one popped out: 'Seeking female roommate, non-smoker, non-drinker, some pets welcome. Only serious applicants please'."

"Hey, Jamie. I found one that might be interesting. You wanna check it out?"

She didn't look up from her text book, but answered. "A job or an apartment?"

"Actually, a roommate wanted. It says female, non-smoker, non-drinker."

"When was it posted?"

"March thirteenth."

"Oh, you can't respond to that one."

"Why?" I asked, kind of miffed.

"Because it's my ad."

"What? Seriously? Did you fill it?"

"Aubrey, seriously, you and I cannot be roommates. And no I haven't filled it yet."

"Why not? I'm clean, you know me… I'll pay rent on time."

She looked up at me sternly.

"Aubrey, I think that it's a bad idea. Besides I'm pretty sure Amy and the Briarwood regulations would forbid it."

I frowned and wrote down all the information anyway.

I went back to job listings, wrote down a few that I could do for a while to bide my time until something else came along and then I found an interesting one. A small fixed base operator (FBO) was looking for a receptionist. 'Must have some prior knowledge of aviation, payroll, accounts receivable, multi-tasking. Must have a vehicle.' Well, I could check all those

boxes except for the vehicle one, which I had unfortunately driven off of a cliff in an attempt to destroy us both. Now, I didn't have a car, but I could get a car. If I got a job. 'Some prior knowledge of aviation'. Well, I had grown up around airplanes, there were several pilots in my family. I could tell the difference between a 152 prop-plane and a Citation jet. I could tell you (from being in my father's plane) what most of the buttons and dials did, but I couldn't fly a plane myself. I wondered if that was enough. I wrote down all the details in my journal below Jamie's ad information. My enthusiasm was returning.

The single apartment rent in the area was between five hundred and eight hundred dollars. If minimum wage was roughly twelve dollars an hour I'd have to work about twenty hours a week to cover rent and utilities. That seemed do-able. But then there was also the other costs, food, gas, insurance, the car I was going to have to buy. I had a decent savings account I could dip into to buy a used car and pay a year's worth of insurance. That left me with just the basics. I could do that. I wrote down the math I had done in my head, scratched out a little budget for myself, and created a little life on paper. There was nothing else to do until the evening meeting so I asked Jamie if I could get into the art supply closet. She looked at me skeptically and reached her hand out for her computer. I closed all the windows, closed the lid, and handed it back to her. "Thank you for that."

"Sure thing. Feel free to get whatever you want out, but please don't leave a mess, and if you tear up Sara's *People Magazine*, I'm pretty sure she will go ballistic. So that one is off limits."

There were always magazines in the art closet, staff brought them after they read them, I think the house even subscribed to a few, but they all ended up in the art closet for 'art therapy'. I stood up and folded the chair back against the wall. I flashed Jamie a quick smile and headed for the empty meeting room. I opened the closet and realized I had a lot of work set out in front of me. The closet itself was a disaster, nothing was in its corresponding bin. There was paper, or pieces of paper everywhere, magazine parts, a stack of *National Geographics* that I could only assume were from the 1980s. My stomach turned. I didn't want to take this on.

I could hear girls in the dining room talking. Some had family members over for their Saturday visits. Others were playing card games. One of the new girls walked into the room behind me and headed for the stair stepper. We acknowledged each other meekly. I grabbed a chair from the semicircle and dragged it over to the closet. I was going to start from the top. I hadn't intended on 'organizing' the closet, but within the span of an hour I had managed to do just that. I had a pile of garbage set to take out, all paints, markers, pens, pencils, strings and ribbons in their proper Tupperware boxes and I had found some things I didn't even know we had. I had put aside a three-ring binder, some *Better*

Homes and Gardens magazines, scissors, glue, and permanent markers. Once I had compiled all I needed, I took the trash to the big bin in the dining room. I headed back into the meeting room and found two girls gawking at my newly refurbished art center.

"Did you get in trouble or something?" one asked.

"No, it just looked like a mess and I couldn't find anything."

"Wow, 'cause that looks like a lot of work."

I wasn't really sure what these girls were getting at. I picked up the things I had collected and took them up to my room.

I was going to ace this exit strategy homework.

I put my iPod earbuds in my ears and lay down on my bed and set to the task of planning my 'perfect next step' in life. I cut out a little white cottage, a calico cat, the bedspread I wanted, the side tables I'd eventually buy. I even cut out some flowers I'd plant and some clothes I'd buy and glued them to sheets of paper from my journal. I arranged it all in the three-ring binder, not unlike a bride getting organized for her wedding, I thought and laughed at myself a little.

I realised there were no people in any of the photos, and the thought saddened me. I went back through the magazines I had again and again, but nothing spoke to me. So I took my *Home and Garden* supply and went back to the meeting room closet to exchange them for something else. When I got there, the two new girls had retrieved the box with strings and ribbons and beads and

were fully engaged in creating friendship bracelets that were quite intricate. “Those look awesome.” I said on my way to the magazines.

“Thanks.” They were already twinning their responses.

I looked through the random assortment of magazines but nothing had what I wanted. I wanted… People. *Frick.* Maybe I wouldn’t get in any trouble with Sara if I borrowed just one magazine. I grabbed one and practically ran back to my room. I felt like I’d stolen something. As I went through the pages, I saw a ‘Celebrities are just like us’ section of the magazine where celebrities were hanging out with their kids, going to the grocery store, buying books, chasing a kid through a park. These were the pictures that were missing. I felt a solid lump start to rise my throat. This was what *I’d* been missing. I had worked so hard to be this person I could never live up to be. That I had missed all the amazing people I could have spent time with along the way. I was always fighting for myself to get ahead, to get an A, to get a PR, I had missed so many opportunities to make a best friend, skip a class to go paddle boarding, let my body recover and enjoy my time running. For what? To come completely undone and end up in Briarwood? What would my ivy league acquaintances say now?

Honestly, they probably would have said, “Aubrey, you were always driving mach-two towards a cliff.” Oh if they only knew.

A song came over my headphones, *Waiting for a Change.* I didn't even know I had any Christina Aguilera on my iTunes. It must have been one of those freebies that you get every once in a while, because I sincerely don't remember downloading it. Then again, alki's do stuff they don't even know they are doing, so it's very possible I bought it at one point. I lay on my bed listening to this song about waiting for a change, cutting out people from a magazine to put into my life. My pretend life. I would have girlfriends and we'd go hiking. I'd have a great guy to ride cruiser bikes with. I even cut out a picture of a mom chasing a chubby toddler down the beach.

Eat that, Amy.

Exit plan… Boom!

I might have been feeling a little too proud of myself, because a few minutes later, Heather returned to our room. Jerry had gone back home. Heather went into the bathroom and washed her face. She came out with face cream and a towel. I wanted so badly to ask her what had happened, but I was lost as to what my place was. Was I a friend? A roommate? Just another resident? I thought about going to look for Angela and changed my mind. After Heather had rubbed her sweet smelling cream on her face and neck she returned to her bed in some very pretty pant pajamas, I turned to ask her how she was doing. Her lips were pursed.

"We were given an offer," she said, not looking at me. She pulled the blanket back on her bed and slid in

underneath them. I waited for an explanation. When she had settled onto her side she looked up at me with sad eyes.

"One year, six months' probation, or take our chances in court."

I let out a big breath. "Are they taking into consideration the time you've spent here?"

"Yes." She began sobbing again into a silk handkerchief that matched her pajamas.

I didn't know what to say. One year was a long time but it wasn't *that long*, she could do a year. She'd been in Briarwood what? Four, five months? I wasn't sure if this was good news or bad. Heather was crying so it must be bad news… but it could have been so much worse I thought.

"The sentencing guidelines for involuntary manslaughter are one to eight years' incarceration with probation. I was given one year, Aubrey. One."

"Honey, you can do a year." I moved to her bed, and was about to console her when she erupted.

"I don't deserve one year! I took someone's life because I was too sick to get help and stop drinking. He did nothing wrong but walk home from work at the wrong time."

"So you think you should get more time?" I was confused but I understood her feeling of guilt.

"I don't know. Jerry paid for the funeral services. He didn't have a family here in the U.S., so Jerry made a promise to keep sending the family the money they

needed. There was some bad blood there for a while but things have mellowed out. It's been almost six months. I've asked to meet them and they've agreed."

"Wow, Heather. I don't know..." My voice trailed off. *I don't know if I could do that, I don't know what to say, I don't know how to help you.* All of these things were tumbling around in my mind but none of them seemed like the correct thing to say.

"Jerry is really happy. I'll be home in six months, it looks like."

"Wow. So you took the deal."

"Yes. I told him to take it today. I just feel like it's not enough."

"I am no cleric or elder or, hell, I haven't even been a deacon at church, but I think you are punishing yourself in a way no jail or institution could. And maybe, just maybe, the powers that be see that."

Heather held out her arms and I practically fell into them. We hugged awkwardly for what felt like minutes. She hadn't stopped crying but it wasn't a heart-breaking sob any more, it was more of a release.

"You're a good one, Aubrey."

"Now don't go spreading rumors."

Heather smiled. Her face was puffy from crying but the small smile was honest. I could hear my grandpa: "You did good, kid."

I'd lost track of how many nights we'd gone to bed emotionally spent... but the tally was up there.

Monday morning I had my meeting with Amy, I

could hardly wait. I was excited to show her what I had put together. Morning meeting dragged on, I could hear the minutes hand on the clock on the wall next to me. Time was taunting me. I had placed my binder and my journal under my chair and sat on my hands. A new woman from the detox unit was introducing herself. She was probably thirty. Her voice shook as she spoke, and I kept expecting her to break out into tears but she never did.

"Okay, ladies. Thank you, Molly. That is all for today, but tonight's session won't be a regular meeting. We are going to have someone over from the department of health to discuss abuse tonight. It's an icky topic, I know, so I want you to be prepared and be respectful to our speaker."

Jill finished with a prayer and I bolted for the door.

I waited outside Amy's closed door for a few minutes while she finished up with someone. When she finally opened the door I almost smacked into Angela, who was trying to exit as I was trying to enter. She had been crying. I gave her a nod, "Sorry," and pushed my way into Amy's office.

Amy was sitting on a folding chair facing the couch.

"In a hurry?" She looked at me over the top of her glasses and I instantly felt remorse for running over Angela the way I had.

"Sorry?" I cringed.

"I think Angela's the one that deserves the

apology." I hung my head. I failed again to put others before myself. "I'll make sure to talk to her." I looked at Amy with regret. "I guess I have been so anxious to talk to you since Saturday I didn't think."

Amy waved me over and I took a seat on the familiar gray couch. It was still warm from Angela's body.

"What have you got?" Amy took her glasses off and placed them on the desk behind her.

I held out my three ringed notebook and felt pride rising in my chest like I'd just finished a medical journal article. Amy took the binder and slowly examined every page. Her lips were pursed, I couldn't read her at all. I suddenly felt very foolish for having done the project the way I did.

"Wow. You really went all in on this didn't you?"

I looked at her unsure of myself. "I did, I actually got pretty excited putting it together."

"You did an excellent job describing a life you want, a home, a job, friends, but there isn't a single thing in any of this that shows how you plan on staying sober."

And there it was. That familiar agitation at the word 'sober' returned. I was annoyed and upset that she didn't applaud me for all my fine work. I had a budget, I had a plan, I had options. My agitation grew into anger in the pit of my stomach. I wanted to yell at Amy that no other resident had done an exit strategy as well as I had. But I couldn't. I had left out any part of my recovery, I had

ignored it all together and skipped ahead to what would be fun and beautiful. There was no mention of a daily routine, a plan to go to meetings or find a recovery group. I had flat out failed.

I inhaled shakily.

"You are right. I think I put in going to the gym, working a steady job, living in a safe place all as things that would help me stay straight but I really don't know what it will feel like to not have the safety and routine of this place. It's hard to wrap my head around the idea that I'm an addict and once I leave all those familiar triggers and urges might just come back and overwhelm me."

"And that's exactly what this exercise was trying to get you to think about. One idea is to apply for the Oxford House like Roz." Amy was serious but that was an idea I absolutely could not entertain.

"I don't think I'd do very well in that environment."

"Why not? There's more structure than living on your own, people are accountable to one another. There are even in-house meetings to make sure people are staying on track."

This was an idea I absolutely had to stomp out but I didn't have an eloquent reason as to why it wouldn't work for me. I just knew it wouldn't. I would feel terrible about myself living with junkies in recovery and I just couldn't do it. *I have a graduate degree. I don't belong in a house like that.*

"I guess I'll think about it. But I'd like to explore

other roommate options." I thought about asking her if living with Jamie would be an option, but I was pretty certain she'd say 'no' and I wasn't willing to suffer that kind of abnegation.

"Very well. I think you have done some good work and you recognize that going back home is probably a toxic idea for you."

"Yes. I can't go there."

"Okay. And I see you've even found some work possibilities? Have you put together a résumé?"

"I honestly haven't needed a résumé in so long. I might need help with that one."

Amy smiled. I had asked for help, even if it was just for building a résumé. "Okay, let's see if we can get Tim to sit down with you for a minute and pound one out. In the meantime, I want you to keep looking ahead. You may come and borrow the laptop when you have free time, just check it out from me, and let's see if you can put some meetings into this new life of yours." She held up my three ringed binder.

Inside I cringed. *Not the meeting type either.* But I would do some research and write down some times and dates.

A familiar feeling of agitation toward the whole program had reseeded itself in my belly. I could go through the motions, enough to get out of here but there was a part of me that knew that that was not enough.

"Remember, Aubrey, we can't do this alone."

I wanted to punch something. "I know." I said as

calmly as I possibly could. I turned and exited her office.

With every step toward my room my anger seemed to grow, and grow, and grow. When I got to my room Heather was there doing some paperwork.

She looked at me. "What's wrong? What happened?"

"My exit strategy was too rosy and failed to have any *plan* on how I'd stay sober." I must have grumbled or sneered when I said 'plan' because Heather let out a snort type of laughter.

"Sorry, honey. How long have you been here?"

"Like two and a half months."

Heather looked at me like I had just added two and two and come up with sixteen.

"Well how *do* you plan on staying straight?"

"I guess I just thought I'd start over you know, things would be different. I'd reinvent myself. Maybe my thinking would be different. Maybe I'd have a less demanding job, I'd make some friends, I'd be less selfish. I don't know. I figured I'd be 'cured'."

"Cured?" Now Heather was looking at me like I was flat out delusional. "Honey, you get out there and nothing has changed. The world is the same blasphemous place it's always been. You are going to step out there and have major stressors, you will feel lonely and have to find a new way to cope with the same old problems you had before you came in here."

I knew she was right. Just because I didn't feel like

driving off a cliff right now didn't mean that I wouldn't feel that way in a week when I was alone, or with new people, in a new atmosphere, with a new job.

"So what the hell am I supposed to do?"

"Come up with a plan. Who will you call when you feel overwhelmed?"

"You."

"Well, I won't be answering the phone for a bit, so who else."

I bit my lip sheepishly. "Jamie, maybe Angela, Sara, I guess I could find like a meeting."

"You know, Jerry is always willing to talk." I was surprised that Heather brought up her husband. "He said that you might be in luck looking for work. His secretary is going on maternity leave in a few weeks and he will need someone to cover for her."

The thought of working for Heather and Jerry lifted a little of the anxiety I felt.

"Thank you for asking him. I hope that wasn't awkward."

"Not at all. I may not have told you this before, but Jerry has been through this. Not rehab, but addiction. Before I met him he suffered alcoholism. He was a major screw up before he met me." She laughed. "He understands this stuff, these complicated feelings. And I think he'd be honored to have you call him. In AA people get sponsors to help guide them and advise them, a person they can call when they feel like they might slip. Typically you do not get a 'sponsor' of the opposite

sex, but it isn't unheard of. Or, he might know someone who is willing to take on a sponsee."

"Would you mind if I called him? Just so I can write his name and number down in my exit strategies book?"

"Of course, honey. Of course. We'll do it tomorrow."

The rest of the afternoon I felt unusually listless. I really just wanted to go to bed and wake up and start over tomorrow. I didn't have the emotional energy to endure a talk on abuse at the evening meeting. When Heather and I got down there everyone had already taken a pillow and found a spot on the floor. Angela had grabbed one for Heather and saved her a seat so I was on my own in the back sitting on the floor when a woman came in dressed in a black skirt and white blouse.

She introduced herself as a resource officer for the state. She helped find people the help and resources they needed to get out of a verbally, physically, sexually or emotionally abusive relationship. She explained all these abuses and the many different kinds of relationships from which they tend to grow.

She explained the entanglement problems people face and codependency issues. The meeting was long but not at all boring. She spoke quite clearly about relationships like Mary's where parents enabled addiction without really knowing they were doing so. She touched on relationships like Ellise's that were complicated and needed legal intervention. She had

pamphlets with all the resources and phone numbers you could ever need, including legal aid, to get out of an abusive relationship. By the time her presentation was over I felt like I needed a shower, a hot shower. When we got up to leave the meeting I noticed that Sara had left her things on the floor. I put her pillow away and grabbed her journal to leave at the base of the stairs for her. Talking about sexual abuse must have been especially hard for her. My gut twisted with guilt and anxiety.

Chapter Twelve
Success Rates

The following day I still felt depressed. I got up, ran for thirty-five minutes, went to meeting. I was just going through the motions. I walked out, still in a fog.

"What's up, lady?" I heard Jamie's friendly voice next to me in the hallway. "You look like someone peed in your Cheerios."

I shoved my hands as far as I could inside my jeans pockets. I didn't want to look at her. I was sure she could see right through me, that all my time here had been wasted. I thought I was getting better when I was thinking about my 'exit strategy' but it had all been in vain. A futile attempt to cover up what was wrong with pretty pictures and delusions of grandeur.

"Nothing." No response formulated in my head.

"Well, it's not nothing, do you want to talk? Did something happen with your meeting with Amy?"

"It was kind of a disaster actually. I showed her my plan and it turned out that I had no 'plan' at all. Just pretty ideas of what I wanted my life to look like."

"I see." Jamie looked at her feet. She had on cute Nike shell toe shoes on with her jeans, the kind I probably would have bought had I seen them in a store.

"Come here." She motioned to the nurses' station.

The door was closed but Jamie unlocked it with one of the many metal keys on a keychain attached to her waistband. She pushed open the door and patted the metal top of a folding chair before sitting on the nurses' station desk.

"Tell me what happened." She crossed her legs at the ankles, and folded her hands in her lap. I loved the way she could make you feel important, like you were the only one in the world she cared about.

"I just didn't have a plan on staying straight. She wanted to know where I was going to live and what meetings I was going to attend. I hadn't given any thought to 'meetings', I guess I want to skip forward to the 'I'm cured' part and live a normal life like everyone else."

"And a normal life to you means that you wouldn't go to meetings?" She looked insulted.

"Well, I wasn't really planning on it."

"I see, so you'd just walk outta here cured, never drink again and life would be great?"

"You're sounding just like Amy."

"I'm sorry, that's not what I am trying to do. Do meetings embarrass you?"

"Yeah, wouldn't they embarrass you if you had to go?"

Jamie chuckled as if what I'd said was sarcastic. "I do go. I meet with a group of people our age at a coffee shop once a week. It's not AA but we hang out, check in on each other. I've been to my share of meetings and

I found walking in at first was a little scary, maybe embarrassing. But getting a public intoxication rap or another DUI would be even more embarrassing. So I guess meetings were the better of two evils for me."

"You were an alcoholic?" The word was thick and awkward coming out, like a dirty word in a foreign language.

"Everyone that works here was or is in recovery."

I remembered that, but Jamie just seemed so 'normal' there was nothing about her that would suggest she'd ever done anything wrong in her life.

"Five years ago I was drinking myself to death. I started as a college binge drinker and just got lost along the way. I couldn't do it alone. None of us could. But I remember feeling like I could just power through and outsmart the disease. I remember thinking I could handle it on my own. That's part of that sick thinking that you have to get rid of."

I wanted to cry *again.* I hadn't cried this much in my whole life. *Why can't I outsmart this? Why can't I think myself out of this one?*

"You will have times in your recovery when you really don't think you can go another five minutes without ripping your own skin off or going for a shot of whiskey. You will have times when you feel so alone you just want to dig a big hole, climb in, and cover it with a rock."

I knew she was right but I still couldn't look her in the eye. I held my face in my hands.

I was suddenly cold and shivering.

"Here." I looked up and Jamie was bent over the desk sideways writing something. When she straightened up she handed me a post-it note with her name and phone number. "You are going to need to start collecting these. These are going to be your first line of defense. I hope you have a good cell phone plan. If you don't, you'd better change it." She winked at me.

I let out a snort of air and gave her half a smile.

"Why don't we go get a cup of coffee in the dining room? You look like you could use some."

I stood and followed her out of the nurses station. She locked the door and we walked without talking to the old dining room, where an old pot of coffee, fresh six hours ago, waited.

The hot coffee felt good in the ceramic cup in my hands. I wasn't really interested in drinking it so much as I was smelling it and holding the hot cup. Jamie sat next to me at one of the round tables.

"Did you find a roommate?" I asked hoping her answer would be no.

"Not yet. I'm waiting for the right person, I guess."

My stomach fluttered. I wanted to press the issue but figured it wasn't the right time.

We sat there talking for a few minutes until my nerves seemed to settle down. Jamie was staring out into space and I was about to ask her what she was thinking about, when Amy stuck her head in the doorway.

"There you are! Jamie can I steal you for a

moment?" Jamie looked at me and I nodded, I was fine.

She stood up and wrapped both hands around her mugh. "Sure thing."

As Jamie followed Amy out into the hall, I wondered about her story. I tried to imagine her as I had been, sick… the image didn't fit. Jamie was just too put together, she had a good head on her shoulders. *Addiction is an unbiased enemy… willpower all by itself is about as effective a cure for alcohol addiction as it is for cancer.*

I opened my journal to a fresh page. 'Exit strategies #2, My call list…"

This time around I was going to accept the hand that was extended to me. I wrote down Jamie's information, Jerry's information, Heather's information, and the names of several other people I needed to get numbers from. I wrote down the time and place of Jamie's meeting. It probably wouldn't count as a true meeting so I went to the foyer and grabbed the AA pamphlet from the front desk. I looked up the closest meeting. All the groups had different names. The Early Birds at seven a.m., the Nooners, the Coffee Mates, I found myself smiling at their silly titles. I wrote them down, the names, times, and locations.

I flipped to a new page. 'Résumé' all of a sudden this seemed harder. Did I really want to reinvent myself, or accept the past as it was, a big ass learning curve. Maybe my leaving law was not so much a failure, as it was a change in direction, a chance for some much

needed self-discovery.

I listed the few positions I'd held since college. Thought of a few references, and then set out to write an objective.

Sara came stumbling in from the foyer. She had been outside on the porch and she looked like she was about to fall over or plow into something.

"Are you okay?"

"Yeah, great." She sat heavily in a chair and drummed her hands on the table looking around like she was going to find something to eat but nothing appealed to her. "Fucking awesome."

Shit, she's high! Oh my God, what do I do? I closed my journal and walked over to her, I placed my hand on her skinny shoulder blade.

"Sara? Are you high?"

She jumped. "What? Fuck no." She stood and we met eye to eye. She smiled at me and her eyes were large pupils. The iris of her eye was only a tiny ring of brown. "Sara we have to get you to your room before you get caught." She was jittery, almost vibrating. "Where did you get the drugs?"

"I'm not on drugs," she said meanly. Sara shoved me and stormed out of the room. I wasn't prepared and was knocked off balance. My hip hit the tabletop and I cried out.

The woman at the front desk came in to see what all the fuss was about. I didn't know what to do, I liked Sara, she had a good reason to get clean and get her life

back together. I didn't want to be a tattle tale, but Sara was on something and if she died because I didn't say anything I couldn't live with that either.

"I think something is wrong with Sara." I rubbed my hip.

"What do you mean?" She looked at me strangely eyeing my hand in my hip.

"I think she's on something."

"Damnit. Okay. Thank you for letting me know, I'll call Tim." She jogged to the desk and grabbed her phone. I grabbed my journal and headed back to my room keeping an eye out for Sara on the way. When I got to my room, I could hear girls' voices in the eyrie. Sara was laughing. Then I heard footsteps. I stuck my head out my door in time to see Tim's legs disappear up the stairs. I ducked back in my room, got on my bed and held my knees waiting for Sara to come charging in yelling at me. But she never did. Heather asked me what was wrong repeatedly and joined me on my bed, terrified that something bad had in fact happened. I just held my knees.

"Sara was on something. I confronted her about it, she shoved me, now she's upstairs and I just saw Tim go up to talk to her."

"Phhhhshit."

It was the first time I'd heard Heather cuss. "There is a guy around the block from here that knows this is a place to sell to. They call him Jim, even though that's not his real name I think they named him after 'Tim'."

She gave me a sideways look. " I've never met him. I've only heard about him from girls who were here before you. They made him sound almost mythical. So I never really believed it happened. My first roommate, a girl trying to get off coke was kicked out for using. Everyone said that's where she got it, she went out on the porch, left a note at the gate, a couple days later she was wasted. It's why they restricted outside privileges so much."

"So Sara's out?" It was more of a statement than a question.

"I don't think she's paying full price so she's most likely out if she tests positive. They have test strips, they will know in a matter of minutes."

"I feel really guilty, Heather, if she gets caught and it kicked out, it's my fault. She's such a sweet kid."

"This isn't on you. Look at me." I looked at her, her graying tendrils framed her face, her brow was wrinkled deeply with concern. "What she does, what I do, what anyone else does, that is *not* on you. You need to know you can't control what other people feel or think, or do. You didnt give her the drugs."

At that moment there were loud voices above us as Tim hauled Sara down the stairs. I was too afraid to get up and look out the doorway but other girls were, I'm sure. Heather and I just sat there on my bed as we heard someone being told to collect Sara's things she was literally being kicked out onto the street. No second chance, no detox. Just here are your things and goodbye.

I wanted to throw up. Where would she go? What would she do? I was so angry that they wouldn't *help her,* take her to the detox unit like they did Mary. I didn't understand. I couldn't wrap my head around the callousness of it.

I wanted so badly to tell Tim that I'd trade her spots. Or I'd find a way to help pay for Sara to stay, but I couldn't put it together fast enough. I felt at a complete loss, like when my dad had cancer and I wished it was me instead. I was mad at the system, mad that I had no control, no ability to help anyone.

I fell asleep that night on an empty stomach. I didn't leave our room until the next morning for meeting.

Jill was there before any of us.

"We have zero tolerance for people who bring drugs in here."

Unless their parents are paying top dollar, then you go looking for them. I bit my tongue. I couldn't look at Jill right now. It felt like a money thing not a tolerance issue.

My time at the Briarwood was rapidly approaching. While they claimed that they didn't put timelines on recovery, your ability to pay was.

When Jamie arrived at work that morning she was surprised but not stunned that Sara had relapsed and been kicked out. She found me in the foyer looking for a new book to read. I was sitting on the hearth reading the synopsis of one when she approached me.

"What the heck, Aubrey? I heard you were here

when Sara came in high out of her mind."

I wasn't sure if she was accusing me of having Sara kicked out or if she just wanted the details of what had happened. "It was horrible. I didn't mean for her to get kicked out, I didn't want that. I feel terrible and honestly scared for her. They just dumped her on the street."

"I heard. You know people have to want to get better." Jamie squatted down next to me.

"I keep hearing that, Jamie but you guys also say we can't do it alone so I'm kinda confused." I didn't intend on lashing out to Jamie, but in the moment, I saw her as part of the problem too. The system was rigged. It didn't make sense. Why pay thousands upon thousands of dollars to end up like Roz or Jamie or Sara, or even worse, like Mary.

"How did you do it, Jamie? How did you want it enough to do it yourself but also get through it without being alone?"

"I wasn't alone. I mean I was given an ultimatum by Devon to clean myself up or he was gone, then after being in meetings and stuff I got really interested in addiction counseling so I went back to school. I worked for Devon's parents at a clinic and had to stay straight there until I could land a job working here."

"You make it sound easy."

"On the contrary it was the hardest two years of my life. I was lucky I lived with Devon and he was good about keeping an eye on me but giving me space too. I had to be busy, constantly. Then I found this group at

the coffee shop I was telling you about… With Devon gone it's been harder but enough time has passed that I don't have the urges I used to. I work so much here right now because I'm still afraid those urges will come back when I'm home alone."

She was squatting down next to me wearing blue nurses' scrubs.

"What's with the scrubs today?"

"Detox unit, I get to spend the afternoon over there." She made a face like it was going to be gross.

I imagined girls sweating and shaking in hospital beds. "You didn't ever do a stint at a rehab?"

"No. I couldn't afford fifteen thousand dollars a month."

I nodded, and felt a pang of guilt. "You've been here long enough to know if it works, what do you think?"

"I wouldn't work here if I thought it didn't work. But then again I think it's working here, and seeing how addiction destroys lives daily that keeps me straight. I could never work at a 'Hollywood' rehab where people just lounge around and do meetings in a spa-like environment. I know rehab isn't for everyone, and the people that come in there have to really want to get better. I've seen a lot of girls just go through the motions and it almost never works out for them."

I wondered what Jamie thought of me, did she think I was only going through the motions? *Is that why she wouldn't consider me as a roommate?*

"I read online that ninety percent of people that come here are successful. There were all these reviews from girls saying that this place saved them." I started to dig at invisible dirt under my fingernails. I was entering foreign territory with my questions. "I mean, that's why I picked this place."

I looked up at Jamie who looked a little puzzled by the number and bit her bottom lip. She was staring down the hall, as if she was hoping someone would interrupt us. She chose her words carefully. "I don't know how they measure success here, to be honest with you. I know that real people wrote the reviews though. I've met a couple of them."

She stood up and squeezed her quads as if they were really sore from crouching down next to me.

I stood up too, to head back to my room. I was thinking about using the gym during lunch time but my stomach growled and reminded me that a snack might be required before I tried to exercise.

"I'd better get back to it." Jamie started to exit the foyer and head down the hallway when she stopped and turned around. Her hands were in the pockets of her scrubs. She looked like a certified nurse.

"Feel free to ask Amy next time you meet with her about your exit strategy."

"Ask her what? About the success rates?"

"No, if she would recommend you living with me. I spoke to Jill about my living situation and she cannot dictate who I choose to live with as long as I stay clean.

But just make sure it's a good idea for you."

"Are you sure?" I asked brightly.

"I'm never sure about anything but you are welcome to apply to be my roommate." She smiled and pivoted down the hallway.

My stomach fluttered. I could feel a shot of adrenaline leave my heart and enter my bloodstream. I rushed back to my room to tell Heather the good news.

Chapter Thirteen
Asking Questions

When I got to my room, I was stopped short at the doorway by the sight of matching luggage on Heather's bed. There were two white suitcases with brown leather trim. One was zipped up and the other lay open full of clothes and toiletries.

Heather startled me coming out of the bathroom I jumped. "Heather?" I couldn't even think of the next words

"Oh, honey," she dropped a bottle of lotion she was carrying on her bed and walked back over to me and embraced me. She smelled amazing, like coconut oil and Oil of Olay cream. A few strands of her wet hair had escaped from the towel on her head. And the wet felt good against my face. My arms were straight down at my sides and I couldn't hug her back. Her off white mohair sweater tickled my neck.

"No," was all I could whisper. My throat was closing.

I felt Heather rest her chin on the top of my head and clear her throat as if she too were choking back tears.

"I'm going to see you real soon. And you can come

visit me at the big house." She pulled back holding my arms and forcing a smile.

"Are you leaving today?"

"Tomorrow. Jerry's coming in the morning with the attorney and we will all go check me in together. You know, make sure everything is squared away."

I didn't know. I couldn't imagine her in jail.

Her eyes were rimmed with tears. "It's going to be okay. It's going to be okay." She petted my hair. She was trying to comfort me but all I felt was rising panic at the thought of her leaving, at the thought of her in jail. I felt panic for me too. Heather had been my roommate, my confidante. I had learned more from her than I had all of our counselors in the last two months. She was my comfort in this place. We talked each other to sleep at night. I knew the sound of her moving through the room on the way to the bathroom or to get a drink of water in the middle of the night.

Her voice was never frantic and neither were her motions. I needed her. She couldn't leave.

She let me go and moved back to her bedside and zipped up her second suitcase. "Did you bring enough stuff with you?" I asked wiping a tear from my eye and trying to lighten the mood. Heather laughed. "Jerry gave me an earful too. I didn't know how long I'd be here or if I'd be able to wash my clothes regularly."

I moved to my bed and sat down. I wished I had something to say.

"You know, Jerry will have that job waiting for you

if you want it. You just need to call him when you get out and let him know where you are. He'll be anxious to know how you are doing. If you give him your address, I'll make sure he passes it on to me and I'll write to you."

"Of course." I looked at my hands, rubbed my eyes, and thought about when we first became roommates.

I looked at the clock on my nightstand. We had less than five minutes to be at our next group. I leaned over and grabbed my journal off my nightstand.

"You coming down?"

"I'll be right there." Heather fussed with the towel on the top of her head and I made my way out of the room and down the hall.

At the entrance of the meeting room Jill and Amy were talking. They both turned and looked at me as if they had been talking about me.

"Do you have a second, Aubrey?"

You tell me. I looked at Jill nervously, then at Amy and back to Jill.

"Hannah is going to be moving into Heather's bed unless you want to move upstairs, then we will have a few switcharoos to do."

I hated how she said 'switcharoo' like I was a kid and this was camp. She made it sound so simple, Heather out, Hannah in, no sweat.

"Oh no, um, I like where I am. Hannah is great." I faked a smile. My palms were wet.

"Okay then, that solves that issue." Amy and Jill

exchanged relieved glances and Jill went back into the meeting room. I followed slowly. My eyes searched for Hannah but she wasn't there yet.

When she did walk in I was expecting the flannel Briarwood pants and sweatshirt, but she walked in casually in keds, a pair of capris and a T-shirt that said I heart Colorado. Heather came in slowly behind her and walked directly towards me, a soft sad smile on her lips.

"Ladies, I hope you are all doing well. We do have some new faces that will be joining us here later today so I hope you can make them feel welcome." Jill was looking down at a sheet of paper. It looked like she was counting names on a sheet.

"We are going to have a full house here tomorrow." She failed to mention that Heather would be leaving.

In my head I counted the beds. There was room for fifteen girls in the house. Fifteen times fifteen was two hundred and twenty five. That was a quarter of a million dollars coming into Briarwood house alone each month. I looked around at the women in the room. So maybe not all of them were paying full price, but shit, that was a lot of money. I thought about the detox unit — I wondered how many people were over there and how many men they housed.

"Aubrey?" I looked up. Jill was addressing me and I had not heard anything she had said.

"I'm sorry, I missed that," I said sheepishly. I could feel the heat rising in my cheeks.

"I was simply saying that you are one of the most

senior girls here right now and so if anyone has any questions they can ask you, right?"

"Um, yeah, sure."

Heather nudged my arm with her pointy elbow.

It's only when you aren't paying attention that people call on you. I fumbled with my journal. Jill handed out a stack of paper to be divided among everyone. I took a sheet and passed it. I read the title of the sheet: 'Preventing Relapse'. There were three specific sections of the worksheet written in bold: 'Emotional Indicators' 'Managing Life's Curve Balls', 'Successful Recovery.'

"As you can see we are talking today about relapse, and why people relapse. Briarwood prides itself on a very low relapse record, but it takes a lot of work to have success in recovery. So today we are going to write down our ideas and share what emotional indicators or 'triggers' we have, what to do when life doesn't go as planned, and being successful in our recovery. Because that's what we want, we want everyone here to be successful." Jill's smile was patronizing.

All of a sudden my hand shot up in the air, I didn't really think about it, it just happened.

"Yes?" Jill looked at me puzzled.

"How do you as a counselor and as a facility define the success rate here? I mean, how many residents actually get 'better'?"

I don't know why I asked or where it came from but the question spilled out of my mouth without me

being able to think about whether it was a question I should ask let alone in front of the house.

Jill met my look directly. Her dark eyes were challenging me. She shifted her weight in her riding boots.

"People don't 'get better', Aubrey. People learn to live in recovery." She paused for a moment and tried to address everyone. "We are proud to have a very high success rate here at Briarwood. We assess success with a variety of clinical measurements and reports, based on patient follow-ups. We consider the length of sobriety residents have, their quality of life, and their capacity to follow through with after care. We try to follow up with all of our patients that finish their programs at six months and one year."

I sat there uncomfortable and slightly agitated by Jill's tone. *Patients that finished their programs.*

"So patients like Mary and Sara don't count because they didn't finish their program?"

Heather nudged me again harder this time.

Jill raised her eyebrows in a warning. "I don't think talking about people that have been here is really appropriate, Aubrey. I think we need to focus on ourselves. If you have specific questions you can come and ask me after the meeting is over."

Hannah came to my rescue, her hand shot up.

"Yes, Hannah?" Jill was looking annoyed and put her hands behind her back.

"What do you mean by quality of life? Like if we

have a house and a job?"

"Well, yes. You will get a questionnaire in the mail and it will ask you what you are doing, how you are doing, if you are happy and functioning well independently."

There it was. I wondered how many girls, or guys, actually filled out the questionnaire and sent it back. So much for 'clinical measurements.'

"What about the 'clinical measurements'?" I almost slapped my hand over my mouth. I instantly wanted to suck the words back in. I was challenging Jill. "Again, Aubrey, if you have specific questions, we can address those outside of this meeting. But for now I would like everyone to look at their worksheets and start to think about your response to the first heading."

I looked at my feet. I knew I was in trouble. I tried to write on the worksheet but I was shaking and all I could think about were Jill's dark and challenging eyes. Part of me wanted to meet her and ask her questions and challenge her back, but the other part of me knew I needed to shut up and play nice if I didn't want to get kicked out.

Back in our room that evening, Heather asked me why I had pushed Jill by mentioning Mary and Sara. I didn't have a good response. I guess I just wanted to know, if we were paying all this money, for real help, or if we were going through the emotional wringer for someone's entertainment.

"I don't think they find our illness entertaining."

She was fussing over the effects in her nightstand drawer.

“Aubrey, a word?” Amy stuck her head in our door. I thought she had left for the evening. She looked like she was headed out, she had her purse over her shoulder and the keys to her car in her hand.

I felt dizzy. I knew I hadn’t done myself any favors by asking Jill about success rates, but now I felt like my place here hung in the balance.

Heather looked at me worried. I nodded at her and she nodded back.

I followed Amy into the hallway. She walked down the hall silently and I followed her. She stopped at the back door. If she opened the door an alarm would sound. Instead, she leaned against the wall playing with her keys. We were out of earshot and out of sight of the hallway cameras.

“Jill wants you out. She thinks you don’t really want this and we can’t help people that aren’t willing to help themselves.”

“What?” It felt like the ground had shifted under me, the blood drained from my head. I felt a rush of panic.

“Jamie came to me and said that she had talked to you about being roommates. She said you had some job opportunities lined up. I think it would be really wise to nail these down.”

Amy was telling me I needed my exit strategy all in place. She was saying I was about ready to get kicked

out.

"But I haven't done anything!" I was forcing tears back. "What did I do wrong?"

"Like I said, they think you don't really want sobriety, that you aren't taking our program seriously, and that you have started to be disruptive in meetings."

"I asked a question."

Amy pursed her lips together and jiggled her keys.

"I'm off tomorrow. But here's my cell phone number." She pulled her card out of the pocket of her peacoat. On the back was her cell number written in blue ink. "If you need anything."

She gave me a half hug and moved quickly down the hall away from the back door and into the foyer. She disappeared from view. I held her card in my hand. I was shaking. I had no way to make any phone calls, no way to get online, I was alone.

I walked slowly back to my room. I was in disbelief, wobbly, my joints felt like jello. I walked into my room and Heather immediately dropped her bag on the floor and rushed to my side. I sat on the edge of the bed and she sat next to me. Her familiar veiny hands grabbed mine.

"It's going to be okay. Everything is going to be okay," she breathed and patted my hand.

"Looks like we are both out of here tomorrow." I looked at her and she bit her bottom lip.

"Do you want Jerry to pick you up? He can come get you later. Or you can come with us?"

I shook my head. “I can’t do that to you guys right now.” I wanted to call my mom. I wanted to tell her how sorry I was for failing them again. I didn’t have the words. I didn’t have the energy. I lay my head down in Heather’s lap. I felt like my flame was blowing out. I had nothing left. I thought of Peekay: ‘Pride is holding your head up high when everyone around you has theirs bowed. Courage is what makes you do it.’

I thought about being Jamie’s housemate and getting a job with Jerry. I sat back up and hugged Heather’s tiny frame. *I am going to be okay. I am stronger than this place thinks I am.* I was going to use their doubts about me to prove them wrong.

I stood up and went to shower. Crying as the hot water scalded my skin. When I got out of the bathroom Heather was already in bed. I quietly put my pajamas on and slid into bed.

It took me forever to fall asleep that night but in the morning I was awoken by Heather in the shower. She was taking an extra-long time and for a second I worried. The water turned off with a familiar squeak of the knob. A few minutes later she came out of the bathroom, steam following her. She looked dazed.

“Are you scared?” It was a stupid question. But stupid things had been coming out of my mouth lately and I was unable to put the words back in once they escaped.

“I’m a little nervous, yes.” She looked up at me with her towel still on her head and another around her

slender frame. "What about you?"

"The not knowing is killing me." I sighed and rolled onto my back. "Maybe it's good if I get out of here too and start something new. I've been sober over ninety days and that's saying something. I don't know if anyone is ever ready to leave a rehab facility, I mean who's to say how long you are supposed to be in here." I took a deep breath and tried to convince myself I was right. "You know someone once told me that because the cells in our bodies are always regenerating or being replaced, we are basically a new human in seven years." I laughed at the thought. And so did Heather.

"Why couldn't my skin cells come back younger?"

I smiled at the ceiling, giving Heather what little privacy we had. I stretched and rubbed my face.

"Maybe I'll be a completely different person in seven years," I joked.

"Yeah, maybe you'll actually be a nice person."

"Hey," I called out and tossed my pillow at her.

She brought it back to my bed and messed up my hair in the way an older sister would have.

"Will you walk down with me?" She looked at me somberly.

"Absolutely." I tugged on a pair of jeans and threw on a sweatshirt. Pulled my running shoes over my baggy socks, and stood to help her with her luggage.

"Thank you." It was barely above a whisper. I grabbed the luggage handle and our hands touched. I felt how cold her hands were.

I swallowed hard and headed for the foyer. Heather and I made it to the landing just as Jerry and an older gentleman entered the house. Heather jogged up to Jerry and they hugged each other tightly. The older man extended a hand and she shook it. He looked at me and nodded. *The attorney.* Angela slowly approached from the dining room, wringing her hands, there to say her goodbyes. I wanted to stick around until Heather left but she and Jerry had already taken to signing papers at the desk. I wiped my face with my hands and headed back to my room.

I pulled my old gym bag out of the closet and started to neatly fold my clothes and put them inside, just in case. I moved quickly, wanting to get it done before anyone came by. I emptied the dresser and left one pair of socks, underwear, jeans and running clothes in a drawer just in case I was wrong. I put the duffle bag back in the closet and shut the door. I showered and for the first time in eighty-something days, I put on makeup, carefully lining my eyes and extending my eyelashes. I looked at myself. My eyes were clearer. My face thinner than when I had entered, puffy from alcohol use. I looked like I did *before.* I thought. But this wasn't before, this was after.

I walked down to the dining room. My heart was pounding as loudly as it did the day I entered Briarwood. Only now, I knew no one could hear it. No one was sizing me up. I was the senior girl in the house.

I wasn't hungry but I grabbed an orange and started

to peel it anyway. I could see Tim and Jill from the corner of my eye, making their way to my table. I was sure a sweat was about to break out on my forehead and armpits. I focused on my orange.

Tim cleared his throat and I looked up as if I hadn't noticed them approaching.

"We need to talk, Aubrey." My name coming out of his mouth sounded foreign.

Tim pulled out a chair and sat down, Jill did the same. *How chivalrous.*

"We have been talking to each other and talking to Amy and we think that it's time for you to go." I felt my body stiffen and go cold. I looked at Tim, knowing my eyes were ready to cry.

"It's been apparent from the first day that you don't appreciate what we are trying to do here. You don't like to share in meetings, and even though Amy has said that you've been making strides on the Prozac, we just don't feel comfortable working with dual diagnosis patients," Jill said. Tim looked down at the lines in the wooden table his mouth clamped shut. "Especially those that aren't really serious about working the program" Jill's voice was almost cynical.

Dual diagnosis patients? Since when? Mary had freaking schizophrenia. I wanted to tell them that every single person in this facility was a dual diagnosis patient. But I wouldn't be doing myself any favors. They'd probably just make this all happen faster.

"We want you to succeed, Aubrey, we really do, we

don't like sending people out without finishing their program, but Jill feels that your disturbance in meeting last night was too much."

"My disturbance? I asked a question." This was ridiculous.

"It has a lot to do with the tone you used with me in your response to my question, Aubrey, it was completely inappropriate."

I wanted to argue that I had heard Roz make statements ten times more inappropriate and she was never kicked out for them. But my words didn't formulate quickly enough. She was kicked out on her basis to pay. I however, had paid.

"It looks like your ninety days will be up in about a week so we can refund you that part of your payment."

My mouth hung open.

"You will have until this afternoon to make arrangements," Tim said.

"But we are doing sheet changes at three so we need you out of your room before then," Jill snapped.

Like a hotel.

"What about my exit strategy? I mean, Amy was supposed to help me figure out where I was going to go, and what I was going to do."

"I'm sorry, but this is the end of the line here. Amy isn't in today and so you are welcome to use the phone at the front desk to make any calls you need."

Jill pushed herself back from the table and stood up.

"I'm sorry," said Tim and he followed his wife out

of the room and into the foyer.

I went to my room and gathered the rest of my things. I opened the nightstand drawer and there was Mary's friendship bracelet. I had tried to retie it onto my ankle after it fell off a few weeks ago but there wasn't enough thread. I shoved it in my pocket and took my bag down to the foyer. I was in 'auto mode' I just needed to get things done. I put my bag down at the front desk and the woman there told me to go to the nurses' station. Morning meeting had just started and I could hear girls' voices coming from the room. The door was shut. As I passed it I felt a twinge of nervous energy. At the nurses' station one of the nurse practitioners I wasn't familiar with was doing inventory. She looked at me like I was a child out of my bedroom at night.

"What do you need, honey?" she asked me in about the same tone.

"I am leaving today and I was told to come down here and get my things?"

"Oh, okay, what's your name, dear?"

"Aubrey." I swallowed hard. The nurse turned around and scanned some shelves and then some cupboards underneath the desk. She rose up with a bunch of pop-out pads of Prozac all rubber banded together — it looked like three months' worth — my cell phone and charger, and an envelope with my name on it. I thanked her and returned to the foyer. I pulled my duffle bag over to the corner by the fireplace and plugged in my iPhone. I was suddenly very aware that I

hadn't really missed it, but now it was going to be extremely helpful. As it charged I opened the envelope.

'Hey Girl,

Sorry I couldn't be there. And sorry things ended this way. I got voted out. I'm sending you with three months of the Prozac you've been on and you have my card in case you need to call me. I'm around. I would be happy to set you up with a local nurse practitioner to monitor your prescriptions and that kind of thing. I just can't do it out of Briarwood for obvious reasons. I think your exit strategy has come along just fine. Use your phone numbers when you need them! Call Jamie, she's expecting you. And honey, take care of yourself. Please.

Yours, Amy

Ps. If you get a chance, look up Penny (360) 665-1219

I wanted to cry. I hadn't been particularly kind to Amy. What had she seen in me that led to this kindness in return. I had no idea who Penny was, her daughter maybe?

I folded the letter back and powered my phone on. I had to leave it plugged into the wall but I dialed Jamie. She answered on the second ring.

Chapter Fourteen
The Power of One

“Hey, housemate.” I said my voice shaking.

“Oh Christ, really?” She seemed to laugh. “Okay, when are you coming?”

“Um, actually today.”

“What? What happened? I heard Jill was mad at you after some meeting but I didn’t think she’d kick you out.”

Tears were rimming my eyes and I knew if I talked I would start to cry. I took some big breathes.

“Do you need me to come get you?” She sounded concerned

“No, you have work today, I just wanted to see if you’d feel comfortable with me coming over and dropping off my stuff while I figure out the next step.”

“Of course. Of course. Key is under the mat. And help yourself to coffee.” I could hear her smile. “I will try to get off shift early this afternoon and make it home to be with you. I could take the day off if you want.”

“Oh gosh, no. No. really. I’ll see you this afternoon.”

“Okay. Hang in there.”

We hung up the phones and I looked at the next

person I needed to call. I couldn't call Jerry yet because he was probably still checking Heather in.

Amy picked up after a few rings. "Hello?"

"Hey, it's Aubrey."

"Oh, hun, how are you doing? Did you get your meds?'

"Yes, yes, thank you for that. I was wondering if maybe you could pick me up and we could run a couple errands. I need to drop my stuff off at Jamie's and figure out what I'm going to do about well… everything."

I started to cry into the phone.

"Okay, okay, okay, it's going to be okay. Just breathe. I'll be there in fifteen minutes."

I left my phone plugged in and walked up to the desk. "I think I need to sign my exit paperwork now." I said to the woman at the desk. Her name tag read 'Meg' but I was pretty sure I'd never seen her before.

"Aubrey?' she asked.

"Yes."

"Okay, says here you don't need an exit interview." I found the statement completely absurd. Grabbed the rest of the forms and started mindlessly signing my name. When I was finished. I returned them to her and walked back to my spot in the foyer by the fireplace. I held my phone and typed 'CarGuru' into the web browser. I didn't care what kind of car I could get, I just needed one temporarily until I could start getting back on my feet. In the filter was 'SUV below eight thousand dollars'. I was thinking a junky explorer would be my

only option, but I was surprised to see several old Range Rovers for sale around five and six thousand dollars. They had just under two-hundred thousand miles, but if they were on a lot and running, they would probably work just fine. I screen shotted two of the cars and their locations. I heard a car drive up and I peeked out the window over the piano. It was Amy. I grabbed my bag and I slipped out the front door. There was no goodbye party, no cake, no people I needed to exchange numbers with. No one to tell me good luck or give me a hug. No one to be notified of my departure. I was alone.

I just needed to get the hell out and fast.

I opened the passenger side of Amy's car and threw myself in. I took a deep breath and tried to hold it together. It was going to crack soon, but not yet. Not until I was away from this place.

"To Jamie's?"

"Yeah." I hadn't been outside the Briarwood this far in nearly three months, the air felt different. Movement in a car felt different. There was music coming from her radio that I hadn't heard before. I looked at the river and the trees as we passed them. I let out a huge sigh that surprised even me.

"Are you okay?" She kept looking at me and I just wanted her to keep her eyes on the road. I leaned against the cool window. "We are almost there," she said turning off the main road and onto a gravel road with tall pine trees on both sides. The driveways were long, and also wooded. She turned up one and stopped in front

of a white bungalow. For a second I thought of my three ring binder and how perfect this house was for my failed assignment. We got out of the car and walked together up to the porch. I knocked, knowing that no one was home. Amy bent over and retrieved the key from under the mat and handed it to me. We both pushed into the house eagerly.

We took our shoes off and walked into a beautiful light blue-gray entrance way and hall that led straight back to a very modern updated white kitchen and a view of the back yard, a small fenced in space about as long as the house and only about ten feet deep. We looked around the living room, a nice sectional, and a few throw pillows. Not much in the way of decoration. We moved on and found the master bedroom which was full of Jamie's things, scattered clothes on the floor. I felt like it was a violation of her privacy to enter so we backed down the only other hallway and found the spare room. It was simple, white, with a metal trundle bed, not unlike one I had as a child. There was a desk, a small closet and an antique armour that served as a dresser. It was stunning.

"My gosh, girl. This place is niiiiiiice." Amy made herself sound twenty years younger. She smiled at me and hugged me. We found the spare bathroom that I would be using, and an extra little living space, where Jamie must have practiced yoga. Her mat was about all that fit in the room.

"What do you think?"

"I think it's perfect." I looked at Amy and smiled. "Thank you so much for bringing me here. Are you super busy today because I don't want to be a burden to you."

"No, not at all. My only date is with *The Bachelor* tonight. I have to see who gets a rose."

I laughed. "Would you mind helping me run a few errands then? I should probably get some toiletries and some food? Maybe an extra set of clothes?"

"Sure thing, let's go to Target. It's just down the road."

Amy took me to Target and I loaded up on soap and food, a few new shirts and pants, a pair of running shorts, and some towels, and we headed back to the house.

Amy helped me put things away and, for a moment, it felt more like we were sisters or ex-patients together. I practically forgot she was my counselor.

"Amy? Why are you doing this for me?"

"Honey, I think you were working really hard on trying to get where we were pointing you. I think you made a few missteps, but who doesn't in rehab?" She was straightening and hanging a towel neatly on a hook in my room. "I don't think it's right that girls get put on the street to fend for themselves after going through rehab. It's only a few of them that they make exit plans for, which are really outpatient programs that patients pay more for. You needed help when you came in. You were angry and scared and I saw that woman change.

She was kind and excited about her future and looking forward, not back. I feel like when girls get dumped back on the street they go backward. I don't want that for you. I don't want it for any of the girls, but I don't want it for you. You did a lot of good work. Now just keep on workin'."

It wasn't the Amy I was used to behind closed doors at the Briarwood. It was a kinder, softer, more empathetic Amy. A friend.

She was on her way to leave when she turned around,

"Call me when you need anything okay? Oh and don't forget to look up that girl I told you about." She gave me a long hug and turned and exited the house.

An immediate sense of loneliness and isolation overtook me. I couldn't be here alone. Again I felt like calling my parents, but I still hadn't figured out what to say.

I grabbed my phone and googled the location of the Lithia dealership. It wasn't too far away, but far enough that I wasn't sure I wanted to walk. But the exercise would do me good and it would kill a lot of time. So I put my shoes on, grabbed my purse and headed out the door to buy a car. This all felt so fast. I kept telling myself to move forward, that I could do it.

Tomorrow my plan was to call Jerry about work, and if that didn't pan out I'd call the other position I'd found. I walked and looked at my phone. I really wanted to call my parents. Another five minutes and I was

walking up the curb of the Lithia lot.

I walked the rows of used cars but didn't see any that were in my price range. Without a job I wouldn't be able to finance anything.

A guy about my age came jogging out to meet me in the lot, eager for a sale, I'm sure. I felt an instant paranoia and overwhelming feeling to tell him to 'go away' but he literally bounced up next to me and introduced himself as Mike. He was so excited to have a customer I couldn't really turn him away, so when he asked me what I was looking for, I told him about the old Range Rover I'd seen on their website. It was old and needed some love but I wanted to take a look at it.

"That one is in the shop right now getting a timing belt, I believe, but let me go check. Don't go anywhere." He smiled at me, his salesman of the year smile, and literally bounced back to the office. I wandered around the used cars, looking in windows and checking out tires, and not five minutes had gone by when I heard Mike's familiar voice. "Look what I've got for ya! Wanna take it for a spin?" He was driving the dark green SUV with the driver's window down. He put it in park and hopped out, giving me the key.

"Don't you need my driver's license or something?" I asked skeptically.

"Not unless you are taking it by yourself. Which you aren't." He smiled and hopped in the passenger's seat. For a second I was nervous. I didn't know this guy and I didn't know if driving around alone with him was

a good idea. But he smiled at me and waved me in.

It was kind of hard to not smile at his enthusiasm and his goofy sideways looks. So I said yes. And before I knew it, we were driving down the side roads, talking.

I didn't want to talk about myself so I led the conversation, asking him questions, first about the car, and then about his life. The car had a ton of miles, but was well maintained, new timing belt, new knobby tires, it was clean and ran smoothly. Mike had bounced around a lot of different jobs in a lot of different places after serving one tour overseas and being medically discharged from the army. I didn't press for details. When we made it back to the lot, he asked me what I thought. I said I liked it but I was wondering if there was wiggle room in the price if I came in all cash. Mike lit up like a Christmas tree and ran inside, once again yelling at me to, "Stay put." I got in the green Land Rover and looked at its tan interior. The old knobs didn't show much wear and tear, it would work. It was the car the new and improved Aubrey would be driving.

Mike came sprinting back out of the building with some paperwork in his hand and got to me just as it started to sprinkle lightly. We got in the car and he showed me what his boss had written down.

"If you can take it down five hundred and throw in an oil change, its sold." I smiled and Mike jumped back out of the car and ran for the building. I felt silly making him run back and forth like my errand boy. But he didn't seem to mind. I fiddled with the radio until I found some

station playing classic rock.

Classical music had too many recent memories, and country was my dad's thing, and right now I couldn't think about my dad.

Mike knocked on the window, I rolled it down slowly. "You ready to come inside and do some paperwork?" I smiled a cheeseball smile.

We signed the hundreds of documents it takes to buy and license and title a car, and an hour later Mike was giving me the keys and a ticket for a free oil change.

"Can I get your number?" he asked, "You know, just in case?"

"Just in case of what? Your car breaks down and you need a ride from me?"

He looked self-conscious and maybe a little silly. "That didn't work as I planned, did it."

"No." He looked embarrassed.

I smiled. "Give me your card." He handed me his card and I wrote my cell phone number on the back and handed it to him.

"Thank you, Aubrey." He grinned. "Call ya soon."

"Well, don't wait too long I might forget who you are," I joked. We both smiled at our stupid one-liners. We were both bad at this.

I drove home to Jamie's and felt a little bit of pride. I managed to get a car. I had a roof over my head. I had job prospects. Once I had a job, then I'd call my parents. I'd explain to them that I was doing well given the circumstance and beg for their forgiveness.

I was afraid to be alone with myself. I looked at my phone. It was past five o'clock. I wondered if I could call Jerry and see how things went with Heather. I paced back and forth on the porch trying to decide until I had built the suspense up so much that I had to call.

"This is Jerry," a kind and tired voice answered.

"Hi Jerry, it's Aubrey." I cleared my throat "I was wondering how it went today with Heather, and if you got any information on when we can visit or write or send her stuff."

"Oh, Aubrey." There was a long pause and some heavy breathing on the other end. "Aubrey, she likes you so much. You have to call her and visit her. I'm so scared that place will kill her. It's just such a terrible environment."

Jerry and I talked for almost an hour, first about Heather and checking her into jail. We talked about visiting schedules and how hard it had been for him to say goodbye. He had thought about running away with her but she had talked him down. It would have only delayed the inevitable or made her sentence longer. We talked about his job opening at the office and I graciously accepted the position. I could start on Monday, shadowing his current administrative assistant. It paid well and had health benefits after a month long probation period. We talked about meeting for coffee but never set a time. Our talk ended when Jamie came home.

She waited politely for me to end my conversation

with Jerry, telling him I'd see him soon.

"Nice ride," she smiled at me. It was dark out so I don't know how much of the car she really saw. "Looks like you got a lot done today."

"I stayed busy. Amy took me to Target."

"And the car?"

"My savings."

Jamie seemed impressed. She gave me the remote to the TV. "Find something," she said and she headed to her room to shower and change. I flipped through channels aimlessly.

When Jamie returned I had settled on a Lifetime movie but I wasn't really paying attention. Jamie put a bag of popcorn in the microwave and settled on the couch next to me.

"So how are you?"

"I'm okay… nervous maybe…" We sat there quietly watching a romantic scene unfold on the television.

"Do you know a girl named Penny?"

"From Briarwood?" Jamie looked a little confused.

"I think so. Amy suggested that I call her."

Jamie looked at me quizzically. "Yeah, I know her. If I remember right, she only stayed a month, I think. She's a tough chick."

I was about to ask what she meant by that but we were interrupted by a loud beeping noise. The microwave signaled the popcorn was done and Jamie got up to it. She didn't offer any more insight.

When she came back she offered me some and we finished the movie. It was past ten and I could hardly stay awake so I said goodnight and made a mental note to call Penny in the morning.

I woke to the smell of coffee and forgot where I was momentarily. I looked around the room and smiled to myself. No morning meeting today. I threw on some sweats and met Jamie in the kitchen.

“Good morning.” She handed me her cup and poured another.

“Thank you.” I smiled and breathed in the buttery steam. It was a trillion times better than the acid served at Briarwood. Jamie was already dressed for work with her lanyard around her neck.

“Plans today?”

“Yeah, I’m going to find the local YMCA, and apply for a reduced membership. Maybe see if that Penny girl would like to meet.”

“Cool. Well stay out of trouble and call if you need me.”

Jamie grabbed her keys and headed for the door. The loneliness was unbearable. I had to get moving fast, I couldn’t let my brain be still for a moment.

I grabbed my cell phone and googled the YMCA. It was about eight minutes away by car. I had a plan I just needed to keep moving. By ten o’clock I had a gym membership and had walked and jogged for forty minutes on a treadmill that overlooked a huge green space. I figured ten was a safe time to call a stranger out

of the blue, so I left the gym and climbed into my car. I didn't want to go home and be alone so I dialed the number Amy had written.

The line rang and rang. I almost hung up before a sweet voice answered. "This is Penny." Suddenly I didn't have a clue on why I called or what to say... "Hello?"

"Um hi, my name is Aubrey, and Amy from Briarwood gave me your number." There was a long pause and I almost thought she'd hung up.

"Hi, what can I do for you?"

This was suddenly the most awkward conversation I had ever had. I had not planned this well. I suddenly felt very foolish for calling.

"Um, well, Amy thought that I should give you a call now that I'm out."

"She did, did she?" I could hear Penny smile on the other end. A wave of relief washed over me. I fidgeted with my keys in my right hand and leaned my head against the cool glass window. "So did you get evicted, or did you finish your time there?"

I smiled, embarrassed. "Evicted."

She sounded amused.

"Would you like to get together for a cup of coffee?"

"I really would."

"Could you meet me at the Starbucks on Main, in like half an hour?"

I looked at the clock on the dash. "Absolutely."

A couple minutes later I was parked outside the café. I should have probably gone home to change but I was afraid of being alone. I almost thought about ordering a glass of wine and I shoved the feeling into the bottom of my stomach. I was not going to let Jill win. That's how I saw it. She had challenged me, claimed I wasn't worth trying to save. I was going to show that bitch.

I found a small round corner table in Starbucks and sat down with my phone. I tried to entertain myself with news articles but I was getting antsy. I finally ordered a latte and went back to my chair.

I was holding my paper cup and nervously looking out the window when a woman approached me. She had long almost orange hair, and wore jeans with a layered top.

"You must be Aubrey."

I stood up and held out my hand. "How'd you guess?"

"You're the most nervous, anxious-looking person in this place." She smiled and sat down across from me. "So you got evicted, huh?" She grabbed my cup and took a sip making a gross face.

"Needs sugar. Like a lot."

I was torn between amused and grossed out.

"How long were you at Briarwood?"

"Almost ninety days"

She whistled. "That's a lot of money. What is that like forty five thousand?"

I didn't want to think about it. I looked down at my coffee and played with the hole on the lid.

"I was there thirty days. My insurance only paid one month. I asked Tim if we could work out something financially but they had already given the bed over. So I was kicked out, like literally on the street. I went straight to a liquor store. Two days later Amy was sitting next to me as I lay in a hospital bed. I guess I had her card on me.

"Anyway. I was a hot mess. I stayed a week in the detox unit of the hospital. When I got out I tried going to meetings, but they were really uncomfortable and I didn't think it was for me." She looked out the window and watched cars drive by. It was starting to rain.

"Anyway, I started my own meeting group with a couple of people I knew from the house. We meet here weekly and talk about what's going on, what we are doing. We help each other find jobs or get rides." She looked at me and her hazel eyes smiled.

"Before I tell you to join our group, what did you get kicked out for?"

"Asking questions." I smiled to myself. "Jill thought that I wasn't wanting to get better. I had asked some questions about the relationship between a person's ability to pay and the house's success rate and it wasn't met well."

"I see. So basically your time was almost up and you wouldn't be able to submit a glowing questionnaire."

She had read my mind.

“Do you have family? Have you called them yet?”

I took a long sip of coffee. Swallowing it was painful and I winced.

“No. Not yet. I’m not sure what to say. I’m afraid to tell them I was kicked out. I guess I’m embarrassed and ashamed.”

“If I’ve learned anything, starting with the truth is usually the best way to start. Call them. They might be more understanding than you think. Especially if you didn’t pull one of my moves and go straight back to your old ways.”

I wanted to believe her. I wanted so badly for my parents to have faith in me again. I wanted a relationship with them again. But the task of picking up the phone seemed insurmountable.

“You should meet up with us on Thursday evenings. My little group will be here at five thirty, we’ll eat coffee cake and drink too much caffeine. It’s usually a pretty good time. You can probably just come with Jamie.”

I looked at her, cockeyed.

“Yeah, yeah, we heard about you last week. Jamie asked us what we thought about you guys being housemates. To be honest I wasn’t sure. I thought for sure you’d relapse.”

“Oh well, thanks.” I looked at her with a furrowed brow.

She smiled.

"Listen, call your folks. You will feel better if you are honest with them." She looked back out the window at the rain that was coming down hard now. "You've made it this far. Just keep moving forward. Find what you love to do, and do it. Don't let this disease define you. Don't let Jill and Tim define you. Always listen to yourself. There is a voice that knows what to do, it just gets muted by a louder one that puts you down and makes you feel small and afraid.

"I have to get back to work, my lunch is only an hour." She was thoughtful for a minute and looked at me. "Do you like to read?"

"Yes. I typically love to read. Why?"

"Well, in one of my favorite books there is this line by this boy trying to be a fighter, he said: 'But I was still alive, and in my book, where there's life, there's hope."

I gaped at her.

Epilogue

Addiction is an extremely lonely disease. It's not a bad word and people who are addicts or addicts in recovery are not bad or dirty people. It's my experience and belief that most addicts feel very deeply and never learned or were never given the tools to deal with emotions that can be crippling.

I was a lucky one. I found someone who understood how hard it was for me to be comfortable in my own skin. He had demons too, albeit very different from my own. We were very honest with each other from day one. And once we were, those demons had far less power over us. We started looking forward. Those forward looking dreams were stronger than any drug for me. But ultimately, it was my decision to be free of my addictions.

I have a beautiful life. My parents still love me and visit me and my children often. But it wasn't expensive rehab that saved me. It was my choice to not let my flame go out. We all need people to talk to and to call when life throws us a curveball. But other people don't make us better. That's all within the power of one.

The characters in this book are fictional. These stories came from my own imagination, but many of the feelings and consequences can be and are very real.

Godspeed.

Made in the USA
Monee, IL
15 May 2021

Made in the USA
Columbia, SC
20 December 2019

About the author

Mariel Gates is a graduate of Stanford University and the University of Oregon School of Law. She is a former world class triathlete and distance runner. An active member of the running community, she lives in Idaho with her husband and three children. This is her first novel.

thing else again and for the faces on the street, looking for Billie or Marilyn or Rider, listening to the radio, cursing the powers that be, making the connections, watching the records stack and fall, lighting the incense, a red pin-star dance in the blackness of the windowless basement bedroom, reading the books of illumination, forgetting the words, talking, saying it again, losing the friends gone straight, burnt out, spitting the words, vomiting the music, imbibing the sacrament bastardized with killing chemicals, the words laid down to the beast, bum-tripping once more, shooting up the poisons for a sense of flavor, watching the blood back up the needle, feeding his ego, losing the friends gone scared, finding others less certain, more confused, watching the records fall, breaking the penultimate capsule with his teeth and discovering the soul of bitterness within...

Mondrian Monochrome

Once he became like so many others, aping the accepted externals of existence, life reduced itself to a simpler matter. His oscillations, which had once soared and plummeted beyond the limits of any standardized graph, now performed a gentle sine weaving about the x-axis. Now he chose to see all things as solid and well defined. When their outlines began to waver and threaten other forms he feigned ignorance of their vagrancy. CONTROL was a key word; CALCULATION was another. It was important to think in numerical terms since it gave one a proper sense for the grouping of priorities. As for his idealism, once he ranked it as pubescent nonsense he could dismiss its relevance with respect to decision-making processes. As for his rage (at the hypocrisy), at first he kept it in a green bottle, nearly opaque due to the darkness of the glass, stoppered with an over-sized cork. His further differences he set apart to occupy private barred chambers within his mind. Other respect-able men had their secrets, the afternoons in uptown apartments, the late evening business engagements, even if they were of a less metaphysical bent. And weren't such indiscretions as these more likely to be un-covered than those locked totally within the self?

Bizarre intoxicants he abandoned for the everyday variety: alcohol, tobacco, coffee, commercial tranquiliz-ers and vitalizers. Socially these were less harmful and in the proper dosage could be effective in their own way. He adopted a SCHEDULE to finalize the regularity of his days and as the years began to accumulate it encom-passed the sum of his visible life. Naturally there were changes and additions – a wife, a house, advancement in his chosen field of endeavor, a budding family – all pointing in one direction, toward a red letter calibration of normality at the peak of the bell curve.

As for his wife, she was sleek and polished. She was well born to her role in life without the adjustments he had found necessary. Her breasts were full, her legs clean as marble. Her eyes shimmered like nickels coated with mercury. When her mouth closed upon him it moved with the accuracy of a machine.

As for his office, the walls were gray-green. He was never sure of what material they were composed since he did not focus on them directly. Certain things were better left without attention, like the illusions which dis-tracted him at the corners of his vision but which he re-fused to turn his head to confront. His rage (at the cor-pulent amid the hungry) was not like that; it required constant attention. It proved to have tumorous inclinations. Benign enough he was sure, yet growing nonetheless. He transferred it to a larger flask, one of slate gray pottery fired to a high gloss at 4000 degrees Fahrenheit so that the contents remained invisible. A stopper of the same material was heat sealed in place and he mounted the oversized vessel atop the mantel in his living room as a weighty reminder of the errors of his past.

His desk changed from metal to oak as his prominence grew. Not all at once. First a handle here or there made the transformation, next an entire drawer or a segment of the side paneling. Finally one morning he entered his office to find the completed product, its richly grained surfaces shining softly and perfectly as if in celebration of his own perfection.

From that day on his lesser needs were supplied by others. His desk was always fully stocked without him lifting a finger. Pencils, pens, erasers, paper clips, rubber bands, scotch tape, masking tape, scissors large and small, date books, rule books, memos, specifications, and six grades of paper each with its assigned use. This desk provided a parallel to his life, right down to the locked-off compartment on the lower left in which he stored confidential papers. As for the locked-off compartments in his mind, these he visited less often, only in the moments before sleep when he began to give up CONTROL, or in his dreams. But dreams were of no matter and could be dismissed upon awakening.

Still, there remained his rage (at the separateness). He knew that any piece of pottery, even heavily cast and perfectly fired, could be shattered in a moment of carelessness. Thus at last he came upon the box. It was a wooden box with a velvet interior and had once held a matched set of long-nosed dueling pistols. It was an appropriate box in which to store and imprison one's rage (at the patronage). A fall could not break it, and the metal sheeting between the lining and the wood made it impervious to fire. There was a sturdy clasp of solid silver with a secret fastening so that no chance guest or curious servant could pry within. Its sole disadvantage lay in the fact that unlike a corked bottle or stoppered flask, it might be opened at a moment's notice. Surely, this was temptation.

Snow Like Static, Like Beast-Roar

He sees the faces that are no longer faces that are blocks of meat, dark and radiant buttons for eyes, empty hooks for teeth. Is it a word which sets him off? An unrecordable chemical accident within the brain, the twitching of a facial muscle beneath a razored jowl? No matter. Although he has compromised again and again and it is but a single moment among many, this once he fails.

In the hall the hose lies curled, a bland and dusty snake within its cage. Beside it rests the axe, potent, shining dully. His hand has forgotten the ways of glass and passing through it bleeds. The axe within his bloodied grip dominates the entire room. With this one action he has brought them instantly alive, all of them, and they scatter like bugs before him as he goes to work. One, two, one, two. So easy, he thinks. Lift and swing. Lift high and deliver the blow and the desk resonates, splits, and begins to crumple. The life of its polished grain is only deception, a surface life. Within, the wood is too dead for sap to flow. Rotted and fibrous it topples away in crackling chunks. Yet his eyes of sweat and rage can perceive another kind of flowing: clips, staples, pennons of unreeling tape, scissors double-jackknifing through the air, six grades of paper, manila folders stamped CONFIDENTIAL and shredded roughly in two.

So easy, he thinks, lift and swing and the pressure wells up and finds release again and again. This was the kind of work any soul could comprehend, destruction clean and simple.

He vaults the midden of the desk and delivers a deft blow to the window. It splinters outward to sprinkle the street far below, soundlessly. He gashes the walls with his own brand of abstract expression, sends a filing cabinet on a clattering journey from one scarred corner to another. He laughs completely and steps into the hall.

Now their eyes are buttons broken, wax grapes crushed underfoot, cheap glazed candies with their tasteless centers exposed. They have retreated and grouped at each end of the corridor, two mindless tides reflecting one another. He controls these tides: when he advances, they retreat. Whirling the axe above his head, sensing its whistle in the programmed air, laughing again, he charges and they disperse to individual droplets running for open elevators and stairwells. He continues his abstract on the corridor walls, in the deserted offices. The artist alone with himself: the axe his brush, all of the immediate world his canvas. This could rival Kandinsky, dwarf Pollock. He is laughing more completely than he has in years. And that is how they find him, laughing still, lift and swing, lift and swing, as they surround him from behind like a cautious hunting pack and drive the needle within.

The plays within his mind, the brain reel running unspliced and without commercial breaks, became far more fascinating than anything on the outside. At times the externals of his existence provided the groundwork for these internal fantasies. Yet often they seemed born unto themselves, or drawn from another reality he had experienced in some other life or plane of being. His waking dreams took on the quality and intensity of sleeping dreams. His unreasoning unconscious held the reins and the whip and together they traveled mightily, with no chosen direction on his part whatsoever.

Example: a dark tree and fern landscape which he had never visited before, a tiger docile as a lamb, a sun which poked about in the hairy branches this way and that as if it had lost all sense of time and did not know setting from rising from burning noon. Right side up and upside down reversed, became as aberrant and interchangeable as the rise-up-fall-down constructions of toy blocks. Here or there a tree chose to grow into the ground and send its roots uselessly soil searching toward the sky. By night, moonless, the constellation of Orion burned brightly in the lake and cast its reflection like an afterthought, tenuous, rippling overhead in the smoky waters of the firmament.

The Master, the Mistress, and the Midwife

The Master was out hunting as he was most days. In the woods from dawn to dusk with rifle by his side. If he wasn't out hunting he would be drunk, working on getting drunk, or having one of his blackouts. As he moved through the dappled light and shadow cast by the sun and the trees around him, sometimes he would find himself firing at the slightest movement of leaf or branch, real or imagined, in the sheer frustration of not discovering the creature who had cuckolded him.

The Mistress was abed, close on the way to giving birth to their second child. For the first five years of their marriage she had been barren. They had nearly given up trying. Then she became pregnant and birthed their first child. If you could call it a child. Most would call it a monster. He took it away from her and she never saw it again. She often wondered what had become of it. Smothered to death? Sold to some sideshow as a freak? Now that she had known the Master for eight years of marriage, she wouldn't put anything past him.

The Midwife had been summoned hours ago. At first she hadn't wanted to come. She had been there at that first infernal birth. The creature had been a normal enough male child in the broadest sense: two arms, two legs, head and torso. Yet its body and limbs were covered with a dark feathery down and its eyes were not human, they were the shiny black eyes of some beast or bird. She had told all this to Father John more than once. Still he said it was her Christian duty and she must go again in the service of the Lord. He explained to her that no life is easy and that the Lord has ways of testing us.

Father John paused for a moment. Then he told her what she should do if another devil child were born. He showed her a pillow, how she should hold it, how to count off the seconds before she could raise it and be sure.

After the Master's dispatch of that first child-monster, the Mistress had argued with him for hours, trying to convince him to bring it back. She claimed it was theirs together, that she had never betrayed him, never been unfaithful to him. He refused to believe her. He laughed in her face, bitterly, called the child an abomination and cursed her as an evil and perverse whore. Now they rarely spoke to one another at all. They ate their meals separately and kept to their own quarters. On the rare occasions when they passed one another in a hallway, she would avert her eyes from him and look anywhere except in his direction.

As the Midwife left the shelter of the woods, she came in view of the manor house. She crossed herself and mumbled a prayer beneath her breath. She dared to glance up across the unkept sward, grasses and weeds growing high, and it was the same as the last time. As she looked into the westering sun she saw dark birds circling the eaves and chimneys of the house. She crossed herself twice more, and again before she raised the iron clapper and knocked on the door. One of the few remaining servants let her in. As soon as she entered she could hear the cries of the Mistress echoing from above. The Midwife hurried up the staircase. Child or monster, it would arrive soon and her duty to the Lord was clear.

The Master always carried a silver flask of brandy with him when he went hunting. And now that the birth of this second child was near, he carried two. He'd finished the first and most of the second. He was stumbling through the woods, wandering off the path and back on again. Suddenly he found himself sitting on the forest floor, a bed of dry leaves crackling beneath him. He must have fallen, he thought, though he didn't remember falling. He laughed aloud, and laughed again, until it turned into a series of strangled sobs.

Using his rifle like a cane he hoisted himself to his feet. He felt dizzy for a moment, his mind a maelstrom of unhinged thoughts and whirling images. Earlier he had killed a stag and a rabbit and let both carcasses lie where they had fallen. He had watched the stag thrashing in its death throes and hadn't felt much of anything. He thought he had spied the monster he sought at least twice, a dark and ragged shadow shifting at the corner of his vision. Yet when he turned swiftly to face it and raised the rifle to fire, it had silently vanished. Even when he charged into the trees after it, there was nothing to be found. As he stumbled on, out of ammunition and headed back to the manor house, he began bellowing out an old drinking song from his short-lived student days. He was off key and his words were unintelligible, yet they stirred memories of a far better life from the one in which he now found himself trapped.

Frantic with her failure, the Midwife hurried from the manor house, praying to the Lord for forgiveness. The child had been born without incident. Another monster to be sure, no different from that first abomination. She couldn't help herself from gasping when she first saw it. Yet there had been no chance to do what Father John told her she must. There were pillows aplenty to perform the deed, yet there had always been one or more servants hovering about. And shortly after she had finished cleaning the creature off, the Mistress had called for it to be brought to her side.

Dusk was settling as the Midwife entered the woods and took the path to the village. The fast and jerky way she crossed herself repeatedly had become a reflex action to all of the darkness she sensed in the world around her. Then she heard the cry of some strange beast, bellowing and roaring, growing louder as it approached her. She looked up and saw it far ahead on the path, shambling toward her in the failing light. She ran blindly into the woods. She crouched there trembling, without moving, until she could no longer hear its bestial cries.

Tomorrow, she thought, she would tell the entire village that not only was the manor house cursed but its evil had infected the forest around it. She would tell anyone who would listen that she had seen the monster who dwelt there with her very own eyes.

He was just like the first one, just as strange and to her

strangely beautiful. The Mistress held the creature to her breast and nursed him. She was his mother, what else could she do? She had carried him within her for nine months. She swore she would not let the Master take this one away as he had the first. She kept a small pearl-handled pistol by her side, even when she slept. She had told the servants not only to lock the door, but to keep the window securely bolted. The window was how he had come to her the last time, though she could not imagine how he had scaled the sheer wall beneath. For now this room would be her life, her self-imposed hermitage. And the child at her side would be her monster alone for better or worse.

Yet as the hours began to pass into a day and more, and she still held the child safely by her side, she realized there was something she feared even more than its loss. She feared that he would come to her again as he had before, during one of his drunken blackouts from which he could remember nothing. He would come with his body changing or already transformed, covered in a satiny sheathe of dark hair and feathers, and with the shiny black eyes of a beast or bird. He would take her against her will, forcing himself upon her, bringing her to one frightening orgasm after another, until he left his monstrous seed within her again.

The Curse of the Magus

with Robert Frazier

Sulak eased his body from a bed made of beach grass and felt around for his glasses. He almost knocked them off the sea trunk, which would have been a disaster for the aged magician, but his little finger, the one twisted with arthritis, hooked them by the wings. His hands shook as he righted them, then pushed the wires back through the dirty gray curls of his hair and over large ears. Now he could see in the dark interior of the hut.

He picked up the cane he'd made from a length of dry driftwood and banged all the pots that hung on pegs or wires until the rats zipped away. Stepping around the assorted debris he'd salvaged over the years, he shuffled toward the door but stopped short. A small, sleek head poked out of the shadows to his left. Its eyes were beady, reptilian.

When he brought the tip of his gnarled cane up between himself and the hidden creature, it quickly slipped away through two ship's planks that framed the jam on which his door latched. The old magician cackled.

Just a damn monitor lizard, he thought. Not his old nemesis the boa. She was too fat to slip between the boards like that. And besides, if the snake had gotten in during the night he would have awakened in her embrace.

Sulak pushed the door open, squinting against the morning light until he could make out the scraggly brush and the ice plants that surrounded his hut.

He stepped outside. It was a sunny day, the first that spring. Before him, black-headed terns wheeled against the sky and dove for ghost crabs along the beach. Their calls reached him scattered by the breeze. Behind him, iguanas and monitor lizards basked on the twisted volcanic rock of Herculius. The wind was warm from across the narrow bay and smelled wonderful, like a breath of glory from his past, from when his powers held sway with the Magi Lords and he had strolled the gardens of the high city with many a court lady on his arm.

An unbidden image rose up in Sulak's mind, the Lady Alcina in a gown of silver strands. He remembered her bare arms, how one minute they could be pale and smooth as polished moonstone, the next instant darkly tanned and downed with blond hair. He recalled her mercurial beauty and impossible treachery, both of which still burned in his chest. Oh well, Sulak mused for the countless time, he should have never bedded a witch in the first place. Damn, it almost felt good to be alive after so many years in exile. Almost.

Sulak cupped rainwater from a battered barrel near the corner of his hut. He slurped it in a single gulp ... then spit out a foul yellow stinkbug and cursed loudly at Herculius, this island prison which kept him from the world beyond, which seemed to destroy his mood every time he felt pleased or satisfied or merely at peace with himself.

But Sulak knew that wasn't true. Herculius was only a jumbled pile of rock and dirt with a volcano slumbering at its core. Long ago he had accepted its rugged landscape, just as he had been forced to accept the spells which held him here and stripped him of his powers, the same spells which also stilled the island's hot lava. If he had any enemies on Herculius besides the boa they were of his own making, the memories he refused to abandon, that plagued his thoughts and seized his consciousness with spells of visionary intensity.

Sulak donned his greatcoat of worn blue velvet, the one with the silver epaulets and tattered silk lining. Though he'd meet no one – for just as he was entrapped here, no other human could enter – he wanted to walk the perimeter beach of his conical prison in style and discover what new treasures the ocean might have washed onto its shores. He had begun every morning like this when he was younger, so after a winter of especially poor health, he yearned for this simple ritual all the more. He took up his cane and started down to the beach.

Where the fine brown sand darkened to the black and grainy sand of an old lava flow, a glint of light caught Sulak's eye. Something was embedded near the shoreline, still lapped by the low and steady waves yet catching the sun's reflection each time the sea receded. Sulak danced gingerly forward and poked at the object with his stick. He gasped as a gold coin rolled free onto the damp earth.

Suddenly oblivious to the cold surf flooding about his ankles, Sulak bent over and retrieved the coin. He quickly cleaned it on his sleeve, marveling at how the heavy metal could have traveled to him across the water. Yet the question fled from his mind as he lifted his glasses onto his forehead and peered more closely at his find.

Intricately embossed upon the gold was a skyline Sulak recognized at once. He saw the slender towers and delicately arched skywalks of his native city. The coin was from his homeland, Myria, the greatest island empire of the Southern Sea, and by the look of it, freshly minted. He turned the coin over and his old eyes widened and froze; the breath caught within his throat. It was true then. All that he had imagined and feared in the years since his exile had transpired. He was staring at the slightly raised and bony profile of his ancient enemy Borgus, now apparently Arch-Magus of the Empire.

A hoarse, incoherent cry broke from Sulak's throat as his breath exploded. He hurled the coin far from him, back out over the water from which it had come. If not for Alcina's betrayal, if not for Borgus' endless plotting and the cronies he gathered about him, minor magicians to a man, Sulak's own countenance would have most likely shone upon that coin.

The old magician waved his stick about wildly as he stumbled up the beach. The past would never let him be, he thought. Not when his present was so paltry. Not when the emptiness of each successive day only foreshadowed the emptiness of his diminished future. All of Sulak's limbs were trembling violently as he collapsed onto the sand and a draught of bitter history possessed him.

The Lady Alcina looked up. Tonight her eyes were deep brown flecked with yellow, warm and constant as the eyes of a cat.

She laughed and pressed her body more closely against his. Standing on the balcony of the chambers Sulak had recently been granted in the High City, they were looking out over the lighted streets below, and a smooth sheet of darkening sea in the distance. The day had been warm and the evening seemed warmer still. The first stars glowed with raw brilliance in a cloudless sky.

They were naked beneath their robes, their flesh still dewy from love-making, and Sulak was intoxicated, both with the protean incarnations of the woman beside him and his own sudden rise to power, for no magician in memory had gained a seat among the Magi Lords while so young. A bit vehemently, he was expounding his theories, ideas he was convinced that he alone had grasped.

"But magic is leaving the world," he insisted. "Each year I've measured the changes with the basic spells. The forces always grow weaker, our sphere of influence shrinks. In the time of our grandfather's fathers the Empire extended beyond the Straits of Gade and onto the mainland. Now only the islands remain to us."

"And what can it matter?" Alcina laughed again. "Surely there is enough magic left in the world to fill our own lives."

Sulak was appalled by her indifference. At the same time he discovered he was aroused again. The witch grasped the back of his neck and pulled him roughly toward her. Her lips and tongue tasted of iced apricots in the heated night. No, rather they held the flavor of almonds rolled in candied grape leaves. And then she was melting in his arms and the balcony on which they stood, the sky above and the city below, faded like foam upon the waves.

Sulak found himself in the High Council chambers, speaking before the Magi Lords. He wore his silk-lined jacket of blue velvet.

"The future belongs not to amulets and incantations," he concluded, "but to reason, to the ordered thoughts of the rational mind. And that is why if we are to survive, our finest magic and finest reason must be bound together."

He clasped his hands with fingers intertwined to illustrate the point. "Our engineers, our architects and philosophers, must be elevated in stature to a rightful place upon the Council."

From the steep and darkly shadowed tiers of the assemblage, only silence greeted this final pronouncement. And then one man rose, illuminating his face with his own magic. Borgus' skeletal visage, aglow in the etheric light, was florid and creased with anger. "We have heard such theories before," he began, flinging one long arm downward in a dismissive gesture to the stage below, "and we have rightly denounced them as the mouthings of barbarians."

Sulak nervously fingered a lapel. How could this be, he wondered, his jacket was not new but worn and falling to pieces? Borgus was not really here, only upon the gold coin he held in his palm. But that was not right either, for hadn't he hurled the coin back into the ocean?

The old magician came to himself, walking along the beach. He felt the sun warm upon his face, the sea wind tousling his hair.

Sulak recognized the spell for what it had been and knew he had survived its passage. The ordered thoughts of a rational mind he had once espoused with such eloquence and vigor, were once again his own. Yet the aged magician suspected that one day his visions would carry him away completely, that he would starve to death or fall prey to the boa while immersed in his own useless past.

He was nearly halfway round the island when he saw the chair jutting out of the black volcanic sand far ahead. At first he didn't recognize it. The wood had swelled and discolored in the waves, and it had soaked in the brine for at least a month, as evidenced by the young barnacles dotting it like liver spots. However, when he stood in front of it, there could be little doubt it was the royal chair of a Magus, and the Arch-Magus at that. It was the very chair in which Sulak should have sat for life. He stared at it in disbelief.

What was it doing on the beach? And what circumstances had prevailed to allow the jeweled chair to become just another bit of driftwood?

Sulak recalled a vivid dream he'd had on the full moon before last. He'd dreamt of Borgus awkwardly seated in this same chair which now rested on the shores of Herculius. In the dream the chair was perched upon the foredeck of a sailing ship. Borgus was leading an armada of war vessels against the mainland republics. His cronies, the very men who had conspired in Sulak's exile, commanded ships of their own. Then a storm blew suddenly in from the north, torrential and devastating. It had scattered the fleet in every direction, drowned more than half the vessels before a single spell could unravel it.

That same night, Sulak remembered, a storm had rattled against the walls of his hut. At the time he had taken the storm for the cause of his dream, but what if the reverse were true? Perhaps his dream had somehow served as an agent of revenge for his long repressed powers. Sulak shook his head to clear the cobwebs. No matter. Simply frustrating Borgus was not a satisfying revenge. Nor was having the damn chair after so many years.

So Sulak's second reaction was one of anger. He kicked at the chair until his chest heaved, then whacked it with his cane. When none of his actions seemed to cause the slightest damage, he conceded that he'd grown very weak during the winter. Then he realized that despite its briny journey, the chair might still contain magic of its own. And that thought struck him dumb. If the chair still harbored magic, he could use it to weaken the spells which kept his own potent powers in check. Even the master spell that cloaked the island and held its volcanic activity to a minimum might eventually be broken.

Sulak made his way back along the coarse sand, through the thin wall of brush which separated it from the barren interior of igneous ropes and rock pillows. He knew that the chair of the Arch-Magus possessed a kind of dim sentience linked to its owner. Steeped as it was with the spells of Borgus, the wood of the chair would recognize and rebel against an unfamiliar touch. Its magic was useless to him now. Sulak must first make the chair a part of his daily existence, until the strength of his own personality began to permeate its being. Only then would it offer up its powers.

At his hut, for the first time in years, the old magician whistled as he cooked himself a hearty breakfast. He would need all his strength to rebuild and rearrange his space so the chair would fit inside, and double that amount to drag the great wooden beast the length of the island.

Rather than rework the old boards of his beach hut, Sulak simply knocked down one wall. As he sat eating his breakfast of crab meat and boiled guillemot eggs, staring inland toward the smoking rim of Herculius, he felt well pleased with himself. However, the problem of moving the chair proved more difficult.

At first he attempted brute force. The chair eventually yielded, and Sulak freed its legs from the wet sand with an audible pop. After that, however, it was impossible to drag on its back. He flipped it onto its front by levering it with his cane. He was then able to drag it on the tips of the armrests. This worked well enough for ten yards or so at a stretch, but the arms were too thin. They kept digging into the sand and Sulak had to wrestle the whole thing free each time. Soon exhausted, he rested against a sunbaked rock and nibbled on some jerky he had dried from lizard meat. He had to face facts. He was nearly sixty, and unwell. Force was not an option for him.

Returning to his hut once more, Sulak pried two boards loose from the collapsed wall. Warped ones made better runners, since their ends turned up, so he lashed these to the arms of the chair and pulled with his spine braced against the top of the back rest. The arms no longer caught in the sand, but he could still make progress only in short, heated bursts of energy which left his temples throbbing and the breath rasping in his throat. There were moments when he swore he could sense the reluctant spirit of Borgus, locked within the chair, consciously resisting him.

The sun had already passed meridian when he decided he could take no more. He estimated that he'd progressed less than a third of the distance he needed to cover.

Sulak retreated to a small rocky lagoon adjacent to his hut, really a tide pool now that the ocean was at low ebb. The old magician stripped off his clothes and slowly eased himself into the refreshing water. He lay with his eyes closed and his head against a bank made spongy by the homes of fiddler and ghost crabs.

The ordered thoughts of a rational mind, Sulak told himself, as he tried to devise an easier way to transport the chair to his hut. Instead he slept, and he dreamt of oxen.

He was back on his native island, once more immersed in the events of his former life. He was instructing the local farmers in the use of a yoke he had designed so that the untilled recesses of the steeper hillsides could be plowed. In some quarters he had been praised for this and for other inventions he had introduced into the daily life of the Empire. However, to most of the Magi Lords it was further evidence that Sulak had been soiled by the commonplace. Only weeks later, Alcina had fed him the potion which heralded his downfall. Even as the drug took effect, the evil witch continued her seduction.

Sulak had returned to consciousness stripped of both power and speech by the consorted spells of Borgus and his minions. In the mockery of a trial which followed the young mage stood upon the public block, his tongue dumb within his mouth, the thoughts raging uselessly within his mind, as charges of treason were leveled against him.

He had corrupted the sacred traditions of the past. He had conspired with the mainland republics against his own nation. Those he had counted as friends and allies in his attempt to transform the Empire watched his humiliation silently, spoke not a word in his defense. While Sulak had plumbed the meaning of life and the natural world about him, Borgus had steadily consolidated his own political strength.

Yet as the convicted "traitor" rode an open cart to the harbor and the ship which would bear him into exile, he realized it was more than Borgus' deceit which had carried the day. Sulak grasped the broader implications of his failure. As the very populace he had tried to save thronged the streets of the capital to rain their curses upon him, as he scanned their angry and righteous faces, he understood that the influence of magic was not only leaving the world, at the same time the very nature of its power grew darker. That darkness had already rooted itself, perhaps irrevocably, in the souls of his countrymen. And it was that selfsame darkness, fixed but unrecognized in his own soul, which had drawn him to Alcina.

When Sulak awoke, he heard an iguana barking only a few yards away. This startled him. The great lizards usually avoided him since he preyed on them occasionally for meat. Sulak raised himself from the pool and felt for his robe where he'd left it on the sand. He needed to wipe his eyeglasses, which he'd tinkered together with wire and the bottoms of apothecary bottles after noting how the glass improved his failing sight. After cleaning them and perching them back on his nose, he was surprised to find the huge iguana squatting beside him. It had slithered up without a sound and now stared at him with doleful eyes.

What a stroke of luck, thought Sulak. Or was it luck? He had pictured the armada destroyed by a great storm and later the chair washed ashore. Now he had pictured oxen in his sleep, and found the island's largest creature upon waking: passive and apparently awaiting his needs. Perhaps his dream time had become something like the bottle glass, it focused his repressed powers into a clear force which could shape reality in the world about him.

Sulak untied a length of sisal he'd doubled around his waist as a belt. He tied a loop in one end of the rope and eased it over the iguana's neck. He was not surprised when it followed him on its tether.

At the chair, Sulak rested flat on his back while the iguana sat beside him. He sensed his old heart rebelling within his chest. Forcing himself to continue, he harnessed the iguana to both of the board runners and placed himself behind the chair. He pushed while the iguana pulled, with a plodding yet effective gait. The creature's long tail swinging back and forth, slapping against the runners.

At last, the two plowed through the damp sand at the lagoon's mouth and stopped by the collapsed wall of the beach house. Sulak untethered the iguana, fed it some scraps of crab meat from his stores, and sent it scampering up the rocks to join what few comrades were still sunning there.

The sun had now dropped low in the sky. Dark clouds were clustering in from the north. Anticipating another bad storm, Sulak did not rest. He tugged until the runners caught against the foundation of the hut. He unlashed the boards from the chair and began the twist-and-twist-back motions needed to inch it up onto the floor beneath the thatched roof. With a final shove he toppled it inside onto its back, and fell with it, exhausted, hurting in every joint.

As he lay half in and half out of the hut, aware that he had bruised his hip in the fall, Sulak stared blankly at the ceiling. His ordeal with the chair had now grown into an obsession. An obsession with many possible origins. The chair was his; he was now the ArchMagus. Also, he belonged to the chair. The more he handled it, the more imperative it seemed to get it sheltered and cleaned up. And he had been wrong about the island; it was more than just a jumble of dirt and rock. It too was somehow involved. He was almost sure of it. The island, or at least the sleeping giant it housed, sensed that Sulak was near his end, and it too desired freedom from the spells which filled its very stone. Herculius had slept far too long.

Sulak ran this over and over in his mind until he could no longer comprehend any of it. He was weary to death of his exile, and weary beyond measure to exercise his powers again. Even if it were for the last time. The chair offered a chance, or so it seemed, to be a Magus again. What mattered was the chair. It always came back to the chair.

A great pain stabbed through him as he pulled himself upright, but he ignored it. Whether he'd broken a rib or broken his whole body, he meant to sit in the seat that was rightfully his. He pushed the chair erect and collapsed into it as something inside him, some last defense, collapsed also. He drifted out of consciousness into a limbo of darkness and pulsing stars.

Sulak dreamed one last time.

He dreamed that as the sun set behind the volcano, it peeked under the quickening storm for a long moment, spreading bloody fingers of light across the underbelly of the clouds. A breeze blew through the open hut and ruffled the tatters on Sulak's velvet coat. He awoke for a moment, or dreamed he did, and with his bare callused palms rubbed the slime and wet sand from the jewels set in the chair's arms. They glowed with appreciative warmth and seemed to draw him onward. His obsession had already linked him to the chair, it now felt familiar beneath his touch.

As he tumbled down the long tunnel of unconsciousness once more, the old magician could feel himself falling through the atoms of the wood and into the cracked and folded bedrock below him. Set free, his expanding awareness spread through the island, and it linked with the power of the repressed volcano. Then he felt his roots spread deeper along the veins of hot magma that carried to nearby islands, especially the island empire of the Magi Lords, his homeland of Myria.

Sulak now sensed more than saw how the coin he had found upon the beach had lied. He learned that he had been wrong again, just as he had been about Herculius, that magic had now fled the world more swiftly than even he had imagined.

The delicate skywalks of his native city, their air-spanning grace more the product of sorcery than architecture, had collapsed. The gardens of the high city grew wild from neglect. The indigent gathered to beg in the market squares, or skulked in alleys by night to await the unwary.

Sulak searched through the devastated and corrupt souls of his former countrymen for the evil emanations of Alcina. He discovered that the witch still lived, yet magic had deserted her also. He sensed how her flesh had aged more quickly because of the changes she had once wrought upon it, how it now hung from her bones in great ugly folds, how she dwelt in shadowy desolation in her ruined apartments where no curtain was ever drawn, no lamp ever lit. Sulak laughed and the magma bubbled in his veins.

Myria too possessed a slumbering giant, a deep caldera ready to burst at the seams as the ancient spells which held it in check continued to weaken. As Sulak's consciousness spread thinner and thinner, his reawakened powers linked through the chair to Herculius, and then from Herculius to the other islands. He realized he was losing touch with his physical body and that his old nemesis, the boa, had found him exposed in the open hut and wrapped herself around the worn husk which now slumped in the chair of the Arch-Magus.

Sulak was passing from life. His last act was to summon all of the magics from the linked network through which his being now flowed: the chair, the spell upon Herculius, even the ancient chains binding vulcanism on the other islands.

The people of Myria had unjustly branded him a traitor. Borgus and the other Magi Lords had cursed him into oblivion. As Sulak died, as the boa's stricture pressed the last wisps of breath from his body, he claimed that brand and returned that curse in kind.

Across the storm-darkened sea, the fury of the earth rumbled beneath his homeland streets where once he might have ruled.

The Immortal Gorgons

Medusa was long and away gone. Barely a bad memory, And so very bad she was! Even if she was Gorgon kin. She had bad looks. Bad taste. Bad disposition. Black sheep of the family. As if the snakes weren't enough, the bat-mad woman had to put jeweled collars on their necks to make them seem attractive.

Then she encountered Mr. Shiny Shield, and it was slice and dice time for poor Medusa. She died young for a mythical monster. But then again, if she'd been a little brighter and less conceited.

That left the two immortal gorgons, Stheno and Euryale.

While the centuries dark and light transpired, there were two things that Stheno and Euryale eventually agreed upon. They both hated Medusa and what they considered her undeserved renown with a manic passion. Why should she be famous, a veritable legend that lived on and on, when they were virtually unknown? And after too many centuries together, they also hated one another almost as much.

I should know. I'm Euryale, the smart one.

We just had nothing left to say to each other we hadn't already said. And looking at one another's writhing or bound snakes only makes you more aware of your own. We never wanted to see each other again. Earth was fortunately large enough to accommodate us.

Last I heard of Stheno, she was going back to nature. Off to find some primitive tribe in Africa or Indian that would worship her as a Goddess.

"Small dreams for a small mind!" That was the last thing I said to her. She just shrugged, turned her back on me, and walked away.

I can see her now in some isolated village, worshipped and feared by a hundred or so ignorant natives. Believe me, natives don't fancy getting turned to stone any more than anyone else.

As for myself, I now live in Hollywood. North Hollywood if you want to be precise about it. I'm part of the cadre of freaks and hangers-on that survive around the entertainment industry. I feed my snakes valium and keep them bound with a turban except when I'm alone. I have my own website where I'm known as Madame Euryale, Psychic to the Stars. I have hundreds of devotees and clients. Even a few legitimate stars. No big deal. I'm just biding my immortal time.

In my private life I'm an avid science fiction fan. I read the books and watch the movies and television shows. I contribute to the organizations encouraging space travel. The sooner we leave this ball of dirt the better as far as I'm concerned. I'm ready and waiting for other planets. Then I'm going to find one I can make my own.

I'll create my very own legend, glorious for me and deadly for any who would dare cross me. It will be a legend that will overshadow Medusa's completely. And I will live on to enjoy it.

That's Show Business

"Cut!" the Director yelled. "That's wrong, all wrong!"

"You have your interpretation of the part," the Actor informed him, standing with hands on his hips, "and I have mine. I'm willing to compromise to some extent, but ultimately, I have to stick with my own vision."

The Director looked at him and snorted. "You call that compromise!"

He was infuriated with the Actor. For the barest moment he considered telling him that he was no more than a solid-state hologram, an artificial construct that could be turned off and replaced at any moment.

He bit his tongue before he could speak.

The Holographic Division had tailored the Actor for the role, an aggressive character with a mind of his own. That meant a like personality came with it, a personality that was causing constant delays because the Actor refused to follow directions. Yet the Director knew if he told the Actor he was no more than an artifact, the persona tailored for the role could begin to disintegrate.

He'd be useless then, and it would take Holographics a week or more to cough up something new. The film was already behind schedule. The Director concluded there was nothing left to do but talk to the Producer. Perhaps the Producer could convince the techs at Holo to make some adjustments.

"We'll discuss this tomorrow," he told the Actor with a malevolent glare. "That's a wrap for today," he shouted to the rest of the set. "Tomorrow. Eight a.m. sharp!"

"I just can't get along with him," the Director pleaded to the Producer. "He won't listen to a thing I say."

"Yes, I can see it's serious," the Producer nodded. "Let me think about it for a minute." He leaned back in his armchair, stroking his beard.

The Director stood before the Producer's oversized desk, hands crossed in front of him, intimidated by the luxurious surroundings.

The Producer considered his options. He knew the Actor was perfect for the role. He had made some suggestions on the design himself. On the other hand, there were plenty of directors that should be able to handle the script. The solution was obvious.

The Producer glanced at his laptop. He called up the file in question and began typing on his keyboard. He found the appropriate entry and erased it.

The Director flickered out of existence.

In his spacious office, near the heart of the Great Studio, the Producer called up a list of director constructs and began scrolling through them for one that was amiable and easy-going.

The Producer spent forty hours a week in his office, though now that everything was hi-tech and automated, there was seldom forty-hours' worth of work to keep him busy. Sometimes he read the sports news online, scanning to the end of each story to use up time. Sometimes he played solitaire online.

Often he'd just sit and stare out the window at the deserted sets and empty buildings. And sometimes, inexplicably, he found himself looking over his shoulder.

An Unrecognized Masterwork

We have before us this week the first authorized translation of the overlooked Portuguese masterpiece *Stamp Your Feet!* by Juan Luis Obregon. Although Obregon was a contemporary, and most likely an acquaintance, of such literary lions as Joyce, Hemingway, and Stein, he has remained in relative obscurity outside his native land. Until recently only two of Obregon's works have been available in English: the early pornographic love poem "Ode to a Thighchilada," and the puzzling yet often anthologized short story "Gherkin," a surreal tour de force that takes place entirely under brine, and which Ford Maddox Ford accused of being "no more than a distended pickling recipe."

Like so many artistic figures of the Twentieth Century, Obregon lived in Paris throughout much of the 1920s. Yet early on he became known as a loner and eccentric, and seldom was he invited to the more influential salons. In one account he is described as "a small dark man with a fiendish chuckle who affected half a mustache, sometimes on the left side of his face, more often on the right." Another casts him as "barrel-chested, a fantastic drinker and womanizer, prone to unreasoning fits of temper." This last point is substantiated by Paris Police reports for 1927. In April of that year Obregon was arrested on the banks of the Seine while trying to drown a rag picker who had insulted his necktie.

Oddly enough, Obregon's only publications during this time were not as a creative writer, but as a critic for the short-lived art weekly *Le Bidet Bouillonne Partout,* where he was best remembered for his classic pronouncement, *"Dada...c'est caca!"* which earned him more than a few enemies and once again showed his tendency to swim against prevailing currents.

By 1930 the bubble had burst, the axe had fallen, the pigeons had come home to roost ... in short, the Great Depression was in full swing and most expatriates had repatriated, some returning home to increasing fame and fortune. This was not to be the case for Obregon. Portugal remained a relatively backward country, in large part illiterate. Although "Gherkin" and the apparently untranslatable "Stuffed Chile" had already established his reputation among a select coterie of his fellow literati, financial support was not forthcoming. Obregon wandered the streets of Lisbon, destitute and in increasingly poor health. Finally he was forced to take a job as a coat tree in a local tavern.

Despite such difficulties, indications are that the writer was mellowing with age. His moustache was now complete and in his only surviving letter, written to his mother, he states: "At last I have found gainful employment, and although it may be below what I consider my just station in life, at least I am serving my fellow man. Send some paella, if you please."

Obregon's new calling was to be a brief one. In March of 1934, only a few weeks after the final pages of *Stamp Your Feet!* had been penned, a premature spring struck the streets of Lisbon. In the space of one afternoon the weather turned unseasonably warm, and Obregon, still loyally at his post, was suffocated by an abandoned overcoat. Yet his masterpiece lives on.

Like so many great novels of the twentieth century – *Ulysses, Gravity's Rainbow, Bushwhacker's Reprise* – the central obsession of *Stamp Your Feet!* is with the nature of time. Time to go to work. Time for dinner. Time to go to bed. Time to get up in the morning.

We follow the protagonist, Manual Emanual, through twenty-seven and a half days of his life as a bricklayer building public lavatories for a soccer stadium on the outskirts of Madrid. The fact that Obregon had never been to Madrid is further testimony to the range of his vision. As each brick is laid in place a whole new reality, both internal and external, unfolds before us.

In the first section of the book, Obregon amply demonstrates why in some quarters he has earned the appellation "Master of the Gerundive."

" ... carrying the trowel, laying the mortar, taking a smoke, eating a box lunch, taking a smoke, riding the trolley, spitting in the street, avoiding the irate landlady, paying the gas bill, killing a cockroach, masturbating, going to sleep ... "

And so it goes, page upon page, chapter after chapter, of accelerating verbal pyrotechnics, until in the closing scene of Part One, Manual is struck upon the head by an improperly secured washbasin and lapses into a coma for the remainder of the narrative.

In Part Two, Obregon evolved a new and radical literary form to portray the comatose state, a form later dubbed "stream of unconsciousness." Note that this was a good thirty years before William Burroughs' so-called discovery of the cut-up method. Shredding fourteen newspapers with his bare hands, and covering himself with flour and water, Obregon rolled about on the floor, placing words upon the page in the same order in which they stuck to his body. The result, needless to say, is more than flatbread. Yet you must dive into this immense and sometimes disturbing novel for yourself if you hope to truly sample its flavor.

Though the translation leaves something to be desired, at times slipping back into Portuguese, we recommend *Stamp Your Feet!* for serious students of twentieth century literature and all inveterate insomniacs.

Published clothbound by Callipygian Press, 743 pages, $34.95. Paperback rights are up for grabs. Yet as Obregon himself warns us in "Ode to a Thighchilada" – "Don't you go grabbing/ more than you can swallow."

Complete Artistic Control

My implants were sizzling. I was on a roll.

Words flashed through my mind. I watched as they transposed to the screen. One sentence after another raced to completion. I had a comlink to the Muse. No doubt about it.

I was finishing the final chapter of my first novel. It may not have been the best first novel ever written, but it was *my* novel.

All at once the screen flickered and my text vanished.

The face of a man I'd never seen before replaced it. A nondescript face. I punched the reset button but the system had locked up.

"Mr. Adamski?" he said. "Lester Adamski?"

"What do you want?" I barked. "Who are you?

"My name is immaterial," the man stated. "I represent the PBI."

An official-looking emblem flashed several times in the lower right of the screen to confirm his authority. It displayed an old-fashioned fountain pen with a circle around it. A thick bar cut across the circle, bisecting the pen.

Of course I'd heard rumors about the PBI. Yet it wasn't until that moment that I began to believe they actually existed. I feigned ignorance.

"The PBI? What's the PBI?"

Immaterial's eyes rolled up to let me know he hadn't bought my ruse. "The Publishers Bureau of Investigation," he nevertheless informed me. "I need to ask you a few questions."

"Can't this wait?"

"I'm afraid not, Mr. Adamski. This will only take a few minutes. Access to your system will be denied until you comply."

I tried the reset button again. Immaterial wasn't kidding. The PBI was not only real, it had long arms.

"All right" I sighed, "ask away."

Immaterial looked down at something he was holding. He cleared his throat before beginning. "On June 16th of last year you e-mailed a story titled 'Ripe Soup' to the *Quixotic Quarterly*."

It was a statement rather than a question, but I answered anyway. "Uh...yeah...I suppose so. I'd have to check my records."

"On March 12th of this year," Immaterial droned on in a portentous monotone, "you e-mailed virtually the same story, retitled 'Give Us Your Stale Fritters,' to *Brain Dump*. This, despite the fact that you had yet to receive a response from the *Quixotic Quarterly*. Despite the fact that both publications stated in their market reports they did not consider simultaneous submissions."

I hedged. "Yeah, well maybe, I can't remember."

"Mr. Adamski," Immaterial leaned forward, his unremarkable face looming to fill the screen, "did you really think a different title and a few words changed would mask your deception?"

"No! I wasn't trying to deceive anyone. I rewrote the story to make it better. I changed the title because I thought 'Give Us Your Stale Fritters' would be easier for readers to identify with."

"Then you admit to the facts as stated and confess to your violation of the International Publishers Code, section 37B?"

"What difference does it make? Neither magazine bought the story."

"I'm afraid that's irrelevant. If you held someone up on the street and they didn't have any credits, you'd still be guilty of a crime."

"But what was I supposed to do? I'd already queried the *Quixotic Quarterly* half a dozen times. It finally took them well over a year to email me a form rejection. What would you have done?"

Immaterial's expression was blank and unfeeling as a dead monitor. "I am not the party in question. My theoretical actions in a comparable situation are hardly germane." He cleared his throat again. "Once more, for the record, do you admit to the facts as heretofore stated?"

"All right, I admit to it. Big deal! I made a simultaneous submission. What are you going to do about it?"

"Since this is your first offense, the penalty is not severe. Your restriction will commence immediately and expire in sixty days."

"What do you mean 'restriction?'"

"You can consider this a slap on the wrist, Mr. Adamski. Future violations of this or any other statues of the Code could meet with more extreme retribution."

"What do you mean by *restriction*!" I shouted.

But Immaterial had already severed the connection.

The text of my novel appeared again on the screen. But by now I had lost my train of thought.. I stood up and began to pace.

A sense of dread tingled up my spine, but I shrugged it off. What could they do anyway? Restrict my data access? Temporarily blacklist me at certain publications? I planned to spend the next few months working on a final draft of the novel. By then it wouldn't make any difference.

I punched up a glass of SlimStim and downed it in three swallows.

I sat down before the screen and centered my thoughts. I accessed my implants, scrolled upward, and reread what I had written earlier. It was good stuff! The kind of stuff that could put me on the bestseller list.

I closed my eyes and began to write. One sentence. Two sentences. A paragraph. The Muse whispered in my inner ear. Creation bloomed within my head. I was sizzling just as I had before.

I opened my eyes, looked at the screen, and started back in horror.

The sense of dread I had shrugged off returned like a hammer blow. I was restricted all right. It no longer mattered what word's raced through my consciousness. It made no difference what brilliant sentences I composed within my mind. My implants would only post one sentence to the screen. The same dozen words glowed back at me over and over again.

I made a simultaneous submission and I will never do it again....I made a simultaneous submission and I will never do it again....I made a simultaneous submission and I will nev-

er….

I've thought about getting a keyboard. Yet where would one find such an anachronism? I don't even know if there's a way to hook it up to my system. And besides, how could I possibly write anything one letter at a time?

South Coast

Sun glances off the white adobe village with enough brightness to strain the unshaded eye.

Joshua looks down into the village from distance, eyes shielded by blue-lens, steel-rim spectacles. Wearing only faded jeans in the afternoon heat, he sits in a broken-down wicker chair in the shade of his veranda. In one hand, a stick of the local weed smolders. By the side of his chair, a glass of lemonade-tequila slowly evaporates. On the other side, a bottle of tequila, its depths clear as stream water.

Joshua draws on the joint in a measured fashion, more from habit than the need for any added high. He idly fingers the stone pendant which clings to the moist hairs of his chest. The sun pulls through the bleached heavens and the afternoon grows longer with shadow.

He sees the climbing native first as an abstraction, a white dot with a black dot head, bobbing up the path and rippling in the heated air.

Joshua calls into the house and Marilyn comes to stand in the doorway.

She has been shielding her complexion from the sun and it still holds the whiteness of winter. Yet her blond hair, banded in back with a red kerchief, has turned dry as straw. Joshua passes her the joint and together, in silence, they watch the approaching Mexican.

"Buenos dias, senor." Voice puffing from the climb.

"Hello," Joshua answers.

The Mexican is stocky, short, and his body is hung in loose folds of white cloth. His dark hair radiates from the back of his head, falling over forehead, temples, neck, until it is chopped off evenly in a soup-bowl cut. The thickness of his features blankets the expression of his face. He climbs onto the porch and lies down on his belly, pressing his cheek against the cool shaded stones.

"I have a story for you, senor."

Joshua nods toward Marilyn and she steps back into the house. When she comes out, she hands him a coin. He flips it toward the prone Mexican and it catches the sun once before clinking flatly to the cement. The man rolls onto his side and scoops the money into his pocket.

"It is a long climb. My throat is dry to tell such a story."

Joshua picks up the glass and empties it over the porch railing. He pours a few inches of tequila and passes it to the Mexican. The man swallows quickly and holds the glass out for more. Joshua refills it and the Mexican drinks again and wipes his mouth before speaking.

"Four days ago three Americans came into town in a big car. The kind with no trunk. Just a big space and windows in back."

"A station wagon," says Marilyn.

"A pale blue station wagon caked with dust," adds Joshua.

The Mexican looks from one to the other before going on. It is not the first story he has told Joshua. He is learning when to speak, when to be silent.

"They came into the town and they went to the cafe. They were a man and his wife and a woman older."

"What were their names?" asks Joshua

"I do not know, senor."

"The man and his wife are Harry and Adele," says Marilyn. *"The older woman is Adele's mother."*

The Mexican drains his glass. Joshua passes him the joint and he pulls deeply. Holds his breath for several seconds, then exhales.

"They came to the cafe," he repeats, *"and there was a fight with much shouting, the two women against the man."*

"What did they fight about?"

"Rocks, senor. They were fighting about rocks."

Joshua allows his head to roll back until he feels its weight stretching the tendons of his neck. The unpainted boards of the veranda's roof, its rough joists and cornices, are invisible. Only a dim and undifferentiated blueness penetrates his glasses. He fondles the stone pendant before speaking. The lines and liniments of the story appear upon this dark blue ground. Some are like sticks randomly scattered by the wind. Others have been placed with careful intention.

"Harry and Adele are geologists on a field trip. Adele's mother has come along for the ride. Harry hates her presence, has always hated it, and the feeling is returned in kind. Their constant exposure since the beginning of the trip has brought tensions nearly to a breaking point. Each trivial difference now holds the potential of a full blown battle. Adele sees herself as the peacemaker in these conflicts, but invariably ... helplessly ... sides with her mother."

The Mexican waits a moment to see it if is all right to continue. The drink and the smoke have raised an increasing dullness in his already leaden eyes. The unfamiliar English words now pass his lips with greater difficulty.

"After the fight they went forth from town four days ago and into the hills. Last night they come back and the old woman was in a sleeping bag on top of the car. Ella estaba muerta! She had been dead in the hills."

"Another fight," says Joshua, "and another, each more violent and irrevocable than the last." He pauses, then goes on, his sentences falling evenly in the heat.

"Still, it is the two women against the man. More suddenly than any of them expect, the situation erupts into violence. In the midst of a meal, without direct provocation, Adele's mother begins to insult Harry. Although it is only noon, she has been drinking heavily. She calls her son-in-law one name after another, all in Spanish ... *bastardo* ... *cerdo* ... *puta* ... and after each insult, she giggles.

"Harry can take it no longer. He explodes, slapping the woman harshly across the face.

"The mother rises, one hand clasping her chest, the other pointing at Harry. Suddenly her face goes bloodless as she staggers back and collapses on the sand. Her heart has failed her. Harry's awkward attempts to revive the woman are to no avail. Adele breaks into wild hysterics and Harry must slap her too before she will be silent.

"There is nothing for them to do but return to town and report the death as an accident. Harry wraps the body in a sleeping bag and ties it atop the luggage rack of the station wagon. Adele breaks down again several times on the way back to town. Their marriage is over, she tells him. There should have never been a marriage in the first place. Each time, Harry stops the car on the empty road. He clenches his jaw and stares across the desert in silence, hands still upon the wheel, refusing to go on until she has calmed herself."

While Joshua has been speaking, the Mexican has edged his body around the chair. His dark fingers close on the crystal brightness of the bottle and he pulls it toward him, its base grating on the rough cement. He takes the cork out with his teeth and refills his glass.

Marilyn has moved out onto the porch and is leaning against the railing, facing the two men. *"All right,"* she says to the Mexican, *"go on."*

"They come into town last night. They go to the police station. They were within for a time and when they come out ... poof! ... the body and the sleeping bag, they are gone!"

Marilyn blinks her pale blue unblinking eyes just once, a rare blink which Joshua savors and adds to the growing catalog of Marilyn, now weighty in his head.

"Faceless thieves," says Joshua, "moving in the night like whispers."

"They drag the sleeping bag to the beach and open it," Marilyn answers.

"They are disappointed because the body is not younger," says Joshua.

"They throw it into the sea and it washes over the rocks," says Marilyn.

"Food for bright fishes," concludes Joshua.

Soft snores bubble from the Mexican's lips. He has rolled onto his back with arms extended.

The light has faded and Joshua removes his sunglasses. The white adobe of the town has turned to coarse cream. Northern mountains are in heavy weave, stretched burlap peaks rising into a gray muslin sky.

Joshua is alone on the porch and as far as the unshaded eye can see, there is not another living soul.

He turns his head slowly, his gaze wandering through the open doorway and into the house.

Upon the table he can see the empty bottles, his typewriter, the steadily growing stack of pages. For the barest moment he perceives the depth of their power welling within him like a trembling he cannot control. Soon his savings would be gone and it will be time to head north, to return to the mercenary world and the rush and clatter of the cities he knows too well.

Joshua fondles the pendant, his talisman and mill-stone. He relights the stub of the joint and passes it to Marilyn.

As always, she appears from nowhere. She is careful not to burn her fingers.

Death and the Hippie

Mulligan got back into school part-time to get back on his father's payroll, but by summer he was out again and into Mexico. He stayed in Guadalajara with an ex-bistro-owner from Greenwich Village who expounded his theories on drugs, women, America, and "dropping out for good" through the tequila-heated afternoons. He disappeared into the Sierra Nevadas for three weeks and came back with eighteen dollars in pan-mined gold. In the fall, speaking Spanish like a native, his hair shaggy and a spare reddish mustache draping his soft mouth, he tramped and hitched farther south through the banana republics of Central America, through strings of tiny villages, each riddled by the sameness of the poverty of exploitation, through tile and stucco cities whose dark inhabitants lounged like droplets of liquid copper against their pastel walls.

At the turn of the year, after a Latin Xmas and with a tropical winter tan covering his freckles, Mulligan started north again. He made it to Mexico before his Irish luck ran dry. One of the multifarious native maladies, which he had thus far been able to dodge, had finally caught up with him. Or it may have been the shellfish he'd caught and roasted on an open fire and eaten the night before. He awoke with a dryness in his throat that after a few swallows turned to pain. All at once it had spread to his stomach and head and chest. He vomited and then began coughing short bullets of white phlegm onto the sand. Fever heightened by the heat of the day swept over him in waves like the ocean rolling in.

The heat was suddenly excruciating. The sun was touching the sand. The heat was a coat of shifting needles.

At his back the rainforest was stretching onto the beach, growing all around him, over him. The roots of living plants curled between his fingers and toes. Vines laced his heaving chest. With each white chunk of phlegm he coughed up he was expelling part of his whiteness. Cough and there went the Protestant ethic, cough-cough, the rest of Christianity thrown in, cough, The Dark Ages, cough, The Renaissance, cough, Karl Marx with a clown's hat and China saucers for eyes, cough, the Industrial Revolution played backwards, cough, the Great Depression, cough, ahem, cough, Sigmund Freud down the drain. If he kept coughing enough he would die or his blood would lose the sum of its whiteness and he'd be transformed into a native. Not a Mexican, but a real native, an Aztec or Navaho.

In his Levi watch pocket there was a battered cap of acid he'd carried throughout his travels. It was the only pill he had and in his delirium and misery, he decided to gamble and take it now. He unrolled it from its foil wrapping and popped it into his mouth. An hour and a half later he knew that it would be death that would claim him rather than nativehood.

He was dying, his whole body told him that he was dying, all of his senses. The sun went down into the sea like a sun going to its death, blood red and with a score of scabby clouds following in its wake. Mulligan was convinced that he would never see it rise again. The sky became darker and more and more like a lid that was shutting down on him. The fever continued to beat against his body. He was aware of a dissolution in his coordination, an inexorable weakness that swept through his nervous system and musculature almost like a release. He could no longer lift his head from the sand. His breath became a labored and monotonous wheezing, the pellets of phlegm rattling like the wooden balls in a whistle. The sand fleas began devouring his flesh, chewing away at his neck and palms and knuckles. They were in on the play. They knew he was already helpless, as good as a carcass. If some vultures showed up he supposed he'd have to put up with their nonsense, too.

Only by that time he figured he'd probably be beyond it all. The acid was objectifying his death drama for him. The acid was helping him to dissolve bit by bit, spreading his awareness over the beach thinner and thinner, as thin as a liquid film.

The beach, thought Mulligan in his stoned delirium, funny that his death should happen on the beach like so much of his childhood.

Night settled down like a burial shroud and each star was a candle lit in preparation for his wake. A broad, white moon slice hung high over the water. Mulligan could just see it out of the corner of his eye. It was an unmerciful moon, a cold steel ingot that paled the sand and cast silent gray mourner shadows with flickering capes that ran shifting up and down the beach and in and out of the trees and brush. Each time these shadows swept by him, Mulligan's body shook with the shiver of a sudden chill that had momentarily banished his fever. It occurred to him that they might be demons come to claim his soul, but it didn't really matter. With the first rush of the night he had ridden the acid high into the freedom of indifference. Now he understood that in all of his short life he had been incomplete – there was the part of himself that he had unwittingly brought to this beach of his death, and there was the other part of himself, the part racing in over the ocean, a giant and misty carrier bird searching out his fleshy shell.

He could hear it whistling as it cleaved through the boundaries of death, slicing the still black-shrouded air, wheeling past the cold moon, skimming in over the low waves, raising a hail of muddy sand clots as it skidded onto the beach, upon him. He could feel it now, enveloping him in the damp and milky embrace of its wings of feathered fog.

And then it had passed through the pores of his heaving chest and become a part of him and he was complete before death.

In its completion, Mulligan's consciousness, if it could still be called that, extended beyond the threshold of indifference. It was not only that he no longer cared, but that he could no longer comprehend the process of caring. He was a sentient stone, he was no-thinking, he was pure sense. His body stopped fighting the infection. His fever dropped away and the disease took over and ravaged at will, carrying him nearer and nearer to death. He could feel it closing the switches that shut down the power in the various segments of his body. His legs and hands were already numb. A tingling had taken possession of his forearms and buttocks. The pain was gone from his stomach and chest. But this self-awareness, this Mulligan-awareness, was only a minute fraction of his total sensory input. At the same time he was aware of and as much a part of the unique audio intricacies of each individual wave as it collapsed upon the beach, the multitudinous cawings and scratchings and rustlings of the tropical forest behind him, the perfect clockwork movement of the stars slowly revolving overhead. He was not yet dead, nor was he waiting for death, no more than a stone waits for someone to throw it. His identity had already rejoined the eternal flow and death had become as inconsequential to him as the ticking of the stars.

Now the moon was no longer white. Farther down the beach someone had set up a projector and they were using its blank face as a screen. Intense jewel colors danced across the Mare Nubium and the Sea of Tranquility. It wasn't a bad light show, particularly for out of doors on a Mexican beach and with the moon as a screen, but it could claim no greater part of Mulligan's attention than the million and one other things that were happening throughout the universe. If he'd thought of it he might have called out to the projectionist for help, but he knew that he was already beyond help and besides, stones don't call.

It must have been around midnight that Death began pulling off his boots. Mulligan sat up. Not because he was curious. Death was of no interest to him. It was only a physical reaction caused by the tugging on his pant legs. If he'd still cared about anything at the time, sitting up would have been worthwhile because he got to see what Death looked like.

Death was a barefoot, walnut-brown old man in gray-white rags. His teeth, hair and eyes were the same color as his clothes. When Mulligan moved he must have startled him, because Death yelped loudly "Aaiie-aah!" dropped the boot he had been tugging on and pranced back away toward the water with several quick hops. As Mulligan plopped back to his prone position, land, sea and Death fell downward spinning rapidly out of sight to be replaced once again by the speckled night sky. Mulligan had never realized before that Death would be so afraid of life. Now that he thought about it, it made sense.

There followed several seconds of silence except for the interminable waves. Whoever had been running the projector at the opposite end of the beach had abandoned it, probably frightened off by Death's scream. The forest was also suddenly and remarkably still.

"Aracamar! Sitioca! Quecotalz!" Death was shouting imprecations in an Indian dialect Mulligan couldn't understand. "Buoymir! Tapeana!"

Mulligan tried to answer in Spanish, but he found it as impossible to speak as it was to move. All his throat could manage was a scarcely audible bubbling. The wooden balls had coagulated to cement.

After the cursing ceased, he heard Death's bare feet come shuffling toward him in the sand and the next moment Death was leaning over him, spreading his palms and grinning apologetically, as if to say: "Sorry, pardon me, I thought you were already gone. You're a particularly hardy one, aren't you? Most are already cold by this time." In spite of this apology, Mulligan soon discovered that Death's behavior was erratic at best.

All of a sudden he grabbed Mulligan's pack, which was lying nearby, turned it upside down, and dancing back and forth began to shake it with all of his strength.

Mulligan's loosely-packed spare belongings fell in a lumpy cascade onto the sand. Death picked up his harmonica to blow a few scratchy off-key notes and chuckle to himself. He wasn't much of a musician. He took Mulligan's pocketknife and opened it. The blade flashed several times in the moonlight and Mulligan thought for sure that Death had decided to finish him off right then instead of waiting any longer for the disease to take its toll.

Although the acid was wearing off, Mulligan still felt removed from what was happening. The dramatic irony of having his throat slit with his own knife almost appealed to him, but Death shut the blade and tossed it back onto the ground. He finally settled on a box of matches, after which he gathered some brush and loose branches together and started a modest fire to combat the cool night air.

From Mulligan's perspective, the fire changed the beach radically. In fact, the beach disappeared. He was now enclosed with Death in the pulsing heat of a liquid yellow-orange pool. He could still make out the stars, fainter overhead. Other than that, all beyond the reach of the fire's illumination was blackness.

Death sat at a respectable distance from him, close by the fire, warming his bare feet and hands. Mulligan concluded that his job must be a lonesome one, because Death started talking a mile a minute. Mulligan couldn't understand a word of it, and even if he had he was incapable of answering, but that didn't seem to bother Death any. Not a bit. He prattled on and on, his tongue clucking like that of a garrulous old gossip. Periodically, he stopped to pepper this meaningless one-way conversation with a few disconnected and equally meaningless toots upon the harmonica.

After a time, Death produced – Mulligan couldn't figure from where – a bottle of wine. Anyway, that's what the label said, Gallo Tawny Port. Mulligan's vision was dimming, he was going now, but he could just make it out in the light from the fire. Judging from the worn condition of the label and the swirling murkiness that filled the bottle, it seemed reasonable to assume that its original contents had been either altered or replaced.

In any case, Death turned out to be something of a sadist.

He took a few swallows from the bottle himself and then moved away from the fire to tilt it over Mulligan's slack jaw. He seemed to take immense delight in pouring long streams of the liquid down Mulligan's throat and watching it gurgle around his esophagus as his lungs gasped for oxygen. It was the first and last time Mulligan ever tasted anything that was gritty, tepid and explosive at the same time.

If it wasn't wine it was at least alcoholic. After several swallows the wrinkles in Death's leathery face seemed beautiful and the fire on the beach had turned the color of a ripe persimmon. Also, the fire that it started in his parched mouth made the other seem inconsequential. It flowed like a congestion of lava erupting through his chest and once it hit his stomach, it was no less than a supernova. The pain obliterated his indifference. The foul mixture was trying to eat a hole in his backbone so that it could empty itself and return to the bowels of the earth from which it had no doubt sprung. But Mulligan's hide proved too tough for it. It finally had to come up the other way. He started vomiting again. Vomiting until he thought he would be turned inside out. It was a hell of a way to go and a rotten trick on Death's part after they'd spent the night together. Vomiting, vomiting into oblivion.

He came to nearly buried in the sand. Death was gone and the only fire was the one high in the sky. His harmonica, his boots and his matches were gone, too, and the sediment that filled his mouth and clogged his taste buds could have competed with the Mississippi Basin. Yet he was still complete. He had become a native, not an Aztec or a Navaho, but a real native, a citizen of the natural and relative universe.

Somehow, one foot after another, he made it back through the trees to the highway and got his thumb out. After that the rides came along as if they'd been scheduled for him – up to the Mexican border and past it, into and out of the smog of greater Los Angeles, through the dusty hot-rod towns of Bakersfield and Fresno, and finally back to the haven called Berkeley. Life had become an ocean and he was the fastest fish in the water.

Cold Finale

with Marge Simon

It is a cold December afternoon shrouded by a slate of swift dark clouds. An old woman shuffles along a city sidewalk, a large cat curled on top of the junk in her cart. She wears several layers of clothing against the cold, topped off by a worn blue sweater and a shapeless black skirt that reaches to her ankles.

The woman has a name, but her few homeless friends don't know what it is, and she no longer cares. Some of them call her Sadie. Once, in another life, she used to take in stray cats. To each one she gave a name. It would be a name of importance, perhaps because she used to read a lot of classic novels. Names like Scaramouch or Homer. The last one was a kitten, whom she dubbed Dorian the Gray. He was the one that went with her into the streets.

She remembers working in a library. Handling book after book after book. She remembers their colorful covers and some of the titles and the names of characters, but for the life of her she can no longer remember the stories they told. Or rather she remembers them like one long story that never ends, all complicated and jumbled up in her head.

After the library, she would return home to cook dinner for herself and a large rough man with tattoos, so she believes she was married at one time,. Did he beat her? Perhaps. Did he steal from her and others? Maybe so. How did they lose their home? What happened to it? She is no longer sure. What street was it on? There are so many streets to keep track of in the city. The streets run every which way so that it is easy to get lost.

The woman's eyes are rheumy and her nose won't stop dripping. She digs a crumpled handkerchief out of her shirtsleeve. Unfolding it, she sees the initials "D. R." She tries to remember who D. R. is, but can't recall anyone by that name. Maybe it was that nice lady who gave her the handkerchief – the lady that smelled like something pink, that was it. That happened yesterday. It had to be yesterday because she could still smell things yesterday and now she can't.

Someone is poking her shoulder. She looks down at a small black boy who is carrying two paper sacks. He sets them down on the sidewalk and looks up at her.

"Hey, lady, can I pet your cat?"

She nods and tells him, "As long as you do it gently."

The boy reaches into the cart and hesitantly strokes the cat, who begins to purr in its sleep.

The boy looks up at her again. "Lady," he says, "can I touch your face?"

She shrugs and nods, so he runs his finger over the trails of wrinkles on her cheek.

"It's all wrinkling yet it still feels soft," he marvels. "I never touched skin so soft, lady." He smiles and tells her his name is Steven and that today is his tenth birthday. She remembers reading books to rooms of children about his size. Not ten but seven or eight, she thinks.

She smiles and reaches into a pocket of her faded skirt. "Do you like peppermints?"

He nods. She gives him the sweet and starts to wish him happy birthday, but suddenly breaks off in a fit of coughing. A few drops of blood land on the pavement but the boy doesn't notice because he's pulling the wrapper off the candy.

He sucks on the peppermint, turns his head this way and that as if he is judging it. Finally he nods and says, "It's good." Then reaching down. he picks up one of his bags and offers it to her. "Ma sent me to the store to buy a bag of walnuts. They were on sale, so I bought two. You take this one, lady. Ma won't mind."

The old woman's face twitches into a grin. "That's really nice of you, young man. You've done a good deed and I thank you for it."

The boy smiles and looks embarrassed at the same time. He's never done a good deed before, never even thought of it that way. It was like the preacher was always saying folks should do, but he thought that was only for grownups.

A chill wind comes sweeping along the street and he clutches his coat tight. It is starting to snow. "Well, see you later, lady. I gotta get home."

The temperature is falling quickly. The old woman knows she no longer has enough teeth left to chew nuts, but she thinks perhaps she can sell them and get something warm to drink and a sandwich. She digs around in the cart and finds a battered straw basket. She dumps the nuts inside, trying to control her shaking hands. Coughing again, she rummages until she finds a rusty old hammer buried under a blanket and other street treasures she has salvaged.

Draped in her dirty blanket and feverish, she sits down on the sidewalk leaning against a brick wall. Dorian the Gray has leaped from the cart and curled up in her lap. She pets him a few times. She can feel his bones and he is so thin it scares her. Beside her is the basket of walnuts. One by one, she places the nuts on the sidewalk and begins cracking them with the hammer. It is getting dark and sometimes she misses the nut and strikes her hand instead. But her hand is so numb from the cold she can't feel it. Soon the flesh of her hand is split and bleeding in several place, but she can't feel that either.

She offers her wares to passing pedestrians, but there are few people on the street and no takers. She knows she should get up soon and find her way back to the shelter. Yet she is no longer sure which way to go. There are so many streets in the city running every which way. It is so easy to get lost.

A man and a woman emerge from a nearby tavern and stagger down the sidewalk. The man stumbles over the old women's outstretched legs. Dorian yelps and leaps from her lap. The man swears and kicks the cat away. The old woman coughs and moans, but she cannot rise. The snowflakes dance and swirl, caressing her forehead. Her lips draw back in a smile. It feels refreshing against her fevered flesh.

Soon the finely powdered snow covers all the sad lines in her face and erases its wrinkles. Frost settles on her eyelashes, makes them long and lush, She is no longer a pathetic old woman, but transformed to an iconic image of some ancient goddess carved in white marble. As the blood grows sluggish in her veins, as her thoughts wind down to nothingness, she remembers herself as young and beautiful and how all the men pursued her, whether that was ever true or perhaps only something she once read in a book.

Dorian yowls, circling her prone form over and again, pawing at her, jumping in and out of her lap. The old woman doesn't respond in any way. Finally, the cat hesitates, then all at once dashes off into the shadows of a nearby alley.

The snow continues to fall on the city, on the streets and the buildings, on the living and the dead.

Mammy and the Flies

He didn't turn on the flashlight.

It was still light outside and the light came through the chinks in the cinder blocks along three walls of the cellar and the flies hadn't come yet. If he looked through the chinks on one side he could see plowed fields and burnt-off hillsides and at night the lights of cars as they passed on the highway. On the other side, only fields and hills. But if he knelt down and looked through the chinks at the rear of the cellar, he could see their yard and the garden Mammy had planted and through the trees and beyond to Mr. Skinner's house in the distance. Mr. Skinner was their landlord. His house was white, whiter than theirs which was once white and Mammy called it dirt white.

He didn't know how she had found this Skinner place. When they left the other place they drove for days, sleeping in the car, Mammy making him stay on the floor in back so no one would see. Then they had come to this place and she started locking him in the cellar. He had been with Mammy since before the other place, but down in the cellar with nothing to do but sit and think and listen, he had begun to remember his real mother.

The cellar had been cold at first with the wind racing through the chinks. He'd found an old mattress and tried to lie on it with the blankets Mammy Jordon had given him, but the mattress was wet and smelled bad. When he pushed up one corner he could see worms and dark crawlies underneath. So he found a dry place on the dirt floor and curled up there with the covers and thought about his mother.

Mammy Jordon was his mother's mother, but she wouldn't let him call her that. She said she was too young to be anyone's grandma, leastwise someone grown up as he was getting to be. His real mother was smaller than Mammy Jordon and she didn't smell like Mammy, always sweet or flowery, still she smelled good, only he couldn't remember just how cause the cellar smelled and the mattress even when he wasn't near it. He'd get this all mixed up with his mother's smell and Mammy Jordon's. And sometimes he'd remember her and she was brown like Mammy Jordon or yellow like he was, and sometimes she was a white lady and once she was soft all over like a kitten. The more different ways he thought about her the less he remembered so she became less and less until finally there was nothing left to her at all. And then he couldn't think about her anymore or pretend he wasn't in the cellar.

So he began to sing to himself in the dark, tuneless nonsense songs which never repeated yet always sounded the same. He kept his voice low so Mammy wouldn't hear. She said he was strange enough already without doing no singing, and she only let him listen to music on Sundays when she read from the book. He loved the music and he could feel it trying to move inside him, but he had to sit still while the record turned on the player. When he sang to himself in the cellar he didn't sit still. He rocked with the nonsense words. Hunched there in the dark, he beat the heels of his palms against his thighs until they were sore.

And that was when the seeing started.

He didn't tell Mammy about the singing or the seeing. He knew she wouldn't like any of it.

Mr. Skinner's dog was chained in its yard barking to be fed and the sun was going down. He couldn't see the dog cause of the fence and the trees. He couldn't see the sun cause that side of the cellar was boarded over, but he could see what it was doing to the land, turning the trees and fence posts golden, the white of Mr. Skinner's house pink and grey, the tomatoes by the back porch as if they were about to catch on fire. It was hotter under the house now, the hottest time of each day at dusk. As the land cooled it gave up its warmth to the cellar which would hold it long into the night. He could feel the warm air flowing in through the chinks in the cinder blocks. And soon the flies would follow.

Each time Mammy sent him to the cellar it was warmer and there were more flies. He could listen to their buzzing in the dark, he could feel them landing and crawling on his skin, sucking his sweat, their hairy legs itching him. He could turn on the flashlight and see them moving in its beam: black and gold-green in the yellow circle of light.

He knew that if Mammy Jordon came back and she didn't have a gentleman with her, he wouldn't have to stay with the flies. If she came back alone she'd unlock the cellar door. She'd come part way down the steps and she'd call "Baby, baby, come up," and when he did she'd take him upstairs and hold him against her in bed and tell him stories – about the animals back home or about his daddy, Pappy Jordon, who was mojo and creole and something special, and since he was part Pappy Jordon that was why his skin was yellow and that made him special, too.

But if Mammy brought any gentleman with her, he might have to stay in the cellar all night. In the morning there would be red bites on his arms, his face and neck. In the morning Mammy would unlock the cellar door and come part way down the steps and she'd call, "Baby, baby, come up." Then she'd have him sit at the kitchen table and she'd cook breakfast for him, special to make up for the cellar, muffins and bacon ends and the eggs which were gooey and ran yellow over the plate. Mammy would hum to herself while she cooked, just like he did when he was in the cellar. And sometimes he could look at her eyes while she hummed and cooked and see the thoughts slowly turning in her head. And he could tell that she didn't know she was doing the humming.

After breakfast she'd let him play in the yard behind the house. He could play there almost every day now that Mr. Skinner knew about him. At first Mammy only let him play a little at a time and he had to promise to stay close by and run back inside if anyone came. Then one day he had been squatting in the dirt watching the ants. Taking little steps on his heels, he had followed one too far from the house. He watched it crawling over pebbles and twigs across the baked earth away from the other ants and farther and he decided it must be running away from home. When he killed it with his thumb its body crushed down like it was empty and there was nothing inside. And then he looked up and saw Mr. Skinner.

Mr. Skinner was a white man and he was big, not big like Mammy Jordon, but tall. He had dark hair on his arms like the flies when they crawled on the light, but the hair on his head was white, dirt-white like their house not like his. Mr. Skinner was climbing the steps to their back porch. There was no way he could run inside without being seen so he ran into the bushes and hid there.

After a while Mammy came to the screen door and she and Mr. Skinner started to talk, so he crawled closer so he could hear. Mr. Skinner was pointing to the yard and saying, "Strange looking boy you got there, strange looking," and he knew Mammy would be mad at him for letting Mr. Skinner see him, but Mammy just said, "He ain't my boy. He's my sister's boy," and he didn't know why Mammy was lying cause she told him it was bad to lie. Mr. Skinner kept saying "strange looking, strange looking," like those were the only words he knew, with his hand on the screen, and Mammy shrugged and said he was "just a boy," and Mr. Skinner said he'd never seen no boy with eyes like that. And then Mammy opened the door. Mr. Skinner looked around the yard once and went inside.

After that Mr. Skinner became one of Mammy's gentlemen. And he could play in the yard as much as he wanted cause Mr. Skinner never came near him anyway.

It was almost dark, but he could see the shapes of the trees and the way the breeze was moving them. There was no breeze in the cellar. It was just as hot and the flies had started to come. He could hear the buzzing of one and then two and then three, so he went over to the crumpled blankets, which he never used anymore cause it was too hot, and he reached under the blankets and took out the fly swatter he had stolen from the hook in the kitchen. It was the same swatter Mammy sometimes hit him with when she was mad.

He went back to where he had been sitting and he watched the trees go away in the dark. Mr. Skinner's dog had stopped barking and that was good cause when the barking went on and on he could sometimes feel the dog's hunger gnawing in his belly and that was bad. He held the swatter between his legs and pressed the metal loop of its handle against his cheeks and forehead cause it felt cooler than the air in the cellar. He listened to the flies coming one by one until their buzzing was together and he couldn't tell how many there were. They began to land on his arms and face in the dark and he brushed them away.

He didn't turn on the flashlight.

He wasn't going to kill the flies yet. He was waiting until Mammy Jordan came back. If she had a gentleman with her he would kill the flies so he wouldn't have to listen to the two of them upstairs. He didn't want to hear their heels on the porch together. He didn't want to hear the talking and the drunken laughter. Most of all he didn't want to do the seeing when Mammy took the gentleman to bed. If he waited to kill the flies, that would be good.

Every Sunday Mammy taught him about the good and the bad. Sometimes he understood and sometimes he'd get mixed up. He knew the music was good, but singing and dancing were bad. The book was good cause it told about the good and the bad. The gentlemen were bad and he hated them, but he knew Mammy had to see them anyway. The cellar was bad and he hated it and knew that. The flies were bad and he hated them. But with Mammy Jordon, sometimes she was good and he loved her and sometimes she was bad and he hated her. Some nights she'd do the drinking alone, and then she was very bad.

Mammy said the drinking was bad, but she did it anyway, just like going with the gentlemen. Sometimes it was different with the gentlemen, but with the drinking it was always the same. She'd sit at the kitchen table and the more she drank the quieter she got. After a while she'd start to cry. Then the crying would become cursing, low at first and under her breath. Pretty soon the cursing got louder and next she'd be yelling at the top of her voice, at no one but like there was someone there, saying how she should of never got mixed up with no mojo swamp man, singing and changing all the time like he did, chasing after his own daughter and the two of them flying off in the sky and leaving her with the sin of it all.

And then she'd see him watching her and she'd curse at him and start hitting him for no good reason. He'd crouch in the corner or under the table and Mammy would hit and kick at him until she got tired. Then she'd go back to the cursing and the crying. Until finally she'd get quiet again and then want to hold him to make his hurts go away. But he didn't like her softness then cause it smelled like the drink.

Sometimes he thought all good things had something bad in them, like the tomatoes going bad when they got old, and he wondered if all old things went bad. Mr. Skinner was old and he didn't seem that bad. But Mammy said that since he was a white man, that made him bad enough.

By the time he heard Mammy's car and the car that followed it, the gentleman's car, the flies had clustered on him, the closed space of the cellar filled with their buzzing. He did not wait for the sound of heels on the porch. He clicked on the flashlight and stood, his knees bent and his neck forward so he wouldn't bump his head on the ceiling. With this movement the flies rose from his body, and some settled back. His shirt was soaked through with sweat so he stripped it off and the flies rose from him again.

In the heat and dark he moved toward the mattress and leveled the flashlight across its expanse. In the dim cone of light he could see its stained ticking and the rips where springs and stuffing were exposed. Its entire surface was alive with the crawling black dots of the flies.

He began to kill them.

He raised the swatter and brought it down – slap! – on the mattress. With the force of the blow the flies rose as a cloud, their buzzing angry, and he brought the light closer and he could see one dead fly and one crushed but still moving, its buzzing broken. He could see they were not hollow like the ants, but filled with goo like the eggs on his plate. And then he went back to the killing.

He put the flashlight at one end of the mattress so that its beam spread in a "V" across the surface and he waited until the flies settled back onto the ticking and started their crawling, and then he aimed and struck – slap! – and the flies which did not die rose up and he waited for them to settle again. He crouched at the other end of the mattress, rocking his body, moving his shoulders so the flies wouldn't settle on him. But each time he waited, he could hear the noises from upstairs. He knew

Mammy's voice too well to pretend it wasn't hers. And the gentleman's voice, he knew that for a white man's voice. So he picked up the flashlight and began shining it around the cellar.

The flies were everywhere, on the walls, the posts, some even crawling in the dirt. He moved about killing them – slap!– and he pretended this one was Mammy's gentleman and this was another gentleman – slap! – and this was Mr. Skinner's dog and this was Mr. Skinner – slap! – and this was Mammy when he hated her – slap! – and this was Mammy when he loved her so he let it go.

His breath heavy, his body bare to the waist, the flies striking him as he moved through them, their buzzing louder and angrier the more he killed, and still they came in through the chinks so he killed them there. As he waved the flashlight about in his hand it began to fade. In the thickening darkness he could sense the life and death and dying all about him. He no longer needed the light so he hurled it against the cinder blocks and it shattered. Moving to and fro, twisting and turning, he killed and killed and still they came. He could hear the buzzing all about him as a music fierce and filling. He could feel his feet pounding the packed dirt floor. He could hear his voice rising from within his chest. He was singing. He was dancing. He was changing.

By the time Mammy Jordon unlocked the cellar door and came part way down the steps and called "Baby, baby, come up," all of the flies were dead but one. A huge and hairy flapping rose from the darkness of the stairs. And it was hungry.

Surreal Chess

Tarashan astounds the spectators with an aggressive hypermodern opening of her own invention. She releases three companies of foot soldiers across the glacial moraine. Horovitz's response is no less unconventional. He advances his panther to the king wolf's forest and fianchettos his hetaera.

> "Chess is a game of beautiful and horrible complications," states honorable Grand Master Tyro Suzuki. "Surreal chess is a game of dream complications." (free translation)

Nearly half of Tarashan's forces perish in harsh mountain storms. The rest suffer severe frostbite. Those who survive the arduous and bone-chilling trek emerge along the perimeter of the coast ensconced in enemy territory.

Horovitz has little choice. He must conscript the fisherman of Port Ligat to defend his eastern flank. Ignorant peasants to a man, they advance against a heavily armed foe with nothing but their tridents and nets.

Yet these poor fisherfolk are only sacrificial bait, a delaying tactic. Not far behind come elephants on stilts, ungainly creatures brocaded in heavy satin with gouts of flame spouting from their trunks and columns of smoke twirling up from the hidden cavities of their ears. Even when such mammoth beasts perish, and they do so by the score, they leave swaths of indescribable destruction in their toppling wakes.

> "*The Dictionary of Surreal Chess* exists in two mediums and versions: hypnagogic and full REM," venerable Grand Master Tyro Suzuki informs us. "The inadequate and contradictory rules in either edition are of little value. Chimerical tales relating many of the incidents and notable matches in the history of the game abound in the pages of both volumes. There is no basis in fact for any of these entries, yet they carry a ring of truth that few can contest." (free translation)

The players, curled fetally in their chairs, settle down to a middle game of entrenched warfare, lobbing elaborate epithets and ultimatums, few of which reach their marks. They pound each other with compulsive images and incendiary nightmares.

The proportions and perspectives of the board begin to evolve at a frightening pace. This is a terrain that can sprout the benign and knowing face of a goddess and young boys in sailor suits, a geology that contains a series of flexible mirages passing through undeclared dimensions.

> "If the board did not keep changing," states often esteemed and rarely reviled Grand Master Tyro Suzuki, "it would not be surreal chess, only a pale imitation for those who cannot sleep." (free translation)

While seemingly bemoaning the slaughter on the eastern front, Tarashan counters in the midland plain with a pack of bloodhounds inhabiting the forms of itinerant preachers. The double entendre escapes no one fully conversant with the literature of pain.

Evacuating churches and citadels, barricading public utilities, Horovitz interposes a division of hallucinogenic toreadors. They appear to be no more than sensitive dandies in their tight red pants and velvet hats, yet they prove a ferocious lot once their blades are drawn.

Fatalities transpire at an uncanny rate. The outcome is virtual obliteration for Tarashan's would-be Inquisition.

> "You understand nothing of the game! Nothing whatsoever!" enraged Grand Master Tyro Suzuki screams to his bewildered students, many of whom have forgotten to remove their sandals. (substantiated anecdote)

Tarashan places her hands across her face and lets her hair hang down in plaited rows. Her body shivers with a sensation hard to distinguish from a clinically perfect orgasm.

Horovitz, enthralled by his own genius, lounges back in his chair with careless strength. He lights a long black torpedo-shaped cigar. But alas, despite all pretensions to the contrary, it is nothing more than a cigar.

Suddenly the flies are everywhere, dark iridescent dots that settle on corpses and corpses-to-be like a species bred for the occasion. Once they have feasted, they clean their hairy bodies with great diligence.

Somewhere in the woods a unicorn screeches its terror, a high-pitched keening that causes the other pieces, the players and spectators, to turn their heads as one.

> Rising up from his narrow bed with one gnarled finger raised in crooked admonition, speaking in a heavily accented yet grammatically perfect English, Grand Master Tyro Suzuki declares: "It is more a question of metaphysics than physics, more pataphysics than meta, the psyche of the human animal in rank and file absurdity."

The end game is upon them before they know it. The pieces lie scattered like symbols across the board, their intent and possibilities so open to various interpretation that both players are left reeling with the implications.

Horovitz's cigar is a withered stump, sputtering in its own ash. He utters the first words spoken aloud at the match. Like most sentences carried from the depths of slumber to the land of the waking, its meaning is unintelligible to all but the speaker.

Tarashan's only response is to glance up and lean back in her chair. The flesh of her aging yet still handsome features recedes to reveal the skeletectonics beneath.

The survivors, heroes and heroines alike, gather at the base of an irregular and top-heavy monument that ignores gravity. The heat of the unrelenting sky beats down upon them. Bleeding from many wounds, some self-inflicted for effect, they pray for the anodyne of rain. And the clouds gather and the rains come down, though they are not composed of water. Assorted distorted objects pellet like hail: howling portmanteaus, pale lavender sachets of a bleak persuasion, proleptic reason stretched upon a rack, the ruins of a petrified railway station, huge metal insects with articulated limbs and fried eggs for saddles.

The puddled mass of the clock begins to reform one molten droplet at a time. Light insinuates itself beneath the curtains and dimples their folds with gray. The game is recessed to begin again in another night's play. The board folds upon itself with a thunderous clap. The spectators dissolve. There are no winners or losers here. Only conscious convention about to cut the cord of sleep at its navel.

> With a vigor that belies the wages of visionary excess, retired Grand Master Tyro Suzuki tends his ornamental garden in the unceremonious dawn. "Believe me," he croons to the stunted trees and the nodding buds of the flowers, "I mean you no harm." (free translation)

Wasp Light

with Lee Ballentine

I was riding black fields in a metal cart when the chronometers shifted and it began to rain heavily. Small explosions as each drop touched the ground. Light and shadow lacquered in the muddy pools. A gate of the city, scrolled with grime, creaked open — and I saw a slash of color. There against the wall. Nothing more.

And now though I watch the streets and alleys each hour from my lab — I cannot trace the source of that aberrant illumination. I do not know why the tocsins suddenly sound with obsessive regularity. In no way can I guess who has fused the lintels over Southgate so they glisten like a nest of glass eels.

The speakers keep hissing. The screen is mired by white files of rain. A woman's leg is brushed by a fist-fall of droplets and seeing the fullness of that leg I desire the image — not so much the flesh itself but its light patina. I bring up one quadrant of the screen. Her sandal swings a few pixels, a silver scrap of foil hangs from the sole — falling halfway to the grille below. A yellow door behind her stands open and from the dark within something gleams. Collective radiation or the white arms of men drinking wine.

The room is a mottled rectangle behind her legs. The rain registers as light hobs — glitter edged. I can see the same oval of foil against the grill, its texture that of sawed stone. The webbing of the grille shows wear, its plastic cracked and dirty. This woman has the leg of a girl. Wine spills across the wreckage of a table. White arms begin to strobe.

When I look again the light is dimmer and the scene has shifted to another sector. Surfaces conspire to deceive me and colors have lost their mastery. The rain continues to fall.

Assuming that spatial correspondence holds within the city's temporal distortions, a hypothesis which has yet to be denied, I might locate this woman and confront her directly. How would she compare with her opalescent image? The phosphors can offer nothing definitive, and I must of necessity consider my own safety first. This leg I desire could easily be diseased. Or merely a prosthetic sheath concealing the withered stump beneath. And why does this woman-girl choose to walk the streets alone? Is her time frame so different that the transmutations have not begun? And if so, how much am I allowed to tell her?

I decant the recorded leg in freeze frame and global search the sectors for its earthbound simulacrum. I scan the files for a possible cross match. Each time I tap the core where the cables are infested the resolution fades. I must reboot from sequence and start again. A window blossoms in one corner of the screen and a list of names scrolls by. All of these files have been retired to Database. To access their contents I must issue a series of electronic requisitions as tedious and convoluted as the streets themselves. And of course the parameters of such a search would be instantly appended to my own file.

Even as I calculate the risks and probabilities of my distraction, a flake of toxined metal drifts past the randomly scanning lens. I pull back too late. A jet of bad light streaks out at me like a wasp and I fend it off with my right arm. In that instant – everything becomes solid. From the speakers issues the syncopated pounding of sub-audible links which vibrate in the dimensions of my bones. A wave of heat pierces the lead across my chest. A murmur sounds in my lungs. A brilliant voice that threatens but does not speak.

Indeed, though my flesh shows no sign of its passage, I believe something did touch and enter my body just then. Perhaps it is that very slash of light I saw splayed against the wall. I must monitor my metabolic rate and watch for signs of transubstantiation.

I link to the Net and discover the attack has not been singular. The toxins now leak from sector to sector. The boards are jammed with calls from others like myself, who watch from their labs, who hour by hour transcribe the city as it may or may not be. Yet within seconds the answer comes down the line:

"Monitor metabolic rate. Watch for signs of transubstantiation."

We are the ones who have been chosen...for our mania, our dedication, our self-denial. Despite the chaos around us...our positions remain secure. The doors to my lab are manually and electronically locked at all times. The fluorescents are never extinguished. The tocsins never disarmed. I continue to preserve and label the chips in their plastic cases. All about me the walls are stacked with a chronological history of my work and my dereliction, an exercise in phenomenology which knows no bounds beyond the birth and death of my own existence.

Beyond which the Net remains.

Once the city ceases its aberrant motion and the tenets of reality are again susceptible to apprehension, our names will be lasered upon stone for all to see. Our files will never be terminated. We will join the phosphors in their lightning dance from core to exalt core and back again. Of this and much more I have often been assured.

In the domed stadium where death is played by night, where those seeking work queue by day, my search statement has turned up a possible cross match. Although it is not night, the overheads are lighted to combat the dimness of the day. One quadrant of the translucent dome is partially collapsed and the rain has covered the field with a series of small lakes. The lines of would-be workers wind across the playing arena while others, who have already been categorized but received no assignment, wait in the bleachers above.

I zero in on the leg in question to confirm its identity. Yes, I do think this is the same woman-girl. Her sandals are darker only because the leather has been dampened by the rain. Other legs mill about her, mostly gray-trousered. For a moment I lose her again as the files advance. Then I pan to her face and discover she is beautiful — wide-set eyes, Eurasian features, dark hair covered by a scarf with a few wet strands escaping to cling to her cheekbones. She is looking up at the man next to her, lips compressed in a tight smile. I realize all at once that she has not come to the stadium to seek legitimate work, but to solicit a liaison.

A small bud of rage blossoms from within me. Yet once I heighten the magnification, my anger fades even as her beauty pales. I see that despite the litheness of her limbs, this woman is no girl. Lines of worry radiate from her eyes. She is well past thirty and as I peel away the surface of her tightly smiling features to reveal what lies beneath, I find neither power nor promise, but merely the dazed glance of another victim.

I pull back from the individual figures, far back from the field itself, until the workers are only dark lines worming their way through a net of rain.

Though I have never visited the domed stadium, I know its dimensions well. In a few hours its stands will be thronged with spectators, its arena alive with combatants. The crowd will feast and roar. Blood will discolor the tiny lakes. As I push the woman from my thoughts, I look forward to the night's games. Like others, I will watch from the relative safety of my personal monitor and thrill to the clarity of their swift and final judgments.

Outside it is dusk. The light has again succeeded in completing its cycle. I have worked through the entire day without remembering to eat. Doing what? The log shows I have formulated no new theories. I have finished the last of the wine. I have recorded that the city is full and loud, the metal catwalks ringing with noise. I have written of colors which threaten to fast-frame the lot of our being.

For a moment I remember none of this. I think I may have a family. My arm begins to throb as if bound by a tourniquet of ice.

Walking on a ledge scattered with thorns to avoid the streets below, I pull my coat tight against the wind. The hills through which the city now passes are creased with snow. Ahead, the gigantic Westend monitor displays a telescoping line of dingy palaces. All different structures I have never been able to track upon my screen. I have heard that their ornate decay is merely a facade, and that strange yet vital rituals take place within their walls. I have also heard it rumored that it is decay alone that finds a place of worship there.

Without noticing I cross the view plane of an active lens. I turn and look back. Past the wild public warrens — the inns, the law-courts and tiered farm dormitories — the rain is falling heavily. The chronometers have shifted once again. A gate of the city, scrolled with grime, creaks shut.

I am riding black fields in a metal cart. Wasp light radiates from the mud-lacquered pools. Small explosions as each drop touches the ground. My legs are those of a girl. Taut and anxious. Diseased as the yellow night.

Biographical Sketch of an Unknown Surrealist

Son of a disgraced Russian nobleman and an industrious baker, Jax was born in Philadelphia, PA, on the fin de siècle, with a full set of false teeth. His peripatetic father kept the teeth for years until they were lost in a typhoon off the coast of Singapore during one of his less successful escapades. Jax's father had the head of a lion and the carnivorous stare of an eagle. He deserted his family whenever he felt like it.

Jax spent much of his time growing up watching his mother build furniture – armoires, credenzas, roll-top desks – and bake loaves of bread that she sold from a small cart on the street. He often sat for hours on end contemplating the intricate geometric expansions and contractions in the freshly baked loaves fresh from the hearth. Though he seldom ate them. They tasted dry and gummy and stuck to the liberal spaces between his young incisors.

Jax believed in absolutely nothing at the time, and when he wasn't watching bread his days were a melee of existential angst as he threaded his way through a veritable sea of armoires, credenzas, and roll-top desks that flooded their once spacious domicile.

His formal education was spare and scanty, except for what he read, but he read anything he could get his hands on. Mustard jars, wine bottles, the warnings on mattresses and pillows, street signs. When he was ten he got a library card. All at once there was no stopping this wild-eyed ingénue who usually need a haircut.

Due to a vastly creative curriculum vitae, later acclaimed as his first surreal work, he was accepted to teach at a university of sorts. It was in a dirty steel town but it was an accredited university nonetheless. It didn't take much to get accredited in those days.

Nearly strangling a student in his second year at the institution, he decided his true calling was art. After two years of near starvation, lean as a rake yet not nearly so clever, Jax left for Paris.

From 1925 to 1938 his hands were often sticky. Due to an art dealer he had met in a hashish haze in a coffeehouse bordello in Amsterdam, his witty and whimsical pornographic collages wormed their way into exhibitions in Paris, Nice, and Berlin. Stealing from newspapers, photographs, musical scores, and olive labels, Jax fashioned a mad graffiti of image upon image devouring image in a cannibalistic bacchanalian orgy. It was all a bit vertiginous, and several spectators were said to have fainted halfway through his first exhibit.

Jax was briefly a name to be reckoned with in the fickle world of avant-garde art. Black and white photos of his work were soon published in wild and self-righteous manifestos issued in numbers so small that even their scattered pages are considered collectible. Although they are not worth very much.

Despite such acclaim, the surreal gurus of the day were not impressed. Paul Eluard dismissed Jax's work as vaguely piquant with the aftertaste of burnt toast. Andre Breton nodded sadly as he caressed the snowy thighs of his latest paramour.

By 1939 Jax could see the writing on the wall, most likely the wall of a public bathroom where he spent an inordinate amount of time lost in transcendental masturbation. This new message, interspersed with the perennial invitations that had so often led him astray, proclaimed that war was on the way.

He fled back to America, penniless and useful as a doorstop.

Fortunately, Jax found work as a polisher in a furniture store: armoires, credenzas, roll-top desks. The years began to drift by in an hallucinogenic haze induced by his constant inhalation of hydrocarbon fumes from the polish. In 1948 he was summarily dismissed from his position for repeatedly trying to polish a customer.

Driven by necessity, Jax penned his last great surrealist work, a curriculum vitae so outstandingly preposterous and exaggerated that he was hired to teach creative writing at a university of sorts. It was in a dirty mill town, but it was an accredited university nonetheless. It didn't take much to get accredited in those days.

Jax's life may not have been a work of art, but it could not be denied that it exhibited a certain startling symmetry.

Jax moved from one teaching position to another with great alacrity, little precision, and less fortune. He spent his declining years at a small unaccredited community college in the Ozarks. By this time he was never quite sure what he was teaching, and neither were his students, but he taught it nonetheless. His lectures were known for a soporific excellence peppered with flashes of insight into the highs and lows of hydrocarbon poisoning.

"You know, man, it was like surreal!" said exterminator and former student Stu Pooley. What more could Jax have asked for?

Jax was buried in a grave high in the Ozarks, where wildflowers bloom and eagles eviscerate their prey. He was buried with a full set of teeth, pearly white and evenly spaced.

References

"Jax Who?" *The Journal of Incomprehensible Art,* Volume 27, Issue Ten, 1946, pps. 17-24.

Surrealists Worth Skipping, Farrar, Straus, and Heidegger, 1973.

"Why Are People Fainting at Art Exhibits?" *Paris Metro,* June 7, 1929.

"Surreal Artists Who May Never Have Existed," Chapter Three in *Frauds, Fakes, and Phonies of the Art World,* Schwarzenegger International, 1979.

Smoke, Song, and the Open Sea

So I'll tell you how it was when I lived on the island. Not so good. Not good at all.

She'd catch me with a smoke, not for the first time, and I'd have to watch her pacing up and down in one of her tirades, scowling like the witch she was, chewing me out in front of all the others. Smoking was a vile habit and would ruin my voice and shorten my breath and send me to an early grave. And how impossibly dumb could I get?

Once she'd finally wound down – and who knows how long that could take? – she'd raise one flabby arm and point one horny finger over the heads of the others, sending me to the very back of the choir. Like I really cared.

So whenever the old bitch would spot a ship through her spyglass and give us the sign, we'd have to drop whatever we were doing and start singing. The same repertoire every time. All rehearsed from the first bar to the last. I was so sick and tired of those songs I felt like screaming rather than singing. They had about as much real passion as a rag doll nailed to the wall.

Pretty soon we'd see them coming across the open sea, straining at the oars, their faces already wild with the sound of us and yearning for the sight and the touch of us. As always they were a hearty lot. How else could they be oarsman? And I don't mind saying I saw more than a few well-muscled young lads I wouldn't have minded tumbling with given half a chance. Not a prayer in the world of that ever happening!

We were forever singing false songs to men who would never reach us before their boats crashed and they died upon the rocks.

Make it more seductive, she would mouth, waving her arms back and forth to the rhythm like she was directing, even though we'd done it all a thousand times before. We'd throw in a few sighs and get real husky-voiced and whispery like she taught us. And then there would be that noise of splintering wood and their screams upon the wind. And their blood pink on the tide. Never mattered a bit to her except as one more notch in her crown.

Believe me, if those poor sailors ever got a good close look at her and her wrinkles upon wrinkles, eyes fierce and mean as those of a roc, the flesh hanging from her bones, they'd start pulling those oars with all their strength in the opposite direction. Though I have to admit her voice held up well enough through the centuries. What a range! Last I heard, she could still out sing the lot of us with tones as solid and clear as temple bells. And she had a vibrato you could feel in your bones. Like I really care.

So enough was enough and here I am in the city. I made the break like a few others had the guts to do before me. Hitched a ride with the deaf fisherman who cast his nets in the shadow of our cliffs where those who knew the score dared not sail. All I had to do was bat my eyes at him a few times and show a little thigh, let him have a touch or two in places that don't really count. He was shy and kind of cute, but not what I was after.

I would like to have seen the expression on that old cow's face when she realized I was gone for good and she had to hitch up her skirts and go trolling the muddy coastal villages for another with a voice like mine.

Like I said, here I am in the city. It wasn't easy at first. It's not easy for many in the city, but I'm doing okay. I sleep most of the day and go out nights to work. I won't tell you where I'm living, but you can find me singing in the right dark dives if you know where to look on the nighttime streets. Now I sing what I want to sing and I do it my own way. I smoke when and what I want, and like the old song says, "Ain't Nobody's Business If I Do."

Of course the men who frequent such places are all over me. Making their moves, often pathetic. Praising my voice and style and beauty, breathing down my neck with clouds of whiskey and gin, trying to take me out, mainly wanting to bed me. I've been down that highway more than a few times and I know all the stops along the way lead to heartache. I sing about that sometimes, but it's not a road I plan to travel again. Now I give such grifters short shrift before they can get very far.

I'm waiting until I find the right kind of guy, one who smells fresh as the air of the open sea, the kind of guy who will crash himself on the rocks for me whenever I want. What can I say? I'm a creature of habit and I had one classic hell of a teacher.

Tales of the Dead Wizard

I. The Wrathful Wraith

My spells were justly famous. Men spoke my name in awe. Kings and princes hired me to tilt their wars with sorcery, cast darkness on their enemies, and concoct subtle potions to command the latent passions of the ladies they found fair. I once changed a river's course. I made the clouds rain fire. I've turned some men to swine and taught others how to fly. Yet even my greatest magics could not dam the flow of time. The years had their way with me and death laid me down.

Yet before I traveled on to leave this earthly plane, to inhabit another world or be shuttered like a flame, I had three scores to settle with those who still remained. My spirit clung tenaciously with all its motive force to a kind of life in death until my tasks were done. My sorcery served me well until revenge was spent and all accounts were summed.

II. The Ignoble King

When Axer was a callow youth and first ascended to his throne, I saved his faltering kingdom and assured his future reign. I made his subjects love him with a blind unwavering love, though he'd yet to do a thing to display the common virtues one should look for in a king to warrant even simple trust. They endured a costly war, driving back a superior foe, to defend young Axer's lineage and secure his regal claims. Yet in the years that followed he proved nothing but a despot who repaid their bloody sacrifice with a reign of terror and pain. He taxed their every breath, their eyelids and their bones, until his royal coffers swelled and burst with wealth beyond what any man could spend.

No longer bound by mortal vows I'd sworn to honor while alive, I stripped away illusion from the eyes of those beguiled. At last they saw their ruler for the tyrant he had been and perceived his evil ways. Once they overcame the shock of the horror that was their lot, they began to plot against him with the same fierce dedication that had once made him king.

Unrest was like an avalanche careening on a downhill spree, gaining force as it tumbled and clearing a path behind for revolution on its heels. In weeks the palace burned. The monarchy was razed. I clapped my ghostly palms and watched with ghastly glee as Axer's crownless head flew from the chopping block. I danced a spirit dance on the bloodied cobblestones.

III. The Faithless Lover

In my own distant youth, in the far land of my birth, I loved the maiden Kara-Lyn, who fed my naive passions with like passions of her own. She swore to love me always, beyond the ruins of time, until the mountains settled and the seas lost their tides. Then she left me for another who could offer more than I.

She chose a wealthy merchant who possessed the gold and servants to sate her every need. He draped her shapely limbs in rare furs and precious silks. He placed a wedding band upon her hand and clasped an emerald choker around the pulse I'd often kissed in the column of her throat. It was Kara-Lyn's betrayal that set my path on wizardry and a scholar's life of solitude.

Though my love had been pure as youthful love can be, it was tainted by rejection and the loss of what I craved. The intervening years had transformed my fiery passion for the maiden Kara-Lyn to a cold and smoldering hate. And now I sought revenge to pay her back in full for her vain and faithless ways.

I found her worn and gray, not a maid but just a crone, her beauty long since passed. Deep wrinkles lined the face I once thought so sublime. I delved within her mind and discovered with surprise I still occupied her thoughts as much as she did mine. I learned that her betrayal had left her scarred for life. She had not fled my arms to satisfy her selfish needs or please her youthful vanity but to meet her father's debts and rescue him from prison. Her marriage without passion was a burden filled with strife, a cross far heavier to bear than my years without a wife.

The need for revenge was extinguished in my chest. An ember of the love I'd felt soon rekindled in its place. Though my magics could not restore her youth they could mend her troubled mind. I made her memories dwell on what there was to cherish in a life that offered little of what most of us desire. I made her errant children attentive and loyal once again. They eased her waning years with companionship and care.

Zagan's spells were infamous. Men shuddered at his name. If you had the gold to pay he would champion any cause regardless of its worth and with no concern for its ends. He was a clever conjurer yet his powers were derived. They lacked creative force and were no match for mine. Each time we fought in life and I gained the upper hand, he retreated like a beaten dog. He cast childish spells behind that I tossed aside, yet they hindered my pursuit until he'd reached the safety of his ensorcelled domain.

While I was flesh and bone I could not broach the shields that surrounded his terrain like a coat of tempered mail. But a ghost can enter anywhere, so I quickly stepped within while he was lost in sleep. I rewrote all his notebooks in a hand just like his own. I turned his formulas to gibberish and intermixed his potions to leave them rotting on the shelf until the only thing they conjured was the stench of death itself.

When Zagan awakened from his dreams and found the chaos I had wrought, he tried to set it right and searched in vain for its cause. And each time he returned to sleep or left his castle walls to pursue his villainous ways, I wreaked my havoc once again until I made him cry and rave. I reduced his agile mind to a state with no more reason than some rabid cat or dog.

When I last saw Zagan he had abandoned magic of all kinds. I left him as a beggar who tramped the roads alone, in search of an answer he was destined not to find.

V. The Wandering Wraith

Each of us has a special door through which we finally pass that leads the way from death to whatever follows after that. But I had tarried far too long stitching up the threads of life. The door that once awaited me closed just like my tomb and will never open again. So I wander disembodied like a wraith across the land, without rest or resolution, neither living nor fully dead, with eternity on my hands

As the years run to centuries and millennia take their place, I watch as nations rise and fall. I see religions share their fate. I travel across the continents and over the open seas with no need for wheel or sail. I observe the pangs of history, the convolutions of the race as it cycles and repeats itself and forever seeks new twists on the same familiar themes.

Yet I've filled my empty hours in a way you might expect from a man who spent his life casting spells and changing lives. Throughout the countless years my magic has not failed me. Far more than a mere spectator, I've made myself a judge and a meddler in the world's affairs.

Some men call me Fortune. To others I am known as Fate. Some mistake me for a lady with the strange name of Luck. Educated men have studied my effects, compiled lengthy tomes on my strange vicissitudes, and concluded without doubt I am nothing more than chance and the laws of probability. No matter what you call me, I don't give a wizard's damn. My own once-famous name has been buried and forgotten in the landslide of the past.

VI. The Idle Meddler

If your days move smoothly like a river straight on course, if the sun is always shining on your bright and smiling face, then all of this comes crashing down like an unexpected storm and the wreckage of your existence leaves you crying in its wake, it may be my wayward spirit amusing itself for a while by playing god with your life.

If your fortune is unfortunate and darkness seems to trail you beyond the realm of night, if every choice you make turns and slaps you in the face, then all at once this changes and you've found a comely mate and children born to please, and wealth comes knocking for an unexpected stay, perhaps my spirit countenance has smiled on your plight.

Don't think about it twice. There's nothing you can do. You can bless me like a saint or curse me like a sin. You can court me like the object of your ultimate desire. You can fill your head with numbers and calculate my game. It will not change my ways and it will not force my whims.

Just remember as you pass me on your journey beyond death, as you make your certain way to the afterlife you've claimed, you will leave me far behind. I will bother you no longer. I cannot follow in your path. For I am condemned to wander this amorphous interim land, with only ghosts for company and nothing left to do but play with human pawns until life breathes its final breath and the human story ends.

Remembering the River Woman

with Marge Simon

i

Simple things. A few hours in a man's life. The rare pleasure of finding someone so close that for a time she filled his skin.

When a man is afraid of himself, everyone knows he's bad company. He was a big man, tall enough, and his shoulders could stand two bushels of grain. By day he worked the docks of a river so vast you could tell time by its tides. He lived alone in a tin-roofed shack near the pier, avoided rum, spoke only when he had to.

Rumor had it he'd once shamed himself and his family. No one could remember how or why.

ii

When the tides rise, crafts from many lands come ashore. One day there was a River Woman among the passengers, dark and slim with smooth hair that flowed with colors in the wind. When he first saw her he forgot to breathe for a moment, and when he did he yelled out.

It was a huge wordless yell, the sound that comes from deep inside a needful man. When she heard him cry, she stopped and turned his way.

One by one and then in groups, the people on the docks gaped when the creature took his arm to walk beside him. River Folk never mixed with humans.

iii

She nestled in his largest chair while he prepared a meal of bread and cheese. They washed it down with a local vintage, laughed often and for no reason. She told him stories he barely understood. He poured more wine, brushed her arm whenever he could.

Yet there came a time when he could tell that she sensed the fear within him like a bright lance of pain. Was it his glance, his touch, or could River Folk share the thoughts of others as the old tales told? And though she stayed to spend the night in his arms, he knew at that moment he'd lost her already.

Afterward, he had to think it out slowly, the way she'd come to him and why. Especially why. A fantasy that took hours to relive: each gesture she made, each word spoken, her webbed hands splayed on the soiled spread. How she had taken his fear in her leaving and left the image of her wild beauty impressed on his mind.

He thought about it all in moments of peace as he watched the tides of the river rise and fall.

The Infernal Itch

I turned up the hot water and let it flow across my body. I took the shampoo that Dr. Pederson had given me, poured a dose between my palms, and rubbed it into my scalp. As the medication penetrated the itching lessened and disappeared. I'd been through this routine before and knew relief would be temporary. Within hours it would again feel as if my scalp was infested by a colony of angry mites.

My life had seemed perfect until a couple days ago. That was when itching started. The dreams began. And the limousine pulled up across the street. All in the reverse order.

I had just started work on my latest novel. Actually I'd been working on it in my head for over a week. After thirty books in as many years I no longer need to put outlines on paper. Only a few of my titles have graced the bestseller lists, but they all sell respectably and are often translated abroad. Although there's never been a film, several books have been optioned. I may not be a literary lion but my writing provides me with an income and a life style that most envy.

The plot of the new book was clear in my mind and I'd set aside Thursday to begin work. I knew I'd have the apartment to myself. Hannah had started on her latest commission. She's an interior design consultant and a successful one at that. The cleaning service had finished its weekly stint. We don't employ a cook because most of the time we eat at restaurants. When we don't dine out we can always fix something ourselves. Hannah has a lamb curry that will take the roof off your mouth and leave you begging for more.

Once I get rolling on a book nothing stops me. Yet wrestling with that first sentence, trying to catch the tone for the first few pages, can be like climbing Everest without a Sherpa. That's why I wanted the quiet of an empty apartment. Yet still it wasn't happening for me. The blank screen stared back at me like the eye of some idiot in on a secret I knew nothing about.

I began to pace. The blocked writer's first resort.

My study is arranged for that purpose. Despite Hannah's objections, I've pushed the furniture against the walls. She's redecorated the apartment more than a dozen times in the seven years we've lived together. Twice it even made the pages of *Interior Design*. Yet my study, unfashionable as it may be, has remained inviolate.

While pacing I chanced to look out the window, across the street and down to the park. That was when I saw the limousine. It had pulled up in a no-parking zone opposite the building. Standing on the sidewalk beside it was a man in dark red livery. He was looking up at my study window. Since I was looking down, he was staring directly at me. There was an air of expectancy about him. He was clearly waiting for someone and had fastened upon the wrong apartment.

I went back to my desk and tried to concentrate. After several false starts I managed to knock out a few pages. But when I read them, they didn't seem right at all.

I decided to extend the limits of my pacing. I threw on a jacket and headed downstairs.

The limo was still parked across the street. As I came down the front steps of the building the chauffeur waved at me. I waited for a break in the traffic and crossed over. As I approached the man, my steps began to slow.

Large and heavily-muscled, he looked more like a bodyguard than a chauffeur. The kind of fellow that spends his spare time in a gym, pumping iron and lord knows what else. His face was one of the ugliest I'd ever seen. Long and sad with features crudely delineated, an unfinished sculpture slapped together from pieces of wet clay. Eyes like slits, red-rimmed and ripe with malice, glinted out at me from folds of gray flesh. It was the kind of face only a blind mother would call to dinner.

Yet as I drew to a halt several feet away, I could see that there was nothing really threatening about the man. He took a few steps toward me and his manner seemed deferential, even hesitant.

"Can I help you?" I said

"Sir... it's time." He glanced toward the car, shuffling from one foot to the other. His overdeveloped torso atop bandied legs gave him a top-heavy look.

"I'm afraid you've got me confused with someone else."

"Sir...if you'll just step into the car."

He gestured toward the limo. He opened his mouth again but nothing came out. There was something he wanted to tell me, yet he seemed afraid to say it. Or at least he was pretending to be afraid. The man was considerably larger than I and if there had not been other pedestrians about he could have manhandled me into the car and whisked me away without anyone being the wiser.

"You've got me confused with someone else," I repeated "I did not call for a limousine."

I turned and walked away, heading across the grass and into the park. I glanced back several times. The driver was staring at me but made no attempt to follow.

The clouds had burnt off and the day was pleasant. Yet as I walked a chill came over me. Rather than easing my mind as it usually did, the unabated green of the park seemed wrong. I had the urge to see it leveled, trees and bushes and grass burnt down to bare earth and charred stumps. Within minutes I decided I'd had enough. I headed back, crossing over at the far end of the block. I could see the limo was still there with the driver standing by its side.

Rather than invigorating me and clearing out my head, the walk had the opposite effect. I felt muddled and drained of energy. I decided to stretch out on the couch for a nap before going back to work. That was when the first dream occurred.

It was the kind of dream that mostly vanishes upon waking. The kind where you have too many things to do and you are rushing back and forth with no time to do them. A single scene from this hodgepodge remained vivid. I was walking down a shadowy corridor, a passage in some subterranean cavern. Along the walls torches were mounted at intervals, offering an uncertain light, imparting a raw smoky taste to the air. The driver from the limo was by my side. He was bare to the waist. Sweat glistened on his exaggerated musculature. He was leaning close to me, whispering in my ear, and I was trying to understand what he was saying. His breath reeked like the air from a dead refrigerator. His words were a hoarse jumble. His hand upon my shoulder had claws. Just as his meaning was about to come clear...

A woman was leaning over me and shaking me awake. She was young and blond and beautiful. I didn't have the slightest idea who she was.

As I said, my life had seemed perfect.

My writing could be deemed a success. My first wife Marie and I, with nothing left to say to one another after twenty years of marriage, had parted amicably. Both my children were grown and had done me proud. Miles, even if he lacked creativity, had chosen a literary life. He was a junior editor at Random House and showed every sign of going to the top. Melissa, a mathematician who worked at Princeton, was also working on my second grandchild. They didn't come by as often as I liked, though they were more dutiful than most children in this streamlined and barbarous age.

Yet the main reason my life seemed perfect was Hannah. No doubt there are more than a few who consider Hannah my trophy wife, and in that they are both right and wrong. She *is* a trophy, but I didn't acquire her in the way usually associated with that term. I'd been separated a few months when I decided to redo the apartment. It held too many memories, most of them positive, but it was time for a change. That was when I met Hannah. It may not have been love at first sight, but it was lust. Spontaneous combustion. Bells and whistles. A hundred and one strings and a ton of heavy metal. Before she'd finished looking over the living room we were at each other's buttons and snaps and zippers. And it's never let up since.

It was Hannah who was shaking me awake.

Why I didn't recognize her I couldn't say. At that moment I probably wouldn't have recognized myself. The dream had left me disoriented and I was shivering violently.

"What's the matter, darling? Are you all right?"

As soon as Hannah spoke, everything fell into place.

"I don't know. I was having the strangest dream." I was trembling, rubbing my arms for warmth. "Turn up the heat. It's freezing in here."

"Do you want some coffee?"

I thought about it for a second. "No," I said, "make me a Bloody Mary. With lots of Tabasco. That should warm me up."

One Bloody Mary led to another. Then we ordered out for Szechuan. One thing led to another and before you knew it we were naked on the living-room rug before a blazing fire. Our sweat-slickened bodies slid against one another as we tried it this way for a while and that way for a while and one or two other ways just to make sure everything was in working order. You'd think we'd been together a few weeks rather than seven years.

Before going to sleep we curled up in bed and watched the late news. For once all the hot spots of the world had cooled. Middle East peace talks were back on track. North Korea had been quiet for nearly a month. There weren't even any natural disasters to report. I was so used to a world full of trouble and strife, it was a bit hard to buy. I kept waiting for the other boot to hit the floor. Most likely with a goosestep.

I slept fitfully that night and at some point began to dream. I was standing alone on the stage of an enclosed amphitheater. High above on the dome of its ceiling a stormy skyscape had been painted, a hemisphere filled with roiling thunderclouds and apocalyptic lightning flashes. Tiers of stone benches rose about me, inhabited by hunched and shadowy forms. They were all waiting for me to say something. My dream thoughts leap-frogged frantically, searching for how to begin. I cleared my throat and...

I came awake suddenly. Though it was not the dream that had awakened me. It was my scalp. It was itching like terminal dandruff. I'd already been scratching my head in my sleep and as I sat up on the side of the bed I began rubbing it even more vigorously. Again I was shivering and I pulled a blanket around my shoulders.

My antics soon woke Hannah, who came out of a sound sleep to minister to my needs. She made cocoa and found some tablets from an old sleeping pill prescription so that I could get back to bed.

"First thing tomorrow," she said "you need to see Dr. Pederson."

"Yes, there is definitely some redness. And there seems to be a little swelling, too."

With her usual insistence, Hannah had managed to wrangle an appointment the very next day. Pederson, who was apparently sacrificing his lunch hour to see me, leaned back and stopped pawing at my scalp.

"I don't think it's anything we need worry about." He gave me a grin that could have charmed Attila.

Pederson boasted a first-rate reputation and an exclusive clientele. Affidavits posted on the walls proclaimed that he had done more than his share of pro bono work. Still I didn't like the man. He was too jovial. His ever-present smile resembled that of some swamified fanatic. I could see him flashing his pearlies with the same beatific radiance whether he was meting out a clean bill of health or hinting at a possible death sentence.

He turned away from me and began digging in a cabinet.

When Pederson turned back, with several small plastic bottles in hand, I nearly jumped out of my hide. "You can start with these samples. I'll write a prescription in case you need more."

I barely heard what he was saying. The man's entire skull was swathed in a flickering golden aura. It made my flesh crawl just to look at it.

"Try to stop scratching. That irritates it. Be sure to keep it clean. Shampoo as often as you need to relieve the itching. If it isn't any better in a week, I'll refer you to a dermatologist."

I took the bottles and shoved them into my coat pocket. I wanted out of there as soon as possible, but the good doctor wasn't through.

"How have you been feeling in general? Anything else bothering you?"

I hadn't mentioned the chills. Or my inability to concentrate on the book. And I for sure wasn't going to say anything about the aurora borealis dancing around his skull.

"I'm all right," I mumbled, glancing out the window, at the floor, at my own hands as they clenched the sides of the metal examining table. Anyplace but at that unearthly light.

"You seem a little tense. Maybe you've been working too hard. Perhaps you should take it easy for awhile. Think about a vacation. Everyone needs a vacation now and again."

A vacation! I've got a rash on my scalp and the man tells me to take a vacation. What kind of a moron was he? A vacation was the last thing I needed. What I needed was to do some writing.

I'd taken a cab to the appointment, but decided to hoof it on the way home. It was about a mile and I thought the exercise might do me some good. I couldn't have been more mistaken. Once I was on the street the hallucination visited upon me in Pederson's office persisted and multiplied.

A blue-haired dowager with a yappy Pomeranian in tow. A cabbie with the hood of his car up, shaking his head in disgust. A bike messenger pedaling at breakneck speed. Two Madison Avenue types in heated sidewalk debate. Everyone I saw sported either an aura like Pederson's, or their faces were grossly distorted — eyes askew, foreheads bulging, mouths twisted in crooked snarls —, as if I were seeing them reflected in funhouse mirrors. I was nearly running by the time I reached our building

No sign of the driver, but the limo hadn't budged an inch.

As Sam the doorman ushered me in I could see his right cheek was a mass of swollen tissue, discolored and oozing clear fluid.

I peered through the slit in the curtains. He was concealed by the limo's tinted windows but I knew he was down there, behind the wheel, staring up at me with those red-rimmed eyes. I watched several motorcycle police and one squad car drive past. Not one of them slowed down. They seemed oblivious to the fact that the limousine was parked in a red zone.

I'd showered and used Pederson's shampoo as soon as I'd gotten home. Although the itching had stopped, I was feeling far from normal. All at once our spacious apartment felt like a prison. Yet I knew that if I went out I'd have to confront the chauffeur. His face was one hell of a sight already without any more distortions or running sores. Or a golden light show dancing around it.

I sat at my desk and through a sheer effort of will forced myself to begin writing. And then it happened. The world I was creating took over and it began to flow for me. I knocked out page after page, making up for the time I had been idle. By late afternoon I took a break because the itching had returned. It was back into the shower for another respite. Then back to my desk, writing like a demon on speed. It was dark outside before I realized I hadn't eaten since breakfast.

I was on my own for the evening. Hannah was entertaining clients or being entertained by them. I pawed through the refrigerator, found some leftover chili verde and popped it in the microwave. A few days ago it had been deliciously spicy. By now it seemed to have lost its flavor. Even when I drenched it with salsa it proved a lost cause. After a few bites I threw the rest in the trash.

Except for one more shower I spent the evening at my desk. I was writing like I never had before. At this rate the book would be finished in weeks. Maybe I could afford to take a vacation after all.

Hannah came tottering in at half past ten, halfway through the news. I could see she'd had more than a few. I was beginning to wonder about these late meetings with clients.

"So what's happening in the world?" she asked.

"Absolutely nothing," I told her. "Dull as an Evnagelical singalong."

If you believed the statistics the talking heads were spouting, crime, drug addiction, and teen pregnancy were all down. Most of the broadcast was devoted to sappy human interest stories because there was nothing else to report. If the news stayed this bland, no one was going watch it.

"How did your dinner go?"

"Same old...same old," Hannah muttered.

She was so out of it she forgot to ask what happened at Pederson's. Once she was undressed and in bed, leaving a trail of clothes across the floor, she came after me as usual. I could smell wine and garlic on her breath. For once I wasn't in the mood.

"We don't have to make love every night!" I snapped.

She turned away with an odorous snort and was asleep in seconds. I popped a couple of sleeping pills and after some tossing and turning...found myself...back in the cave with the driver by my side.

We were approaching the end of the tunnel. There was a room from which a red-orange glow and a loud clanging noise emanated. I knew there was something horrible in that room, so horrible it was beyond human imagination. Yet I wasn't in the least bit afraid. My pace quickened. I was eager to see what the room would reveal....

The itching woke me before I had the chance.

I stepped out of the shower and toweled off. Morning light was eddying in around the curtains. Hannah was sound asleep, her mouth open, snores escaping from her lips. Her familiar face looked strange to me. As I came closer, I saw that it was covered with pink scabs.

In my study I looked over what I'd written the day before...and it made no sense whatsoever. Most of it was gibberish. Words and sentences strung together at random.

Already I could feel a tingling spreading across my scalp. The shampoo was losing its effectiveness.

The dreams and visions. The itching. The chauffeur and the limousine. I didn't know how, but I knew they were all part of the same lumpy stew. I pulled on a sweat shirt and baggy corduroys and slipped into my running shoes. I couldn't do anything about the itching or the visions, but I could at least take care of that limo.

The driver was out of the car before I crossed the street.

I strode up to him. "Just what are you doing here? What do you want from me?"

"Sir...," he held the rear door open. "If you'll just step inside, I can explain everything."

I could see the interior was upholstered in a deep red that matched the man's livery. Somehow I knew it would be that way. I hesitated for a moment. They tell you never to get into a car with a stranger, even if you are being held at gun point. Yet the chauffeur had been so present in my life the last couple of days, both in fact and in my dreams, he hardly seemed a stranger anymore.

As soon as I sank into the leather of the seats and saw the mini-bar stocked with expensive liqueurs, as soon as the door swung shut and the unearthly warmth of the car's interior enveloped me, it all came back in an instant.

Everyone needs a vacation now and again. And what better vacation than one where you can leave your everyday cares behind and lose yourself completely in another world, an entirely different life? Which was exactly what I had done. The reason it felt as if I'd been with Hannah only a few weeks was because I had been with her only a few weeks. I was not a novelist with thirty books to my credit. I had children to be sure, both living and dead, but none of them worked for Random House or taught at Princeton. Their work and their lives were of more import than that.

I leaned back and surrendered to the itching. Within moments I felt my scalp begin to part and the horns breaking through. I felt my stature growing and saw the talons sprouting from my fingers. Of course I now recognized the man in the livery. I understood why he had approached me so circumspectly. He was my right hand man and had been so on and off for centuries. He had also experienced my wrath more than once and been banished to the deepest pits. He had now taken his place behind the wheel and was looking back at me expectantly.

"Take me down, Asmodeus," I said. "It's time to get back to work."

I watched the news that night with satisfaction. Things were starting to heat up again. As they always did.

Curse of the Alien's Wife

He has become the darkest star of her erotic obsessions, the critical mass beyond which her personality can no longer ascend or even express itself. Whenever she considers leaving, he launches the precise sensual bullet that slaughters her resolve and elevates her consciousness to new heights of excitation. He is an incendiary of the flesh who ignites her neural corridors with undivided passion.

At first she is ashamed of the incoherent cries that rise so freely from her throat, at how her limbs thrash beneath the artful invasions of his touch. Yet she soon learns to embrace her abandon, to find a sure purchase on his slippery flanks, to revel in the fluid guttural oh-so-foreign purr of his elaborate and fiercely whispered endearments.

And now that his supernal caress has become the familiar sanctum of her nights, she fears that no mere human partner could ever satisfy her again.

All of his kind, so he tells her, are masters at the art of love...both somatic and sublime. Or is it nothing more than sex, she wonders.

Has he transformed her to a nymphomaniac? A nympho-xenomaniac? She laughs to herself, for she knows if she laughs aloud he will hound her unmercifully until he knows the reason why.

In the darkness of the anonymous motel rooms they occupy in a seemingly unending chain, a pale lime radiance leaks from the corners of his eyes. Other than that he can pass easily enough for human. Large and well-built. The planes of his face perhaps a trifle too flat and sharply angled. The green of his eyes an odd shade, rife with the stuff of dreams even by daylight. Yet at first or second glance one would never suspect the star-flung distance of his origins. It is not his appearance, no gross physical anomaly, that threatens to betray him. Rather it is his curiosity and naiveté regarding the human condition, his inability to leave the slightest need or suffering unattended.

Even in the midst of their headlong flight from one assumed identity to the next he forces her to stop the car for hitchhikers. He tips extravagantly at rundown coffee shops and squanders the pittance she earns at temp jobs or waitressing on every homeless soul he encounters in the street. Although he speaks the language with no trace of an accent, the idea of him holding a job is more absurd than the thought of leaving him. She must manage all the particulars of their life, financial and otherwise. No matter how often she instructs him in the proper behavior, his personality resembles that of some gentle intense madman, a cross between Quixote and Van Gogh. Matters of ordinary survival on the planet Earth, the give and take of daily hypocrisy, are beyond his grasp.

In contrast, his performance each night grows more accomplished and bizarre as he masters the limits of her flesh, as he plumbs the depths of her psyche and devastates her final inhibitions. And each night she continues to learn from him, buoyed by the vague promise that someday her sensual repertoire could equal his own and she might return in kind a portion of the ecstasy he dispenses so freely.

She knows if he is discovered for what he is, she will lose him to a media hungry for sensation. Or to some acronymic government agency with an even greater appetite for secrecy. In one nightmare scenario that spools across her imagination she sees him stretched upon a laboratory table, gladly assisting a team of scientists in his own dissection. In another reel he has become a darling of the talk-show circuit, his sexual prowess already legend, a line of long-stemmed starlets clinging to his arms.

So at her direction they flee from one city to another...one under-culture to the next, where his eccentricities are no less noticeable but more readily accepted...until even among the social misfits who become their circle of "friends" he begins to draw curious stares and questions...and then she decides they must move on again.

To her friends and relatives she has become a stranger, or at least persona non grata. In increasing numbers they refuse to accept her calls or respond to her pleas for cash. When her car breaks down, unable to afford the repairs, she must sell it at a fraction of its worth so they can continue their haphazard flight and happenstance existence.

Only her mother continues to speak to her, and then it is no longer in the voice she knows as that of her mother. It has become reproachful and strident, any shred of motherly tenderness lost in the bitterness engendered by what the old woman considers a filial betrayal.

"If I could prove what I know," she screeches across the wires, "if anyone would listen to me, I'd send the police after you right this minute! You and that thing you call a man."

She is past the point of hope or redemption, resigned to her addiction. She has already accepted a life of flight and poverty punctuated by interludes of blinding passion, when the tiny rescue beacon that never leaves his side begins to pulse with a radiance that mirrors the pale green fire of his eyes.

They must dash more than halfway across the continent to rendezvous at the designated coordinates, first by bus, next by thumb as their funds are depleted, and finally leaving the highway and civilization behind, they travel by foot in an exhausting trek through the desolation and chill of a desert night. His eyes flare, brighter than before, lighting their way like ghostly headlamps.

He has at last taken command of their fate and no longer seems the least bit helpless. Without compass or map, guided by some inner sense of direction akin to the migratory savvy of birds or dolphins, he strides forward as surely as if their path were marked. In the eerie illumination that he casts, the cacti and desert rocks take on the shifting dimensions of a fluid otherworldly landscape. When she stumbles, reaching out to him for support, she is startled anew by the wrongness of the bones and muscles beneath his flesh.

Waking near the end of night, about to experience the last earthly dawn she will ever know, she finds herself huddled within his arms for warmth rather than pleasure.

As the sky bleaches and the stars begin to fade, a single star among them grows brighter. The sand beneath their feet trembles in subsonic vibrations as the craft silently descends. Looking to her lover's face she sees that the exertions of the night have bled the color from his eyes. They are like curdled milk, the green fled to the corners of the iris. Yet it is not their lack of color that causes the breath to catch in her throat so much as their expression. His eyes now watch her and look away with a glance he has henceforth reserved for beggars in the street.

All at once she understands that their roles will soon be reversed. She will become the alien, inept and unable to comprehend the simplest conventions of a strange new existence. She begins to wonder if the media, the government and the scientists of his world, are as hungry for novelty as those of her own. She realizes that this is the first night they have spent together without making love.

My Grandfather, the Carver

One night when I was about six-years-old, my mother, father and self were grouped about the kitchen table consuming a common meal when an uncommon event transpired.

Both my parents rocketed to their feet, accompanied by flying string beans and toppling chairs. At a distance from one another, circling, never coming together, shouting at the top of their lungs, they paced about the floor, with faces changing a mile a minute. My father's cheeks went all lumpy, his forehead accordioned. My mother's nose seem made from clay, and her hair blew and crackled about her temples like the uncut weeds and grasses in the vacant lot by the corner, dead but still rooted.

By the time things settled down we were all bundled up and packed into the family car, our new '49 Ford, speeding through the night and out of the city. I heard train whistles and watched telephone poles looming and shrinking against the blackness. I was sure I had done nothing wrong, yet my parents were making me sit in the backseat instead of upfront between them, though there was plenty of room between them. And their faces still looked odd. Like other adults in the market or on the streets, they had become strangers. Their eyes didn't know me and I could no longer recognize them.

That night we drove to my grandparents' house, where I was to stay for the next several weeks. My father and mother, I was told, had a trip to take. Years later I learned their "trip" was a trial separation to contemplate a divorce that never happened.

My grandparents lived in a rangy two-story wood frame with open country all about and more rooms than I could count. This house, which I promptly and most naturally dubbed "the castle," was lavish with accumulation: stylish old clothes, ancient magazines, congeries of porcelain figurines (such as long-haired French gentleman who danced at arm's length from their coiffured ladies), umbrellas whose handles had faces, and packed in trunks at my disposal the left-behind toys of all the children who had grown up there. In the backyard my grandparents raised animals, only chickens and pigs, but still, real live animals. When I was six I rode a pig and, most naturally, pretended it was an alligator!

But best and worst of all, curse and bless their souls, my grandparents had dipped into their savings and invested in the most wonderful of the newest wonders of the wondering electronic age: they had purchased a television set. It cast its spell upon me with great immediacy from the very first day.

Three weeks, twenty-one days, say approximately four hours of viewing per day ... equals a grand total of eighty-four hours of 1950s television gluck streaming unfiltered into the open reservoir of my six-year-old mind. How much of that debris I've sloughed off with expiring brain cells, how much still circles in my unconscious, I have no idea. Consciously, I can't call back a word or image. What I do remember is the process, its particulars.

After dinner each evening we would gather in the dim living room. My grandmother: a tall erect woman with a sharp jaw and a mass of pure white hair that she always kept piled and pinned atop her head. My retarded Aunt Bertha, who had never left home: although she must have been nearing forty her demeanor still reflected the questioning glance and awkward grace of an adolescent. Myself: a blond, nearly pretty boy, too thin, with dark circles beneath darker eyes. My grandfather: spectacled, baggy-skinned, suspendered, with a full head of gray-yellow-white hair and an unlit cigar stub protruding from between his false teeth. And of course, our mentor, the television set, which had more to say than any of the rest of us, but which my grandmother, nevertheless, controlled. She would set the volume, pick the programs, and change the channels. When the picture went out of focus or began to flip, she'd grumble and fool with the rabbit ears (which my grandfather called "antlers"). She was an energetic old lady, no doubt of that. During the commercial breaks she would jump up with Aunt Bertha in tow to finish another two minutes of housework, then return with a flurry once the show had resumed.

I remember my aunt giggling unexplainably at certain programs, and on several occasions bursting into tears at some tragic occurrence on the screen. My grandmother would console her and explain that it was only "actors pretending," and that she shouldn't be upset because things such as that didn't happen in "real life."

Through this assorted activity my grandfather remained for the most part stoic. Since he had cataracts on both eyes, I doubt very much if he could make out anything but the most obvious images that flipped across our magic screen. Instead he had created another pastime for himself, his own magic. At some point in the evening, usually in the middle of a show, he would rise from his chair and shuffle to the linen closet in the downstairs hall. When he returned he would be carrying a fresh bar of Ivory Soap, still wrapped. Resuming his seat he would fish out his pocketknife. With one clean stroke the wrapper would be sliced away and he would begin to whittle. Though my grandmother would say nothing, her head would often shake with firm disapproval: after all, soap was for washing as clearly as the sun was for shining.

Soon my grandfather's trousers would be covered with white chips and his large, freckled hands would turn glossy and gummy. It occurred to me with great delight that he was actually getting himself dirty with soap. As his knife pared the dimensions of the bar, an animal would begin to take shape beneath his fingers. Now I had two shows to watch. When the television grew tiresome, I would glance over to see how my grandfather's creation was progressing. For certain he was no Rodin, no Giacometti, but he did have what is known as "the touch." Often his animals were stiff-legged and out of proportion, yet if you looked closely enough, certain details – an eye, the splay of a paw upon the ground, or even the texture of fur – would jump out with amazing accuracy. Each of these soapy carvings stood upon a base of soap, where my grandfather added the final touch. So there would be no mistake as to their intended identity, he would scratch a label for each of his tiny statues.

My mother, a woman with ambitions for her son, had already instilled in me the rudiments of reading. My meager knowledge coupled with my grandfather's representational ability allowed me to decipher most of these scrawlings. "RooSter" or "giraFFe" or "Wild boaR" they would read, in a random mix of upper and lower case letters, as if my grandfather did not know the difference between the two. Since none of his menagerie ever survived the evening, this labeling proved pointless in any case.

Inevitably, my grandfather would doze in front of the set, often even before his carving was complete. then, careful and deliberate, my grandmother would move into action. While the television continued to play, she would cross to his chair. With one had she would pluck the newborn animal from his lap; with the other she would scoop up the larger chunks of soap from his trousers. Her palms would come together. Still standing over my grandfather, she would begin to knead. The tendons in her long white wrist stood out, her fact strained. When her hands came apart, there would be a bar of soap, a bit lumpy, but once again usable. Usable, that is, by all except me.

Having watched my grandfather bring "a stone to life," I had, most naturally, invested the product with a kind of life. To my eyes there was something horrible about my grandmother's ritual actions each evening. Though I could not give it a name at the time, I saw those hands as none other than those of the castle executioner, and the resultant bar of soap, for certain, as a still-warm corpse. If I had not been such a reticent and trained child – who was already well aware that he hallucinated too much for his own good – I would have cried out my anguish as soon as her knuckles went bloodless with their dirty work. Yet one night I finally conquered my reticence. I did take action.

My grandfather had begun his carving early, right after dinner. Rather than the regular bar of Ivory he had taken a bath size. His tarnished blade seemed to dance with special ambition that evening. He whittled at the bar lengthwise and the form which began to appear was tall and thin. Another giraffe, I thought. But no, for the first time to my knowledge it was a human figure that my grandfather fashioned. The television lost out. My awareness became centered on the shifting apertures left my grandfather's moving fingers. I spied a floppy broad-brimmed hat, a curving nose, the ragged tails of a long coat. I saw a man, stretched beyond human dimensions, yet remaining true throughout to his elongated proportions: an angular cartoon hobo, lips pursed in a whistle, with a stick and a knotted rag over his shoulder.

I was already six years old. Civilized morality, most naturally, had its grip on me. Crushing an animal back to dumb substance was one thing. A man with a song upon his lips was something else. Resolve took form within me. For the first time in my life I really understood what waiting was. I learned to wait.

I waited.

The commercial came. My grandmother and aunt scurried, the former barking directions. My grandfather's work was complete. His eyelids had slipped low over his cataracts and his fallen belly pumped in and out with a regular rhythm. I lifted the hobo gingerly from his lap and with fear-faltering steps began the retreat to my bedroom, cradling the creation in my open palms so as not to alter a line of its form. In the hallway I met my grandmother head on, a giant dust mop in her hand.

"Christopher," she reprimanded gently in a voice like a pear, "we can't have you playing with that. What would your mother say?" Her hand reached out, wrist fluid, long finger opening as delicately as a flower about to taste the rain. "Now give it to your grandmother." Her eyes beamed, her voice became a plum. "And I'll let you have something *very special* to play with!"

But all that sweetness wasn't fooling me.

I had heard of the wolf in sheep's clothing and I knew an assassin when I saw one. Most naturally, I turned and ran.

The castle stairs I took two at a time. Painted tapestries flew by. From the ornate balustrade faces winked and leered at me. My grandmother's black laced shoes clackety-clacked behind. On each floor we passed I glimpsed the empty rooms, the flickering tapers. Higher and higher we ran. The air grew thin and musty and my breath began racing faster than my feet. I found the last hall, the narrow, winding stairway that led to the turret. Kicking off my cumbersome shoes I kept running in my stockinged feet. I reached the final room in blackness, the bejeweled and ivory statuette clutched against my pulsing chest.

"Christopher! Christopher!" I heard the voice not far below, edged with ice.

I unlatched the window. Pushing with all my might I forced if free from its metal casement and it creaked outward to the moon and star-speckled sky. She towered behind me in the open doorway. A wave of her arm and the room was flooded with blinding light. I glanced at the base of the figure I held. A pattern of dewdrop rubies shimmered, spelled a single word – "motLEY." With long strides she bore down upon me. As the wind whipped my hair about and banged the open window against the mortared walls, I hurled my prize far over the dark landscape.

Hard fingers closed upon my shoulder. I looked up. It was the Wicked Witch of the North. Her face looked like a fairy tale with an unhappy ending. And her eyes, most naturally, were brimming with evil.

As for Motley, he escaped across the dark landscape to live on in my imagination

Bruce Boston lives in Ocala, Florida, once known as the City of Trees, with his wife, writer-artist Marge Simon, and the ghosts of two cats. He is the author of sixty books and chapbooks. His poems and stories have appeared in hundreds of publications, most visibly in *Analog, Asimov's SF, Amazing Stories, Weird Tales, New Myths, Strange Horizons, The Pedestal Magazine, Realms of Fantasy, Daily Science Fiction, Year's Best Horror* (Daw), *Year's Best Fantasy and Horror* (St. Martin's) , and the *Nebula Awards Showcase* (St. Martin's), and received numerous awards, most notably the Bram Stoker Award, a Pushcart Prize, the *Asimov's* Readers Award, and the Rhysling and Grand Master Awards of the Science Fiction Poetry Association.

http://www.bruceboston.com
http://www.facebook.com/bruce.boston.50